Experiencing and Explaining DISEASE

prepared by the U205 Course Team

THE OPEN UNIVERSITY
Health and Disease   U205   Book VI
A Second Level Course

THE OPEN UNIVERSITY PRESS

The U205 Course Team

U205 is a course whose writing and production has been the joint effort of many hands, a 'core course team', and colleagues who have written on specific aspects of the course but have not been involved throughout; together with editors, designers, and the BBC team.

Core Course Team

The following people have written or commented extensively on the whole course, been involved in all phases of its production and accept collective responsibility for its overall academic and teaching content.

Steven Rose (neurobiologist; course team chair; academic editor; Book VI coordinator)

Nick Black (community physician; Books IV and VII coordinator)

Basiro Davey (immunologist; course manager; Book V coordinator)

Alastair Gray (health economist; Books III and VII coordinator)

Kevin McConway (statistician; Book I coordinator)

Jennie Popay (social policy analyst)

Jacqueline Stewart (managing editor)

Phil Strong (medical sociologist; academic editor; Book II coordinator)

Other authors

The following authors have contributed to the overall development of the course and have taken responsibility for writing specific sections of it.

Lynda Birke (ethologist; author, Book V)

Eric Bowers (parasitologist; staff tutor)

David Boswell (sociologist; author Book II)

Eva Chapman (psychotherapist; author, Book V)

Andrew Learmonth (geographer; course team chair 1983; author, Book III)

Rosemary Lennard (medical practitioner; author, Books IV and V)

Jim Moore (historian of science; author, Book II)

Sean Murphy (neurobiologist; author, Book VI)

Rob Ransom (developmental biologist; author, Book IV)

George Watts (historian; author, Book II)

The following people have assisted with particular aspects or parts of the course.

Sylvia Bentley (course secretary)

Steve Best (illustrator)

Sheila Constantinou (BBC production assistant)

Debbie Crouch (designer)

Ann Hall (indexer)

Rachel Hardman (designer)

Mark Kesby (illustrator)

Liz Lane (editor)

Vic Lockwood (BBC producer)

Laurie Melton (librarian)

Sue Walker (editor)

Peter Wright (editor)

External Assessors

Course Assessor

Alwyn Smith   President, Faculty of Community Medicine of the Royal Colleges of Physicians; Professor of Epidemiology and Social Oncology, University of Manchester.

Book VI Assessors

Mildred Blaxter (medical sociologist) School of Economic and Social Studies, University of East Anglia.

George Brown (medical sociologist) Department of Social Policy and Social Science, Bedford College and Royal Holloway College, University of London.

A. Hamid Ghodse (psychiatrist) Drug Dependence Treatment and Alcohol Research Unit, St George's Hospital, London, and at St Thomas's and Tooting Bec Hospitals.

Peter Maguire (psychiatrist) The University Hospital of South Manchester.

Acknowledgements

The Course Team wishes to thank the following for their advice and contributions:

Sheila Adam (community physician) North West Thames Regional Health Authority.

John Ashton (community physician) Department of Community Health, University of Liverpool.

Val Box (cancer education advisor) South West Thames Regional Cancer Organisation.

Jocelyn Chamberlain (cancer specialist) South West Thames Regional Cancer Organisation.

Graham Currie (cancer researcher) Director, Marie Curie Memorial Foundation Research Institute, Surrey.

Roland Littlewood (psychiatrist) Department of Psychological Medicine, Guy's Hospital, London.

Tim J. McElwain (clinical oncologist) Professor of Medical Oncology, The Royal Marsden Hospital, Surrey.

Heiner Schuff (consultant psychotherapist) Hill End Hospital, Herts.

The Open University Press, Walton Hall, Milton Keynes MK/ 6AA.

First published 1985. Reprinted 1988. Copyright © 1985 The Open University.

Designed by the Graphic Design Group of the Open University.

Printed by Adlard & Son Ltd., Letchworth, Herts. SG6 1JS

ISBN 0 335 15055 1

This book forms part of an Open University course. The complete list of books in the course is printed on the back cover.

For general availability of supporting material referred to in this book please write to: Open University Educational Enterprises Limited, 12 Cofferidge Close, Stony Stratford, Milton Keynes, MK11 1BY, Great Britain.

Further information on Open University courses may be obtained from the Admissions Office, The Open University, P.O. Box 48, Walton Hall, Milton Keynes, MK7 6AB.

About this book

A note for the general reader

Experiencing and Explaining Disease is the sixth of a series of books on the subject of health and disease. The book is designed so that it can be read on its own, like any other textbook, or studied as part of U205 *Health and Disease*, a second-level course for Open University students. As well as the eight main textbooks and a Course Reader, *Health and Disease: A Reader**, the course consists of eleven TV programmes and five audiocassettes, plus various supplementary materials.

Open University students will receive an *Introduction and Guide* to the course, which sets out a study plan for the year's work. This is supplemented where appropriate in the text by more detailed directions for OU students; these study comments at the beginning of chapters are boxed for ease of reference. Also, in the text you will find instructions to refer to the Course Reader and to audiotape sequences. It is quite possible to follow the argument without reading the articles referred to or listening to the audio sequences, although your understanding will be enriched if you do so. There is also a TV recording associated with the text. Major learning objectives are listed at the end of each chapter along with questions that allow students to assess how well they are achieving these objectives. The index includes key words (in bold type) which can be looked up easily as an aid to revision as the course proceeds. There is also a further reading list for those who wish to pursue certain aspects of study beyond the limits of this book.

A guide for OU students

In *Experiencing and Explaining Disease* we choose a variety of diseases and disorders to explore problems in the

* Black, Nick *et al.* (eds) (1984) *Health and Disease: A Reader*, Open University Press.

understanding and interpretation of disease in general. The conditions we have chosen are headache, appendicitis, cancers, depression, schizophrenia and the addictions. This range is intended to cover conditions that are of major importance in Britain today and, between them, illustrate a series of contrasts and similarities. These contrasts include those between chronic and acute conditions; between minor and major disorders; between debilitating and life-threatening diseases; between those that are treated with sympathy and those that are socially stigmatised; between subjective experience and objective explanation.

We use these diseases and disorders also to explore themes which are of importance to wide areas of health and disease. They include the problem of classifying disease (nosology) and its relationship to the 'reality' of disease states (ontology); the relationship between 'biological' and 'mental' causes and explanations of disease; the dilemmas of treatment of sickness; the relationships between the sick and the well, between patients and doctors; and the politics of the disease state.

The book falls into three main sections, preceded by an introduction and followed by a concluding chapter. Chapter 2 is concerned with headaches and appendicitis; Chapters 3–5 with cancers; Chapters 6–9 with mental disorders and diseases; and Chapters 10–12 with addictions. Each of these explorations illustrates different aspects of the main themes of the book and you should be on the lookout for them as you work through the text. Look, too, for the way in which apparently very different conditions show some deep similarities just below the surface. Finally, in Chapter 13 we reflect on the preceding chapters in the context of what we can call 'sick-role politics' — the micropolitics of the sick person, their family and friends, and the macropolitics of the relationship between definitions of health and ill-health, the policies of the state and the larger economic and ideological forces of society. Associated with the text are a TV recording and audiotape sequences. In this book we mainly use the audiotapes to record the voices of sufferers from some of the conditions we discuss, and their doctors, family and friends.

The time allowed for studying Book VI is four weeks or 40 hrs, including study of the reader articles, audiotape sequences and TV. The table below gives a more detailed breakdown to help you pace your study. You need not follow it slavishly, but do not allow yourself to fall behind. If you find a section of the work difficult, do what you can at this stage and return to rework the material at the end of your time on the book. Remember, use the chapter objectives as a guide, especially if you are pressed for time.

Study time for Book VI (total 40 hours)

Chapter	Time/ hours	Course Reader	Time/ hours	TV/audiocassette	Time/ hours
1	$\frac{1}{2}$			Audio sequence: *Headache, Abdominal Pain and Appendicitis*	$\frac{1}{2}$
2	3				
3	$2\frac{1}{2}$	9		$\frac{1}{2}$	
4	3	Frei (1982) GMBATU (1984)			
5	$1\frac{1}{2}$			TV programme: *A Cancer in the Family*	
6	$1\frac{1}{2}$	$5\frac{1}{2}$		Audio sequence: *A Cancer in the Family*	2
7	$2\frac{1}{2}$			Audio sequence: *Dilemmas in Cancer Treatment*	
8	$3\frac{1}{2}$				
9	$2\frac{1}{2}$	Brown (1978) Goffman (1969)	$1\frac{3}{4}$	Audio sequence: *Mental Distress and Disorder*	$\frac{3}{4}$
10	$\frac{1}{2}$	9			
11	$2\frac{1}{2}$				
12	2	Poshyachinda, Azayem and Jaffe (Edwards and Arif 1980)	1		
13	$3\frac{1}{2}$	$5\frac{1}{2}$			
		Asher (1972)	1	Audio sequence: *Disability and Sickness*	$\frac{1}{2}$
		Macintyre and Oldman (1977)			
		Shearer (1981)			

Assessment: There is a TMA (tutor-marked assignment) associated with this book. Three hours have been allowed for its completion.

Contents

The Scream by Edvard Munch.

1

Introduction

What does it *feel* like to be ill — whether with a relatively minor disorder such as a headache, or a life-threatening disease such as a cancer? How does a person experience bodily pain or mental distress, and how do people respond to others who are in such types of pain? As you read through this book, you will discover that, just as with all other aspects of life, there is a politics to being well or ill, or to being disabled: a micropolitics of relationships between the ill person and lovers, friends, relations and those who are in authority over illness — health workers of many sorts — and a macropolitics of their relationships with economic and political institutions.

These issues are explored in relationship to a number of diseases and disorders: headache and abdominal pain, cancers, depression, schizophrenia and addiction, some of the main medical problems of modern industrial society. We have chosen them partly because they are sufficiently common to be within the range of experience of everyone reading this book. Cancers kill 1 in 5 of us; 80 per cent of us suffer from headaches; 1 in 8 women and 1 in 12 men will undergo psychiatric treatment at some point in their lives; most people are addicted to something, if 'only' tea or coffee.

The disorders and diseases we have chosen also represent apparent contrasts: contrasts between *chronic* disorders, which may last a life-time, but do not necessarily kill, and *acute* diseases which last only a short while; contrasts between temporarily disabling and permanent or life-threatening conditions; contrasts between conditions that seem clearly to represent a physiological or biochemical malfunction, and those that might seem to be 'in the mind'; and contrasts between conditions over which an individual seems to have no direct responsibility and those that may seem, like drug addiction, to be self-inflicted. Yet as we explore these several contrasts we shall again and again find underlying similarities. Conditions that seem clear-cut and 'biological', for example appendicitis, turn out to be problematic of diagnosis and share a number of features in common with seemingly 'mental' conditions such as depression. Ambiguities of definition

and of diagnosis abound. Throughout this book, you should be on the lookout for these surface contrasts, and for the deeper themes of similarity.

The book is about both *experiencing* and *explaining* disease. By experience we do not mean just the experience of, say, suffering from depression or having a cancer, but the experience of pain or discomfort, the experience of trying to diagnose whether or not one is ill and, perhaps just as important, doctors' and nurses' and relatives' experience of illness — the way in which the medical condition of an individual affects those around them — their family, their friends and colleagues and those whom they consult or who care for them.

From experience, we turn to explanation. Why do particular people get a cancer, become depressed, or go down with appendicitis? Why are some substances most of us use defined as addictive — and why do some people become defined as addicts? 'Explanation' means different things to the different sciences. To the doctor, it means diagnosis, naming the disorder and identifying a proximal cause or symptoms which can be treated and perhaps relieved. To the clinical scientist, it may mean taking a life history of the patient — especially if the diagnosis is one of mental or psychiatric disorder. To the biologist, it may mean defining the molecular and cellular changes that occur when a disease 'strikes'. To the epidemiologist and sociologist, it may mean asking just what characterises those who contract a cancer in comparison with those who do not. Do they differ in class, or gender, or geographical location, or occupation, or ethnicity, or . . .? What is more, amid this babel of seemingly mutually contradictory (or at least exclusive) explanations, how does one distinguish main from minor causes, causes from mere correlations or consequences, and proximal causes from distal ones, or mere predisposing conditions?

There are three main ways in which we can try to explain health and disease. There are explanations based on assumed abnormalities in an individual's biochemical make-up, explanations that define the problem as entirely located in the social order to the exclusion of biology and explanations based on an individual's unique personal life history*. We shall endeavour to show how these three broad classes of explanation can be applied to the six conditions of headache, appendicitis, cancer, depression, schizophrenia and addiction, and how they might be integrated, despite formidable difficulties.

Let us take some examples of the problems that run through the book. The first is that of the definition and classification of disease. The study of the classification of disease is called *nosology*, but its definitions cannot be absolute. As new knowledge is produced so the way in which disease is classified undergoes constant revision and there are many obscurities and contradictions in the standard method of classifying diseases. For all this, there is now some degree of certainty and a considerable measure of international agreement. Appendicitis and cancers are clearly defined. On the other hand, the nosology of mental disorder, of the addictions and of 'psychosomatic' complaints is in a very problematic state, and the whole area is split into rival schools.

Underlying the question of nosology is the question of *ontology* — the word philosophers use to describe the study of whether things actually exist in the real world, as opposed to being just the products of our own ways of studying and classifying the world. In the nineteenth century there were fierce battles over whether the individual complaints from which people suffered were discrete entities, each with their own origins and course, or merely surface phenomena, underlying which there was a single disease-state, a disease that expressed itself in a different fashion in different people and according to different circumstances. The struggle over these different interpretations went on for many centuries, but eventually the modern view — that there are many different diseases, each with their own separate existence — triumphed over the traditional belief that there was just one underlying disease. Today the major ontological battle is over the status of mental disorder — does it exist at all? If so, can different types of mental distress be categorised as representing ontologically different types of disorder?

This discussion of the ontological status of diseases flows into the second problem area with which the book is concerned. Where does a disease originate — in a person's 'biology', that is, in their body, or in their 'mind'? Medicine and psychology have tried to understand the implication of such distinctions for many years now — hence the confusion of terminology. Diseases 'in the body' are sometimes referred to as 'physical' or 'organic' or 'somatic'. Those 'in the mind' are termed 'mental' or

'psychological' or 'psychiatric' or 'functional'. Yet the very phrasing of the question in this way — mind *or* body — disrupts the unity of the individual person, who is simultaneously mind *and* body.

The roots of this mind/body dichotomy run deep in modern Western medicine and philosophy, as opposed, for example, to the medieval European concept of the 'sickman' or of traditional Chinese medicine with its more holistic approach. Polarising a disease between mind and body increases the dilemmas of diagnosis, from appendicitis to schizophrenia. We shall continue to refer to 'biological' and 'mental' disorders and explanations for the sake of defining two different domains of analysis and in order to relate our discussion to that in many standard medical and psychiatric books — and, indeed, to everyday language — but we want to emphasise that in the last analysis 'mental' and 'biological' are one and the same. A headache may *simultaneously* be 'caused' by changes in the blood flow through the brain ('biological') and be the effect of 'pressure of work' ('mental'). Which explanation and which language we use depends on the purposes we have in mind in endeavouring to, for instance, treat the condition — drugs to change the flow of blood to the brain, or altering the conditions of work to lower the 'pressure'. We shall discuss these issues more fully in later chapters.

These difficulties of nosology and ontology, of biology and mind, are reflected in the problem of diagnosis — the identification of a disease in a particular individual. The diagnosis even of clearly 'biological' diseases can present tricky problems. First, there is considerable variation in human anatomy, and the disease itself can take many different courses and present itself in many different ways. The classic signs of appendicitis are, for example, found in only just over half the people with this condition. On top of this, the diagnosis of many diseases requires their sufferer to report on how they experience their symptoms — a task of some difficulty, and one that is often heavily shaped by their personality and social circumstances, and by those of the doctor. Finally, biochemical tests may be inaccurate and some mental conditions seem to mimic biological diseases.

The core of illness, of disease, for each person is their own subjective experience. How does it feel to have a pain, what sort of pain is it — grumbling or stabbing, continuous or 'only when I laugh'? How does it feel to have a cancer, or to be told that you have a cancer? What sort of personal distress is one in to be called 'depressed' or 'schizophrenic'? What does a person who is desperate for their next fix of heroin feel? What explanations do we offer for our *own* ill-health, or that of people we love and care for — quite apart from the explanations offered by the professionals? When and how do we decide that our condition cannot be treated by self-medication, and that the professionals need to be

*There is a more detailed discussion of these types of explanation and the ways in which they are related in *Studying Health and Disease*. The Open University (1985) *Studying Health and Disease*, The Open University Press (U205 *Health and Disease*, Book I).

called in? This experience of ill-health is the starting point for all the subsequent discussion in this book. Because of this we make extensive use of direct statements from individual sufferers, their relations and close friends, and from the doctors and the health workers in immediate contact with them.

Understanding the experience of disease is one thing; classifying, diagnosing it and explaining its occurrence is another. Treating disease is quite a different matter. Cure, or the alleviation of suffering, is one of the main goals of health sciences. Like explanations of disease, treatments tend to be concerned either with direct intervention into the biology of the individual — the reductionist methodology of drugs or surgical approaches or, alternatively, with social interventions — moving patients to a different social environment, or modifying their economic circumstances. Which theory of disease causation is embraced tends to determine the treatment you are offered, but, as we shall see, there is no necessary relationship between them.

Note that statements about a person's having a particular disease or disorder are not neutral. They are also expressions about relationships, between the clinician who gives the patient a disease label (of cancer, depression, or addiction) and the individual so labelled. These relationships involve questions of power and responsibility.

Being labelled as a patient may entitle one to expect certain privileges, certain types of consideration, from sick pay to absolution from certain family responsibilities. The label may also constrain the patient. Persons regarded as psychotic can be compulsorily detained in mental hospitals on the authorisation of appropriately qualified medical and social workers. A person with an infectious disease may be quarantined and kept in isolation. A very ill person may be deprived of knowledge about their own condition and probable imminent death. A person addicted to certain types of drug may find themselves violating the law, and liable to imprisonment rather than hospitalisation.

The power of relatives, friends, doctors, social workers, the law over the individual diagnosed as diseased or disordered is therefore an important part of the relationship. In one sense, the doctors and related professional groups are acting as part of the apparatus for maintaining social order. Too many heroin addicts in the street, and a medical problem is redefined as a legal one, of keeping society safe. Certain types of socially disapproved of activity become defined as mad, as psychotic, as cancerous of the social order. Individuals are then denied their personal feelings and commitments by being defined as an 'invalid' — their behaviour and beliefs are seen as products of their illness, rather than as manifestations of different ways of understanding the world, or of attempting to organise it. By defining people as an *invalid* they are, in a way, *invalidated*.

The borderline between therapy and social control is at best a fine one, as we see in the final chapter, especially in the definition and treatment of mental illness and addiction. Where does treatment end and restraint or even punishment begin? Where does treating the victim begin to take precedence over the treatment of the social conditions that make victims what they are? Doctors have to deal with individuals, to alleviate their personal suffering, while biologists may be committed to the belief that it is the individual's biology that needs adjusting. If, however, some cancers are the result of environmental pollutants produced by particular industries, and if depression is a common feature of the experience of inner-city working-class women with children and economic insecurity, then should we continue to treat the individual, or should we look for wider social change? These questions are real. They do not permit glib answers — or even single answers.

Why have we chosen to discuss particular diseases? Consider the similarities and contrasts between headache and appendicitis. Headaches may be recurrent, relatively minor conditions, although they can be debilitating and may prevent people living a normal life. Just occasionally, they can be a symptom of something worse, such as a brain tumour. Acute abdominal pain may indicate appendicitis which, if untreated, could result in death. The two conditions therefore seem to be contrasted, but if you ask questions about who gets a headache or abdominal pain and under what type of social conditions you will find unexpected similarities. In addition, neither headache nor appendicitis is altogether straightforward to diagnose from the outside. Abdominal pain can be the 'bodily' manifestation of 'mental' distress; in the same way a headache can be produced by mental distress, but it may be a symptom of damage to the blood supply of the brain.

A major portion of this book is concerned with the disease that will eventually kill one in five of us, cancer: lay beliefs, biological and social explanations and treatments. How do cancer sufferers *experience* being told (or not being told) they have a cancer? What do they believe caused it, and how do they regard the medical treatment they have received. Why do many people apparently regard cancers with a special fear, even as a source of stigma and even 'uncleanness', by comparison, say, with heart attacks? What are the possible *explanations* of cancers? How are they distributed and what are the causes? Do we look inside a person's biology, to their immune system or their DNA, or is there a politics of cancer? Are some cancers caused by environmental pollution or living in an industrial country, or are the major causes some aspect of our lives over which we have apparent control, like smoking?

How should cancers be *treated*? There are contrasts between the reductionist and technology-oriented approaches of chemotherapy, radiotherapy or surgery and the so-called 'holistic' approaches involved in changes in diet, meditation or psychic therapy. How do cancer sufferers themselves feel about these alternatives, and why is there such massive investment in drug treatments and relative neglect of preventative strategies? Unlike headache and appendicitis, or the diseases dealt with in the later part of the book, there are few ambiguities of diagnosis with most cancers, but they present doctors, patients and relatives with a set of choices about truthfulness and treatment which many people regard with ambivalence.

The book then turns to the question of what we describe as mental distress and disorder, of psychiatric illness. About a quarter of all the visits people make to their doctors are directly concerned with their mental well-being, about half the hospital beds in the country are 'psychiatric' beds and psychoactive drugs are prescribed at the rate of about one prescription per head of the population per year. What does this vast scale of mental distress and disorder signify? Is there a psychiatric epidemic, or is it a new way of explaining and dealing with old problems? Is it just that 'physical' medicine has become so successful that all we are left with are pains in our heads?

These later chapters weave together the themes of experience and explanation, but we also use the study of mental distress and disorder to explore in more detail the apparent contrasts between biological and social explanations. Mental disorders arouse deep controversy — over nosology, over the ontological status of the states of mind which are being classified, over the appropriate methods with which to study them and over the issues of individual treatment and responsibility versus social and economic measures to alleviate the distress.

If these chapters have moved us increasingly away from apparently easily defined areas of disease and disorder into an uneasy penumbra, Chapters 10–12 continue the journey into a half-world between pain and pleasure, between medicine and the law, between self-induced biological damage and social dereliction, the world of addiction. What is 'an addict'? Does the condition even exist at all? What are addictive substances? Why is alcohol accepted in some cultures, marijuana in others and caffeine in all? Where are the boundaries between acceptable and unacceptable uses of addictive and intoxicating drugs? Is the appropriate treatment for addiction concerned with cure or containment?

Finally, we stand back in an endeavour to summarise some of the issues raised throughout the book. What does it mean to be sick; in what way is being sick a *political* question, from the micropolitics of the family to the macropolitics of the state. How are the boundaries between therapy and social control set within the changing context of contemporary industrial society? How can one avoid explanations and treatments which reduce individuals to nothing but their biology, or regard them as merely the constructs of their class, gender and ethnic position? Is a truly integrative biosocial account of health and disease really possible?

2

Headaches and abdominal pain

In this chapter we discuss two relatively common conditions, headache and stomach-ache. Both can be chronic, but one form of stomach-ache, appendicitis, can be acute and, if untreated, life-threatening. There are, however, surprising similarities between these conditions and the problems of diagnosis that surround them, which you should look out for. An audio-tape sequence *Headache, Abdominal Pain and Appendicitis* (AC806, Band 3) is associated with this chapter.

Most of this book is about diseases or disorders, but let us begin this chapter by looking at *symptoms*. Symptoms may often indicate disease but they are not the disease itself. Symptoms — pains, rashes, lumps, itches, weakness — are what people complain of and worry about: Am I ill? Should I see a doctor? What have I got? The relationship between diseases and symptoms is a tricky one. Some diseases have very few symptoms; many diseases share the same symptoms. Deciding whether a symptom is temporary and trivial, or whether it presages something far more serious, can be a complex matter. Just how it is done and the problems this may involve are the subjects of this chapter. To illustrate these issues we have selected two of the commonest of all symptoms, headache and abdominal pain.

Normally, a headache is one of the most minor symptoms, so minor in fact, we tend to treat it ourselves and around three billion pain-killing (analgesic) tablets are bought every year in the United Kingdom. Just occasionally, a headache can be more than a passing irritation. It can represent a disease such as migraine, acute mental distress such as depression, or most frightening of all, a brain tumour.

Most abdominal pain has a trivial cause, yet this is not always so. Some abdominal pain is caused by gall-bladder disease, some by duodenal ulcers, appendicitis, or a cancer — all of which, if left untreated, may result in death. Sometimes abdominal pain can be a sign of acute social and mental stress.

How do doctors — and patients — distinguish one symptom from another, determine which complaint is caused by what disease? Diagnosis is not something unique to doctors. All of us engage in it and, as you will see, the most basic diagnostic problems and methods are shared by laity and professionals alike.

What is diagnosis? It is often thought of as just choosing a correct label to match a particular condition, but of course, we can only choose from among the labels we have currently available to us. As the classification of disease (nosology) changes, so too does diagnosis. Moreover, the actual process of diagnosis usually has far more to do with excluding possible explanations than with finding the correct label.

The importance of making a diagnosis lies in the fact that it is a recipe for action. If action is not available or is thought to be a waste of time, then it is less likely there will be a precise label for the condition. For appendicitis (and for the classical forms of migraine) specific actions are prescribed, but for an ordinary headache, or abdominal pain with no obvious serious biological problem involved, non-specific palliatives, tranquillisers or even placebos tend to be offered.

The incidence of headache and abdominal pain

Most people experience headaches from time to time, women more than men and the young more than the old (Figure 2.1). A study of 2 000 people, conducted in Pontypridd, found that 63 per cent of men and 78 per cent of women had had a headache within the previous year and, of these, one-tenth of the men and one-sixth of the women said they had suffered in this way several times a week. Headaches are therefore one of the major sources of morbidity and are also a major reason for medical consultation. Another British study, this time in Southampton, found that of those reporting headache during the previous year, 12 per cent of the men and 19 per cent of the women had actually consulted a doctor for this reason.

Abdominal pain is common also. A study conducted in Oxford by three doctors, Rang, Fairbairn and Acheson, in the 1960s showed, much to the surprise of the researchers, that unexplained abdominal pain was the sixth most common cause for women's admission to hospital and the tenth most common cause for men. Figure 2.2 shows the

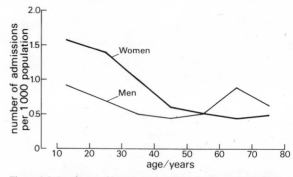

Figure 2.2 Incidence of hospital admissions in the Oxford Region in 1962 and 1963 for patients whose abdominal pain was undiagnosed at the time of discharge. (Rang *et al.*, 1970, p.48).

rate of hospital admissions for unexplained abdominal pain among men and women of different ages.

☐ Describe the distribution of unexplained abdominal pain shown in Figure 2.2

■ The rate is much higher in the young than in the old. It is also higher in women than in men, except among the over-fifties.

The causes of headaches

The causes both of headaches and abdominal pain are still the subject of considerable controversy. Headaches, for example, take an extremely varied form and are hard to classify. One recent American study of 726 patients suffering from headache produced a total of no less than 57 different signs and symptoms. Another claimed to identify 19 distinct types of headache. There is also debate over the origins of the everyday kind of headache. A popular medical encyclopaedia compiled by doctors and nurses in the 1930s took a fairly biological line. It identified five main classes of headache: 'sick headaches' or migraines suffered by 'brain workers', and four other types caused by eyestrain, fatigue, rheumatism and constipation:

Constipation causes another type of headache which is of common occurrence. Everyone is familiar with the dull, early-morning headache accompanied by an out-of-sorts feeling and a distaste for food, which usually coincides with an omission from the regular habit of bowel activity. (Robert Macfarlane (1934) in *The Hygiene of Life and Safer Motherhood*, p.344)

Contemporary views side more with social and mental theories, though it is debatable whether these theories are any more accurate than those held fifty years ago. It is interesting to speculate as to why our level of understanding of headaches does not appear to have advanced to the same degree as with other symptoms. It may be because headaches are often unaccompanied by other symptoms

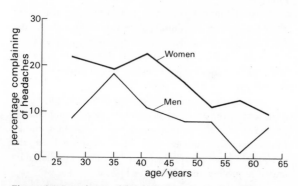

Figure 2.1 Prevalence of headaches by age and gender in the general population in a single month (Bungay *et al.*, 1980).

that would help to distinguish one type from another, or because they are rarely life-threatening. Perhaps they are so common, they are readily dismissed (by others) as of little consequence. In comparison, pains in the abdomen or chest are the subject of detailed analysis and elaborate rules for distinguishing one type from another.

Broadly speaking, headaches are distinguished as either primary or secondary. Secondary headaches refer to those that arise as part of a disease, such as influenza or sinusitis. With primary headaches there is no other disease present. Apart from the symptom of a pain in the head, the person appears to be unaffected in any other way. The two main types of primary headaches are tension and vascular (migraine) headaches.

Tension headaches are thought to affect most of the adult population. The pain is typically on both sides of the head and usually persists for a few hours. It may sometimes, however, last for days, weeks or even months. The pain itself is thought to arise from chronic tension of the muscles of the scalp and neck, which is in turn often thought to be a response to stress, anxiety and depression.

Vascular or migraine headaches affect rather fewer people, between 5 and 15 per cent of the population. Women, once again, suffer more than men. The episodes of pain last from 2 to 72 hours, with total freedom from pain between attacks. These episodes are associated with visual or gastrointestinal disturbances. Visual symptoms, some of which are very striking, occur before the pain starts, though during the attack people often experience photophobia (a dislike of light). They are also likely to vomit. The cause of migraine is thought to be rather different from that of tension headaches. Mental factors may well have a role, but there is also evidence that biological factors are important as well. The immediate, or proximal cause of migraine headaches is thought to be the dilation of arteries, both in the scalp and inside the skull. Why this should cause pain is not understood. Moreover, although there are several theories to explain why these arteries dilate, none of them has gained general acceptance. In recent years research has concentrated on the role of serotonin, a neurotransmitter. One of its actions is to cause arteries to constrict. It may be that low levels of this chemical result in arterial dilation and hence migraine headache.

Migraine is known to be associated with a variety of factors. It tends to run in families. It also occurs more often in women than in men. Changes in oestrogen and progestogen during the menstrual cycle may well account for this. They may also explain the tendency for migraines to start around puberty and to occur in association with menstrual periods. Certain foods may also produce an attack of migraine in some people. Chocolate, some cheeses (which contain relatively high amounts of the amino acid tyrosine) and some drinks, especially red wine, have all

been implicated. Finally there is evidence that some attacks are related to particularly stressful occasions, though sometimes in an unusual way, the attack occurring only after the stress is over.

There has been an emphasis on the role of stress in our accounts of both types of primary headache. Just what is the evidence for this? Research has focused primarily on people who regularly consult their doctor about headache. One such study was conducted in Leicester. Tension headache was by far the most common diagnosis for headache sufferers referred to the department. These patients were reassured by a specialist that there were no serious underlying biological causes. What effect did this have on them? The researchers selected 38 patients at random from among this group and examined their visits to their general practitioner before and after their visit to the specialist (Figures 2.3 and 2.4).

☐ Examine Figure 2.3. What was the effect of seeing a specialist on the number of visits about headaches patients subsequently made to their GP?

■ There was a very dramatic fall in the extent to which patients complained of headaches, at least to their GP. None of the 38 patients now visited their GP more than once a month with this problem.

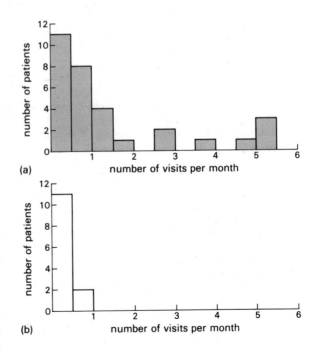

Figure 2.3 The number of patients attending their GP complaining of headache, both before (shaded) and after (unshaded) their referral to a neurologist. (Grove *et al.*, 1980, p.196).

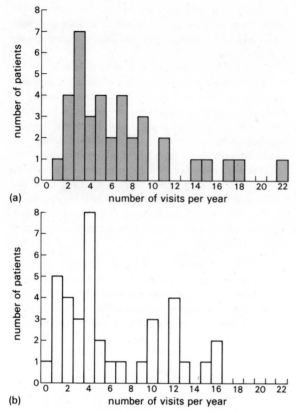

Figure 2.4 The number of patients attending their GP for any reason both before (shaded) and after (unshaded) their referral to a neurologist. (Grove *et al.*, 1980, p.196).

□ Look at Figure 2.4. What was the effect of a visit to a specialist on the rate at which patients consulted their GP, for any reason, in the subsequent year?

■ It would seem that there was little, if any, change, despite the fact that, as you have just seen in Figure 2.3, few of these patients were now consulting their GP about headaches. The headaches had apparently gone only to be replaced with other symptoms.

The researchers concluded that this illustrated what any experienced practitioner knows: tension headaches are only one factor in an illness profile that is likely to continue to manifest itself over succeeding months. In other words, the complaint of headache was only a manifestation of an underlying distress, such as depression — although it is important to consider whether in some people, the distress of frequent headaches may have accounted for their depression. One other important point should be noted. A study by two medical sociologists, Fitzpatrick and Hopkins (1981), found that 60% of the patients attending an out-patient clinic with headaches were worried that they were suffering from a serious, even life-threatening,

condition. Although all were reassured that no such condition was present, 40% of those who were worried were found still to be concerned about the possibility of serious disease some three weeks after the consultation. There appeared to be two factors related to a failure to reassure: the patients did not feel the doctor had understood their perspective as an individual and that the doctor had not supplied them with sufficient information about their problem.

The causes of abdominal pain

Let us turn now to the causes of abdominal pain. We need to consider two broad types. The first is episodes of acute pain. These have received so much attention from doctors that they have even established a special label for the symptom: 'the acute abdomen'. Causes include the inflammation of abdominal organs, such as the appendix, gall-bladder and pancreas, general inflammation of the abdomen (peritonitis) after perforation of a gastric or duodenal ulcer, kidney stones which get stuck in the ureters and obstruction of the intestines. In contrast to these causes of acute pain are the conditions that give rise to chronic pain. These include gastric and duodenal ulcers, various conditions affecting the large intestine and, in women, pain arising from the ovaries and fallopian tubes.

Clearly, we cannot attempt to consider all these conditions in detail. Instead, we shall concentrate on just one — inflammation of the appendix. The appendix is a small organ (up to 10 cm long) that opens into a part of the large intestine known as the caecum. An inflamed appendix can lead to peritonitis, a serious condition which, if untreated, results in death. There are several mysteries about appendicitis. To begin with, the appendix appears to serve no useful purpose and is therefore known as a vestigial organ. It is presumed to have had a role to play in the body's functioning at one time, though exactly what this was is unknown. At present, its only role appears to be as a source of infection. For this reason, some surgeons remove it while performing other operations in the abdomen. This prophylactic or 'incidental surgery' is frowned on by some of their colleagues.

The existence of the appendix was for many years unknown in the Western medical tradition. Leonardo da Vinci in 1492 seems to have been the first person to describe it, though his drawings remained unpublished until the nineteenth century (Figure 2.5). The first illustrations of the organ to be published were produced by the Belgian anatomist Andreas Vesalius in 1543 (Figure 2.6). However, although it was first identified in the fifteenth century, there was no suggestion at that time that it was responsible for any serious acute condition. Indeed, what we now call appendicitis would appear to have been rare at this period. The earliest known descriptions of the condition date from

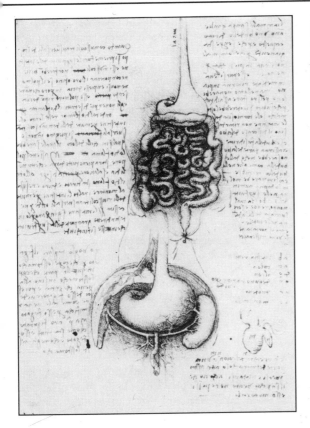

Figure 2.5 The first illustration of the appendix; Leonardo da Vinci, circa 1492.

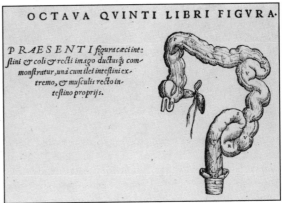

Figure 2.6 The first published illustration of the appendix; Andreas Vesalius, 1543.

the sixteenth century and were ascribed not to the appendix, but to an inflammation of the caecum called 'perityphilitis'. Suspicions that the appendix was responsible for perityphilitis grew only slowly and were not definitely proved until 1886. Shortly afterwards, in 1889, an American surgeon, Charles McBurney, developed the principal method of diagnosing appendicitis when he identified a point of greatest tenderness on the lower right-hand side of the abdomen — subsequently known as McBurney's point.

The operation was undoubtedly popularised by the disease's most famous sufferer, Edward VII. On 13 June 1902, twelve days before his Coronation, the King complained of abdominal pain. His surgeon, Frederick Treves, decided to wait to see what happened. By 23 June the King was much improved and held a small banquet, following which he suffered a serious relapse. His surgeons concluded that an immediate operation was necessary:

The King insisted, 'I must keep faith with my people and go to the Abbey'. 'Then Sir,' Treves reportedly said, 'You will go in your coffin.' At 12.30 p.m. the

operation was performed ... the King did well, but Treves did not sleep for a week. Appendicectomy became instantly fashionable ... in 1902 patients with appendicitis were commonly admitted to the medical wards, but within a year or two it became customary for them to be admitted to the surgical floors and for operation to take place within 48 hours of the onset of symptoms. (Seal, 1981, pp.431–2)

In modern times it is estimated that up to 12 per cent of the population of Western countries will suffer an acute attack of appendicitis at some point in their lives, and in the United Kingdom, more than 80 000 people are admitted to hospital each year with appendicitis. The surgical removal of the appendix, appendicectomy (known as appendectomy in the USA) is now the most common of all emergency operations. What causes inflammation of the appendix? Here again there are still some puzzles. The standard approach has been to see the inflammation as the result of an obstruction. The appendix opens at one end into a part of the intestine called the caecum. If this opening is blocked, the appendix may become inflamed. What might cause such an obstruction? There are three theories.

The first, 'lymphoid hyperplasia', ascribes it to the enlargement of surrounding lymphoid tissue located in the wall of the gut. Some studies have suggested that as many as 60 per cent of cases of appendicitis arise through lymphoid hyperplasia. A similar process occurs in children who suffer enlarged tonsils, which are also composed of lymphoid tissue. Just as the tonsils may enlarge during an acute respiratory infection or an infection such as measles, so the lymph tissue around the appendix responds in a similar way. This process would explain why seasonal outbreaks of appendicitis in children have been reported.

The second theory holds that the opening of the

appendix is obstructed by a 'faecolith'. A faecolith is composed of some vegetable fibre (cellulose) in the gut, surrounded by calcium-rich mucus which is secreted by the lining of the gut. The faecolith grows in size until it obstructs the opening of the appendix. It has been suggested, however, that the presence of faecoliths in the opening of the appendix may be a consequence, rather than cause, of the condition. This debate has not yet been resolved.

The third type of explanation involves a mixed bag of other causes of obstruction. Those suggested include worms (such as tapeworm, roundworm and threadworm), vegetable seeds, cherry stones, gallstones, intestinal tumours and even the barium used during special X-ray investigations such as barium meals and enemas. At most, these factors are thought to account for only a small proportion of cases of appendicitis.

So there is still a good deal of uncertainty about the immediate cause of this disease, particularly as any acceptable explanation must be able to answer several questions. Why should women suffer from this disease more than men? Why should it affect the young so much more than the elderly? Above all, why does it appear to be so common in the industrialised world, but so infrequent in the Third World, as the following quotation illustrates:

> Of 25 mission hospitals in East Africa who replied to a recent questionnaire, none saw more than an estimated 3 cases [of appendicitis] a year .... Four senior doctors responsible for all the surgery in their hospitals had seen no cases of appendicitis in 30, 28, 18 and 17 years respectively .... (Burkitt, 1971)

There appears to be a possible answer — diet. In 1920, a Bristol surgeon, Arthur Rendle Short, suggested that the main cause of appendicitis lay in the growing consumption of white flour. He also pointed to the absence of the condition in less-developed countries and to the fact that in Britain itself the condition affected the richer rather than the poorer social classes. He also noted an interesting difference between an orphanage and a boys' public school. In the public school, Clifton College, where the boys ate a good deal of cakes and pastry, appendicitis was common. In Miller's Orphanage, however, where the food was far less refined, it was a rarity.

Relatively little attention was paid to Short's work at the time, but subsequent research has suggested that this dietary hypothesis may well be correct. For example, urban Africans, who eat a good deal of refined flour, are far more likely to develop appendicitis than are rural Africans and, as Africa modernises, so its rates of appendicitis are rising.

Similarly, although appendicitis in Japan was once rare, it is now rising, and is higher still among Japanese living in Hawaii — which is an American state with an American diet.

The precise mechanism by which a high-fibre diet might protect the individual from appendicitis is unknown. However, it is assumed that refined food must somehow enhance the production of faecoliths. Nonetheless, association is not causation. Some other aspect of the lives of richer people and richer countries might explain the phenomenon.

Although appendicitis seems to be a biological condition, some people who are diagnosed as suffering from this disease are found to have a normal, uninflamed appendix when they are operated on. This is referred to as a 'lilywhite' appendix. What might be the cause of this apparent misdiagnosis? For women, one possible explanation is a confusion with menstrual pain. There is evidence both that young women are significantly more likely to be misdiagnosed than young men and that unnecessary operations occur more frequently during menstruation and ovulation. It has also been suggested that male surgeons may be readier to operate on young women than on young men.*

However, there is also evidence that suggests that mental problems may play a role. In the study of hospital admissions for undiagnosed abdominal pain that was cited earlier, such patients were found to be twelve times more likely than average to be admitted to a mental hospital in the six months preceding and in the two years following the abdominal pain. (The total number of such admissions was nevertheless small.) Such evidence has been reinforced by a recent study by a British psychiatrist, Francis Creed (Creed, 1981). One hundred and nineteen appendicectomy patients were interviewed a few days after they had had the operation. All the patients were aged between 17 and 30, and the interview focused particularly on whether they had recently experienced any severely distressing events. Such 'life-events' included serious illness, a death in the family, the break-up of a long-term relationship with a boyfriend or girlfriend, or a court appearance for a serious offence. Creed took several precautionary measures. He interviewed a similar set of people, matched for age, sex and social class, but who had not just had the operation. In addition to using this control group, he compared the results of his own study with those of previous research into the relationship between life-events and the onset of

*The issue of misdiagnosis of younger women is discussed in the context of hysterectomy in *Medical Knowledge: Doubt and Certainty*. The Open University (1985) *Medical Knowledge: Doubt and Certainty*, The Open University Press (U205, Book II).

depression conducted by two sociologists, George Brown and Tirril Harris (see Chapter 8). Creed also interviewed some of the patients' brothers and sisters to see if their accounts tallied. (They did.) Finally, he arranged for the pathologists' examination of the appendix to be conducted only after the research was over. Thus, the research was done blind, neither the researcher nor the patients knowing whether the appendix was diseased or not. Eventually, after the interviews had been undertaken, the pathologists examined the organs that had been removed and sorted them into those that were acutely inflamed and those that were 'lilywhite'. Creed then compared the incidence of acute inflammation with the incidence of severe life-events. The results, along with several other findings, are given in Figure 2.7.

☐ What do these results show?

■ Four groups of people are compared in Figure 2.7. Of the appendicectomy patients who had an acutely inflamed appendix, only a small proportion (just over 10 per cent) had experienced severe life-events in the nine weeks immediately preceding the operation. In this respect, there was little difference between them and the control group who had not had an operation. However, of those who had had a 'lilywhite' appendix removed, nearly a third had experienced a severe life-event in the nine weeks before the operation. In this respect they closely resembled the people suffering from depression.

As with the Leicester study of headaches, it appears from these data that depression may manifest itself in physical symptoms. Thus the shock caused by major personal changes can have a variety of (overlapping) effects on people's health. Some of these are straightforward changes in mental state resulting in the sufferer becoming severely depressed. (What this means will be illustrated in detail in Chapter 6.) Other changes may take a more biological form. The sufferer may experience severe pain in the head, the abdomen, or many other parts of the body. Given the way some sufferers from recurrent headaches come back to their GPs with a new set of symptoms, it may be best to talk of a pool of symptoms associated with anxiety and stress.

Such a pool may include many other symptoms besides those discussed here. One medical study described three hundred patients all of whom suffered from migraines, but who also had bowel or urinary problems, each of which can sometimes be hard to pin down in terms of a person's biology. The first of these is sometimes known as 'irritable' or 'spastic' colon — and the second includes recurrent problems such as cystitis. Another study showed that there was little difference between those patients whom their GPs had classified as depressed and those whom they were treating for recurrent conditions for which no biological cause had been found. The mental state of patients in both groups was very similar.

A cautionary note must be added. Although there is a good deal of evidence that some undiagnosed abdominal pain may be associated with certain mental states, this evidence, like that for the biological causes of appendicitis, is still inconclusive. There may well be some important biological causes of this condition that have yet to be discovered. Moreover, the pain may sometimes be the result of a problem that surfaces in an identifiable form only months, or even years, later. In the Oxford study of undiagnosed abdominal pain, the death-rate in the two-year follow-up period was considerably higher than would normally have been expected. Of the 427 people with mysterious pains, 6 later turned out to have abdominal cancer.

Let us turn from the incidence and explanation of the pains to their diagnosis and treatment.

Diagnostic dilemmas

Medical practice is not confined to doctors or nurses. All of us are obliged to engage in it and everyone who has to deal with illness, whether they be sufferers, relatives, friends or medical professionals, face certain problems in common. Imagine you have a pain in your abdomen, or that someone else tells you that they have. How do you decide whether you, or they, are ill? If it is an illness, what sort of illness is it — mental or biological? What sort of action needs to be taken, and what sorts of methods and evidence will you use to make up your mind?

There is an audiotape sequence, *Headache, Abdominal Pain and Appendicitis* (AC806, Band 3), in which we

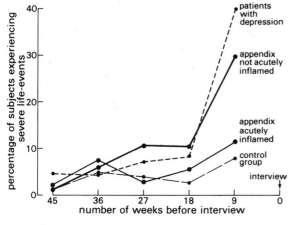

Figure 2.7 The proportion and timing of severe 'life-events' in different groups in the period prior to interview (Creed, 1981, p.1383).

investigate these matters further. This contains interviews with members of the general public, hospital patients and doctors. Listen to the cassette now and then work through the following questions and answers.

☐ What are the main problems that patients experience in describing pain?

■ Three problems are mentioned. First, some pain is so overwhelming that it is hard to describe: 'I just felt that everything was unreal. I was submerged in this sensation'. Second, people vary in how practised they are at experiencing and describing pain: 'Obviously, when you're talking to women, they relate it to, say, period pains when they describe their pains, which men can't'. Third, people vary in the extent to which they feel it right and proper to describe themselves as in pain: 'I was brought up in middle-class, sort of, you must grin and bear it, don't make a fuss, and it's come and gone'.

How far such stoicism is in fact a middle-class quality is debatable. There is little doubt, however, that people do vary widely in the manner and extent to which they describe pain. In a recent review, two American psychiatrists, Arthur Barsky and Gerald Klerman, described several different mechanisms through which this variation in descriptions of pain may arise (Barsky and Klerman, 1983). First, it has been shown that different people have very different *pain thresholds*, so events which, measured objectively, should give the same pain may be experienced quite differently by different people. Second, there is considerable variation in the extent to which individuals pay attention to normal bodily sensations. Some people, for example, are constantly conscious of their heartbeat, others rarely notice it. Third, anxiety itself seems to increase awareness of normal bodily sensations in some people. They may both amplify and misinterpret normal bodily sensations, a process that is considerably augmented by mental and social stress. It may also be augmented by a fourth factor, the kind of culture from which we come. Both patients and doctors have theories about the extent to which people of different ages or social classes are stoical in their response to pain. This area is relatively little researched, but American studies have indicated clear differences between different ethnic groups. Italian immigrants, for example, seem to report pain more readily than do native-born Americans.

☐ What are the problems that doctors experience with patients' descriptions of pain?

■ Several problems are touched on in the audio-tape. First, when patients are themselves overwhelmed by pain, this may affect the story they are able to tell: 'I was as confused as I made the doctors'. Second, given the way that patients' descriptions of pain are shaped by

their mental state and social background, doctors must try to take this into account. Third, how far should doctors treat the pain seriously? Should they really be searching elsewhere? One general practitioner commented on the importance of, 'exploring what the real problem is that they've really come up with and which the abdominal pain has been a ticket of admission for'.

The importance of this background exploration was emphasised particularly by a British psychiatrist, Michael Balint, whose work has had a major influence on many general practitioners (see Balint, 1968). He argued that most doctors were far too quick to impose their own diagnosis on patients without giving them time to express what their main concerns were. Even providing patients with terms to describe their pain might seriously bias their description. Balint called this the 'apostolic function' of doctors and urged them instead to spend far more time just listening to what patients had to say and to the way they said it.

☐ How do doctors assess whether a pain is primarily mental or biological in origin?

■ Doctors use a great many means to this end. They look for involuntary signs of pain: 'People look in pain, that's a common expression, and with experience you know that'. They use their own previous knowledge of the patient, or consultants may look at the GPs referral note. They make an informal social and psychological assessment of the patient. They also assess the statistical likelihood of particular diagnoses: 'The . . . hit rate of a tumour with people presenting with headache is one in many more than a thousand'. Diagnostic tests may be used. Ideally, they take a thorough history from the patient and, finally, they may conduct a physical examination.

Most of these latter methods depend in part on highly specialist knowledge, knowledge that is often kept secret from the patient:

There is one point which will help in trying to sort out the rare genuine case from the spurious: the pain of onset in acute appendicitis is typically in the mid-epigastrium [above the navel] not at the umbilicus [navel]. But don't let our patients get to know this. (Lewis, 1979, p.552)

Only the doctor normally knows what interpretation to place on certain symptoms: 'of the sorts of things you think about, the classic one is, did it wake them up in the night?' Similar subtleties can be found in the conduct of the physical examination. A tense and rigid abdomen may be caused by an inflamed appendix, or even peritonitis, or may simply be the result of the patient's being very tense. Doctors therefore get patients to relax by placing their arms by their trunk and chatting about other things during the physical examination. In other words, diagnosis is a form of detective work in which no evidence and no witness can be completely relied upon. (The character of Sherlock Holmes was in fact modelled upon an Edinburgh doctor.) As was previously mentioned, diagnosis is also concerned more with excluding serious causes than establishing a specific cause. This can be seen in the use of the white-cell count (a blood test that measures the density of white cells in the blood) in diagnosing the cause of abdominal pain. A normal white cell count is taken as evidence that the pain is *not* caused by appendicitis. On the other hand, an abnormal count can, but does not necessarily, indicate appendicitis.

☐ List as many similarities as you can between the patients and doctors as regards the following: (a) their beliefs about the origins of pain; (b) the types of action open to them when presented with the possible signs and symptoms of illness; (c) problems in the diagnosis of pain.

■ The similarities of note on the audio-tape were: (a) doctors and patients both held that pain could be mentally as well as biologically caused; (b) both referred to four distinct options when faced with a potential medical problem (dismissing it as trivial, treating it there and then, referring it to someone else and postponing a decision. As one surgeon commented, 'If you're ever at all worried, then you sit on them ... you admit them and observe them'); (c) Each group seems to face similar problems of how to know when something has a biological or mental basis or how much allowance to make for anxiety and social circumstances, as the following account suggests: 'I had felt unwell, but very often these things are related to other circumstances. One of the things that happened to me was my husband died very suddenly, so that all causes were put down to [the] emotional effect of this, rather than anything physical. And I am 60 and that adds to the dilemma, because again all causes are put down to being a 60-year old, recently widowed woman'.

You may have also noticed that one further matter mentioned by a general practitioner on the tape is also common to the laity. After reflecting on the many uncertainties involved in diagnosis, he commented:

What I think is a great danger is that if you have a doctor who always feels insecure and always feels that he's got to have the back-up of some specialist, or back-up of investigations and so on, it's very difficult for him to acquire the confidence and experience of knowing that in fact a clinical judgement is something which it is reasonable to make. And he learns by

making the clinical judgement and finding that in fact it was a good judgement, as it, of course, almost invariably is.

☐ What is the parallel between this doctor's statement and lay decision-making about illness?

■ Everyone is faced with the problem of interpreting a vast amount of minor aches, pains and miseries, a problem that is amplified by the many difficulties involved in working out precisely what is going on. In order to cope with life, everyone must arrive at some faith in their own judgement. The only alternative is to refer our problems to others, whether these be relatives, friends or doctors. To do so continually is unlikely to make us popular.

In short, for all the doubts and uncertainties that surround the diagnosis of illness, both patients and doctors are obliged to have some faith in their own judgement. Decisions do have to be made even when the evidence is highly problematic, a fact that often leads to major variations in clinical judgement.

Variations in professional clinical judgements

There is variation in clinical judgement in all branches of medicine. For example, wide variation exists in the extent to which doctors diagnose their patients as suffering from mental disorders. The most systematic British study of such disorders in general practice found a nine-fold difference in the extent to which general practitioners classified their patients as suffering from mental illness. Some reported psychiatric consulting rates as low as 38 per 1 000 of the population. Others went as high as 323 per 1 000 (Shepherd and Clare, 1981).

☐ What might explain these differences?

■ There are several possibilities. There is considerable disagreement over whether, say, migraine should be classed as a biological phenomenon or as a response to social or mental stress. There is also the problem that such illness may take a variety of different forms and switch from one form to another. In addition, some doctors might take a special interest in mental problems. This might lead more of their patients to bring such problems to them. It might also mean that more such problems are uncovered. (Remember the general practitioner, cited earlier, who spoke of 'exploring what the real problem is that they've really come up with and which the abdominal pain has been a ticket of admission for'.)

There is, however, one important snag with such studies. Although they show that there is an extraordinarily wide variation in the extent to which doctors identify mental

Table 2.1 International variations in appendicectomy rates

Country	Year	Population	Incidence per 100 000 population
USA	1930–50	six representative samples	520
USA	1963–64	representative sample	213
USA (Hawaii)	1961	sugar plantation workers	127
UK	1956–57	total population	210
West Germany	1966	total insured population	540 (men)
			604 (women)
West Germany		armed forces	1 040

(Data from Lichtner and Pflanz, 1971, p.325)

problems in their patients, these studies do not reveal how far any of these assessments are accurate. Doctors who do not identify many patients as having mental disorders are perhaps missing some cases, but it might also be that those who diagnose mental disorders in a large number of patients are creating problems where none existed before. Research that takes a standard method of assessing mental health and then compares the results with those given by general practitioners suggests that some doctors are, in fact, very good at identifying such problems whereas others are very bad (Goldberg and Huxley, 1980). The identification of minor mental disorders therefore presents a lot of problems.

In contrast, variation in clinical judgement about biologically caused disorders offers the possibility of outcomes that are relatively easily measured — whether or not an appendix is inflamed, for example. Surgeons therefore know, fairly immediately, just how good their judgement is. A surgeon comments:

> The truth of the matter is that you get better as you get older. When I was a registrar, my error rate, in other words the number of normal appendices I removed was about a third. And when I got to my best, which was as a senior registrar, about a quarter. And now I'm back to a third, because as a consultant I don't see them so frequently.

We might therefore expect there to be far less diagnostic variation between surgeons as regards appendicitis than there is between general practitioners as regards minor mental illness. Is this in fact so? A classic study of appendicectomy was undertaken in the 1960s by two epidemiologists, Sigrid Lichtner and Manfred Pflanz, in Germany. Table 2.1 gives details of some of the more striking international variations in the rate at which this operation has been conducted.

□ What could account for the large variations in the rate of appendicectomy?
■ One explanation might be international and historical variations in clinical judgement. The other

candidate is variations in the incidence of appendicitis.*

If variations in morbidity is the answer, there is nothing dramatically askew about surgeons' judgement. It is the incidence of the disease that varies — a variation that might perhaps be explained by differing amounts of fibre in the diet. Hawaiian sugar-plantation workers might have had lower rates of appendicitis because they had a much higher proportion of fibre in their diet. Similarly, the halving of the appendicectomy rate in the United States between 1930–50 and the 1960s might be the result of a change in diet. The West German armed forces would have been fed an institutional diet, which might have been lacking in fibre compared with that chosen by the Germans with health insurance (the great majority of the population). And so on.

Consider another piece of evidence: the differences in national death-rates from appendicitis in the late 1960s (Figure 2.8).

□ What was the relationship between the appendicectomy rate (Table 2.1) and the death rate from appendicitis (Figure 2.8)?
■ Countries with a high rate of appendicectomy also seem to have had the highest mortality rate from appendicitis.

This initially suggests that German surgeons were correct in operating so frequently for this condition. There is however, one snag in the argument. Death rates from appendicitis include patients who died as a result of surgery. It is possible, therefore, that part of the reason for the high death rate in Germany was *too much* surgery. Faced with a patient with abdominal pain, German surgeons were perhaps trained to operate, whereas others may have been taught to be more cautious.

□ What evidence might be examined to test this hypothesis?

---

* Another debate on clinical judgement versus variations in morbidity can be found in *Medical Knowledge: Doubt and Certainty* (U205, Book II). There the operation in question is hysterectomy.

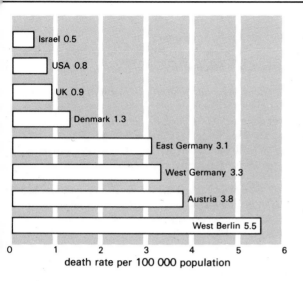

Israel 0.5
USA 0.8
UK 0.9
Denmark 1.3
East Germany 3.1
West Germany 3.3
Austria 3.8
West Berlin 5.5

death rate per 100 000 population

Figure 2.8 Deaths from appendicitis per 100 000 in 1966. (Lichtner and Pflanz, 1971, p.314).

■ One could look at the proportion of appendices that turn out to be normal or 'lilywhite' in the various countries.

In fact, German surgeons removed three to four times as many normal appendices as those in the United Kingdom or the United States. The thesis about the importance of national variations in clinical judgement therefore seems correct. It should not be concluded, however, that within any one country every surgeon uses the same criteria. A recent study of Welsh hospitals showed that, although the overall appendicectomy rate was fairly low as judged by international standards, there was still a three-fold variation in the rate at which the operation was performed in different hospitals.

In summary, although something is known about the distribution and causes of pains in the head and abdomen, there is still much that remains uncertain. The diagnosis of the cause of these symptoms presents many tricky problems. For all the advance of medical science, the problems of lay judgement still have their counterpart among the professionals. Such problems, it is worth emphasising, are not confined just to these particular symptoms. Nor are they simply a product of mental disorders, for even when there is no question of a possible psychological cause, doctors can still show remarkable variation in their judgements. A major survey by Lorrin Koran investigated the *reliability* of the diagnosis of diseases that are clearly biological in origin — reliability is the extent to which doctors agreed with one another in their judgements. The researchers came to this conclusion:

The reliability of many signs, procedures and diagnostic and therapeutic judgements has never been studied. As for available studies, most are limited to small unrepresentative samples of physicians, most fail to use statistics that correct for chance agreements, many do not disclose the participants' training and experience, and many examine tasks, such as interpreting electrocardiograms, performed in a manner different from that in which these tasks are performed in clinical practice. On the other hand, if the results of these studies are representative of the reliability of clinical data, methods and judgements, there is little room for complacency.... The physicians studied almost always disagreed at least once in 10 cases and often disagreed more than once in five cases, whether they were eliciting physical signs, interpreting roentgenograms [X-rays], electrocardiograms [measurements of heartbeat] or electroencephalograms [measurements of brain waves], making a diagnosis (from incomplete information) recommending a treatment or evaluating the quality of care. (Koran, 1975, p.700)

Objectives for Chapter 2

When you have studied this chapter, you should be able to:

2.1 Describe the distribution and some of the possible causes of headaches and abdominal pain (in particular, appendicitis).

2.2 Discuss: (a) some problems and methods in the description and diagnosis of pain; (b) similarities and differences between lay and professional assessments.

2.3 Outline some reasons for major variations in the professional medical diagnosis of appendicitis.

Questions for Chapter 2

1 (*Objective 2.1*) Consider this quotation. 'Headache represents one of the most disturbing of the minor ailments of civilisation and since it is such a universal experience, it is only natural to expect that it should take its origin not in one or two causes but in many'. (Macfarlane, 1934, p.343)

(a) Just how universal is the experience of headache and what is its distribution?

(b) What are the main types of headache according to current medical classification?

2 (*Objective 2.1*) Here is another quotation. 'Curiously a condition as common as appendicitis was not recorded in the medical literature until about five hundred years ago?' (Sabiston, 1981, p.1 048).

What biological explanations have been offered to support a real increase in appendicitis?

3 (*Objective 2.2 and 2.3*) A general practitioner has said: 'I find that some obsessional academics are absolutely marvellous at describing their symptoms to a minute degree.' What other sorts of things may influence people's description of their symptoms and in what way are these common problems for both doctors and patients?

4 (*Objective 2.3*) Consider the data in Table 2.2. What different explanations might be put forward for these variations in the death-rate from appendicitis?

Table 2.2 Age-specific death rates from appendicitis in selected European countries, 1966

Country	Age group/years					
	1–4	5–14	15–24	25–34	35–44	45–54
Sweden	—	0.2	—	—	0.2	0.5
England and Wales	0.6	0.4	0.3	0.3	0.3	0.7
Austria	2.5	1.3	1.1	1.0	1.4	2.2

(Data from Lichtner and Pflanz, 1971, p.313)

3

Cancers: beliefs and realities

Miss Gee knelt down in the side-aisle,
   She knelt down on her knees:
'Lead me not into temptation
   But make me a good girl, please.'

The days and the nights went by her
   Like waves round a Cornish wreck;
She bicycled down to the doctor
   With her clothes buttoned up to her neck

She bicycled down to the doctor,
   And rang the surgery bell;
'O, doctor, I've pain inside me,
   And I don't feel very well.'

Doctor Thomas looked her over,
   And then he looked some more;
Walked over to his wash-basin,
   Said, 'Why didn't you come before?'

Doctor Thomas sat over his dinner,
   Though his wife was waiting to ring,
Rolling his bread into pellets;
   Said, 'Cancer's a funny thing.

'Nobody knows what the cause is,
   Though some pretend they do;
It's like some hidden assassin
   Waiting to strike at you.

'Childless women get it,
   And men when they retire;
It's as if there had to be some outlet
   For their foiled creative fire' ...

(W.H. Auden: *Collected Shorter Poems, 1927–57*)

Cancers are only one group of the many chronic diseases: chronic heart disease, arthritis or multiple sclerosis all show similar uncertainties about causes, treatments and strategies for prevention. Those who suffer from them share a similar struggle to cope with prolonged anxiety, progressive or unpredictable disabilities and (except for arthritis) possible death. Cancers, however, seem to have attracted more than their fair share of despondency and alarm, together with a confusing jumble of knowledge, beliefs and speculations in both the lay and medical domains. Although people with chronic heart disease, arthritis or multiple sclerosis know all too well the disruption to normal life that these conditions entail, many people believe that a heart attack is a 'lovely way to go', or equate arthritis with rheumatism, unless they have observed its crippling effects. Many know little about demyelinating diseases such as multiple sclerosis. Cancer, on the other hand, is 'the big C', a death sentence only to be talked about in whispers and euphemisms.

One in four people in the industrialised countries of the northern hemisphere will develop a cancer at some point in life and one in five will die from it. There are, therefore, rational reasons for this concern, but what are cancers and how are they caused? As with all the conditions we discuss in this book, we can look at explanations at levels varying from the biological to the social. Indeed, the range of explanations offered for cancer is exceptionally wide and we shall discuss this in Chapter 4.

Only coronary heart disease, the other major fatal disease in the industrialised world, has attracted a similar debate — presumably because neither cancer nor heart disease has yielded to a unifying explanation or strategy for prevention and treatment. There is worldwide agreement that cancers are a distinct, recognisable group of biological diseases. Malignant cells look different from their normal counterparts; tumours often show up on X-ray films; a surgeon can remove a cancerous growth. This is very different from the disputed diagnosis that we discussed in relationship to headache in Chapter 2 and from what you will find in later chapters in relationship to mental illness and addiction, though mental distress has been indicated as a possible cause of cancer.

One further ground clearing point at this stage. Lay and medical conversations commonly refer to *cancer* rather than *cancers*. Yet there are numerous different cancers, classified according to the tissue in which they originated. The symptoms, prognosis and treatment of each of them varies considerably. In these chapters, we attempt to refer to cancers in the plural wherever possible and to concentrate on three of the commonest cancers affecting adults — cancers of the lung, breast and cervix — and on leukaemia, a relatively rare group of blood cancers which none the less account for about half the cancer deaths among children. These cancers illustrate the range of variations in mortality and incidence, prevailing arguments about prevention, causation and treatment and the dilemmas facing medical staff, patients and their families.

The *experience* of cancers for those who have them, treat them or care for sufferers is typified first by a very high degree of uncertainty about prognosis and, second, by dilemmas about treatment strategies that may be unpleasant and cannot be guaranteed to cure. We have attempted to provide an insight into the emotional impact of this chronic, sometimes debilitating, disabling or fatal group of diseases by quoting extensively from interviews with patients, their families and medical staff and from published sources.

Let us begin by comparing people's perceptions about the incidence of cancers with the epidemiological evidence.

☐   You may not agree that cancers are particularly frightening, but note down as many reasons as you can why many people view them with a special dread.

■   You may have thought of some of the following.

They kill thousands of people every year in the UK alone, some of them children or young adults.

There are reports in the media that cancer rates may be rising and more people seem to die from cancers nowadays than years ago.

A cancer diagnosis is seen as a death sentence and a 'very nasty painful end'.

There is a high degree of uncertainty associated with cancers — treatment cannot be guaranteed to produce a cure and, even if the disease appears to have been 'cured', it may start up again.

Treatment by orthodox methods may have unpleasant side-effects, such as hair loss and nausea.

Some people consider cancers to be 'dirty' or shameful diseases and, even if you do not agree with this view, cancer is still a taboo subject.

This is a daunting list, but it bears closer examination

because some aspects of 'cancer phobia' are realistic, whereas others are based on misinformation. We shall begin with the details of cancer mortality in the UK and work through the items in the list in sequence.

Deaths from cancers

In the industrialised world, cancers remain capable of killing us prematurely, even in childhood. In the United Kingdom in recent years about half a million people die annually and around 120 000 (22 per cent) of these deaths were from cancers, with approximately 10 000 more men dying from the disease each year than women. Only the cardiovascular diseases account for more deaths overall, but for women between the ages of 30 and 59 cancers are the commonest cause of death. Figure 3.1 reveals another aspect of cancer mortality that generates anxiety.

☐   In Figure 3.1, how are cancer deaths distributed by age in comparison with other causes of mortality?

■   For both men and women there are two peaks of mortality when cancers make up a large proportion of all deaths. One is in childhood and a larger one occurs in middle age. Both peaks are at ages when (in an industrialised country such as the UK) death is considered to be 'premature' or untimely. The larger peak for women is at 45 years of age when almost 50 per cent of all deaths are from cancers; the peak for men is about 10 years later and accounts for 30 per cent of all deaths at that age.

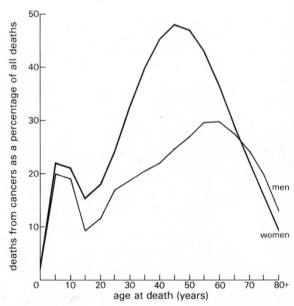

Figure 3.1 Deaths from cancers as a percentage of all deaths in men and women of different ages in England and Wales during the period 1971–75 (Michael Alderson, 1982, Figures 2.5 and 2.6, pp.8 and 9).

In numerical terms, the majority of cancer deaths occur late in life. Of the 120 000 people who die of cancer in the UK each year, around half are over 75 years of age and three-quarters are over 65. We do not mean to imply by this that it is acceptable to die of cancer if you are elderly, but cancers cause a more conspicuous *percentage* of deaths in younger age groups. These are the deaths that are most often felt to be tragic or a waste because of the years of life lost.

People have always died of cancer (papyrus scrolls from Egypt 4 500 years ago record symptoms and treatments), but the threats of malnutrition and infectious diseases have retreated, leaving deaths from cancers exposed like a rock emerging as flood waters subside. Despite strenuous research efforts and large amounts of money being spent, this rock has proved difficult to erode, although the complex genetic and biochemical events that result in a cell becoming malignant are now beginning to be understood and progress in treatment and prevention should logically follow.

Trends in cancer rates
The fact that cancer deaths have become more conspicuous as other fatal diseases have declined has done much to arouse fears that cancers are on the increase:

There's such a lot of this cancer now.... I think it's more advanced. A lot more people seem to get it than years ago.... I don't know why it is so increased. You never used to hear of it years ago, did you? Perhaps they never used to find the lumps, and you just had them there and just died of them I suppose ... and nobody was ever told what they'd died of.*

□   The person quoted (a cancer patient herself) wonders whether there has actually been an increase in the incidence of cancers. What other explanation is she considering?

■   She suggests that deaths from cancers may have gone undetected (or at least unrecorded) in the past. (This may have led to an apparent upward trend as medical training and diagnostic aids led to better detection of the disease and more accurate data on its incidence).

Improved detection and accurate records have certainly made some contribution to increases in the rates of certain cancers in recent years, but they are not the whole story.

□   What does Figure 3.2 reveal about cancer death rates since the First World War?

■   During the 60 years from 1911 to 1971 the *proportion* of cancer deaths among men over 55 years of age and women over 75 has shown a steady increase. This means that nowadays an older person is more likely to die from a cancer or to know someone who has the disease. Among younger members of the population the death rate from all cancers has not changed much this century. (In fact recent data shows it to be declining slowly, as you will see in a moment.)

One possible reason for the increased incidence is greater longevity, but this cannot wholly account for the increase in cancer deaths among older people since the First World War. The most important single factor is the huge rise in

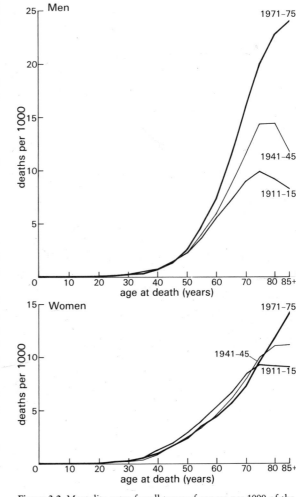

Figure 3.2 Mortality rates for all types of cancer per 1000 of the population of England and Wales in three five-year periods 1911–15, 1941–45 and 1971–75 (Michael Alderson, 1982, Figures 2.3 and 2.4, pp. 7 and 8).

*This is an extract from one of a number of interviews conducted by a member of the Course Team. Other extracts from these interviews are given in this chapter.

cigarette smoking because this causes lung cancer, which is predominantly fatal in later life. This is discussed in more detail in the next chapter. For now you should note that on present trends, lung cancer will exceed breast cancer as the commonest fatal cancer among women in industrialised countries by about 1990 — in some parts of the USA (e.g. Texas) it has already done so. Conversely, fewer men (especially younger men) are dying from lung cancer: in the past 30 years the mortality from lung cancer has dropped by 40 per cent among men aged 45 to 49 and by 60 per cent for men in their thirties as smoking has declined. The association of tobacco with other diseases such as bronchitis, pneumonia and coronary heart disease is also well established and smoking accounts for hundreds of thousands more 'avoidable' deaths worldwide. Lung cancer is also caused by inhaling asbestos fibres, a material once used widely in industry and in fire-proofing buildings. Regulations have controlled its use in recent years so the number of lung cancers caused by asbestos will decline, although we have probably not yet reached the peak.

The contribution of lung cancer rates to fears of a 'cancer epidemic' can be readily seen from Figures 3.3, which shows deaths from various cancers for middle-aged people since 1921. Confining the data to people under 65 avoids the problem of controlling for demographic changes in older age groups.

The decline in deaths from all cancers except lung cancer is particularly marked in generations born since the 1920s. A report produced jointly for the Medical Research Council's Environmental Epidemiology Unit and the Office of Population Censuses and Surveys by C. Osmond and his colleagues in 1983 provided abundant evidence of this. Within this overall decline, however, some cancers have increased while others have fallen. The report by Osmond carefully distinguishes between trends that are apparent across all age groups in the past few decades — a *period*

effect — and progressively higher or lower rates in each succeeding generation — a *cohort effect*. For example, the incidence of breast cancer is slowly rising in all age groups as well as in recent generations, whereas the incidence of stomach cancer has been falling steadily in the UK (as elsewhere in the industrialised world). Cancer of the cervix increased sharply in the two generations of women who were in their late teens and twenties during the First and Second World Wars and in the generation maturing during the 1960s. (As these are regarded as being periods of greater sexual freedom, this has strengthened the view that a sexually-transmitted infection may cause this type of cancer, a subject to which we shall return in Chapter 4.) Since the cohort of 1920, testicular cancer has also increased in succeeding generations, and there have been increases in cancers of the pancreas, brain, kidneys and in the leukaemias. Nevertheless, these increases have been outweighed by decreasing trends in stomach cancer and cancers of the uterus, thyroid gland, bone and lip. In Chapter 4 we shall examine the political dimensions of the debate about preventative strategies for cancer; as you will see, some authors engaged in cancer research believe that cancer rates are rising overall, and have called for government action to halt the trend, even though the weight of evidence points to an overall decline.

☐ List the factors put forward in this chapter to account for the incorrect view that a cancer 'epidemic' is underway.

■ The factors are: (i) improved rates of diagnosis and collection of data; (ii) the relative decrease in fatal infectious diseases making cancer a more conspicuous cause of death; (iii) the rising proportion of older people in the population who are most likely to develop a cancer; and (iv) the substantial increase in the incidence of smoking-related cancers.

Fatality and pain

A cancer diagnosis is often seen not only as a sentence of death, but as a very nasty, painful end. That cancer is held to be synonymous with pain is revealed by this woman's reluctance to accept her diagnosis:

> There was no lump, and I thought you'd get a lump or something. And I pressed it... and no pain. I always understood you had dreadful pain. I thought if it was cancer, I should have felt it.... Then it spread to the bones and I *did* start to get some pain, so I thought well ... maybe I *have* got it.

Some people do suffer pain as cancer spreads through tissues, damaging nerves and infiltrating bones, but pain can usually be controlled during terminal illness.

Yet, for most people who actually have the disease,

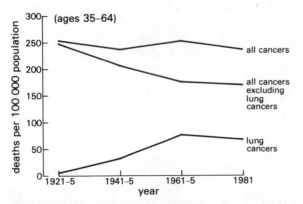

Figure 3.3 Death certification rates for cancers in England and Wales for 1921–81 per 1000 of the population aged 35–64 (Richard Peto, 1983).

Table 3.1 Average relative survival rates at 1 year and 5 years after diagnosis in 1971–73 for the commonest cancers in England and Wales

Primary site	Number of men diagnosed	Percentage of men surviving after 1 year	Percentage of men surviving after 5 years	Number of women diagnosed	Percentage of women surviving after 1 year	Percentage of women surviving after 5 years
lung, trachea and bronchus	71 525	23	10	16 340	21	9
breast	—	—	—	57 232	84	57
skin*	25 817	98	99	22 814	99	100
stomach	19 619	19	7	12 938	19	7
prostate	17 943	67	36	—	—	—
colon	14 564	47	30	19 703	45	29
rectum	13 003	56	31	10 537	55	33
cervix*	—	—	—	11 965	76	83
ovary, Fallopian tube	—	—	—	11 472	46	25
uterus	—	—	—	10 341	79	66
bladder	16 172	71	54	5 629	61	47
pancreas	7 051	10	4	6 071	10	3
testis	1 981	80	67	—	—	—

(Data from Office of Population Censuses and Surveys (OPCS), 1980)
* For cancers with a high relative survival rate (e.g. skin and cervix), the percentage of patients surviving after 5 years may be *greater* than the percentage surviving after 1 year. This is because survival rates are adjusted to take account of the possibility that patients may die from something *other* than their cancer and people who have been 'cured' of cancer are statistically less likely than others in their age group to die from some other cause.

cancer is a chronic condition — periods of treatment may be interspersed by months or years of symptom-free life, in which the principal strain is anxiety about a possible recurrence. Even if the disease has spread to many parts of the body (as described in the last quotation) and all curative treatment has ceased, some people survive a very long time in reasonable comfort. Once a cancer has been diagnosed, the patient and his or her family usually try to make the best of it and may be surprised at how soon they get back to normal after treatment.

> Initially, I really was frightened because cancer's a bad name — anyhow you know a lot of people die from it. But then you learn that a lot of people live as well, you know — the cancer's taken away and people do live through it.

The pessimism with which many people view cancer probably stems in part from the widespread misconception that cancer is a single disease. Individuals who contract particularly unpleasant forms of cancer with a high fatality are therefore taken to represent all cancer patients, whereas those who go back to a normal life after the initial period of treatment are forgotten unless a recurrence of the disease again threatens their life. Some cancers are indeed rapidly fatal in the majority of patients, but most have a much better prognosis. The *average* relative survival* in the UK from all cancers is shown in Figure 3.4. It reveals that

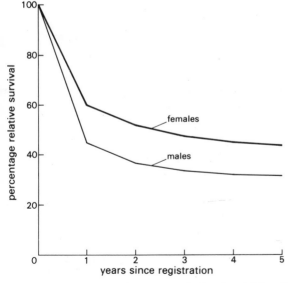

Figure 3.4 Relative survival rates in England and Wales for all cases of cancer initially diagnosed between 1971 and 1973 (Cancer Research Campaign, 1982, p.19).

*The crude survival rate, say two years after registration, would be just the percentage of cancer sufferers who are still alive two years after diagnosis. The *relative* survival rates are calculated by adjusting the crude survival rates to exclude from consideration those patients who might be expected to die from a cause other than cancer, given their age and sex.

3 out of 10 men diagnosed with cancer and 4 out of 10 women remain alive for at least 5 years. This may not seem particularly good odds, but conceals some striking variations in prognosis for different cancers (see Table 3.1).

Note that the commonest cancers among men (those of the lung, trachea and bronchus) are among the most rapidly fatal. Thus a significant change in smoking habits could have a profound impact on the *average* survival of all cancer patients taken together. Cancers of the skin (other than the malignant form that can arise in the pigmented cells in moles) are the second commonest cancers in both sexes, but are very rarely fatal.

To put cancer mortality more firmly into perspective, it is worth noting that of the people who develop a cancer, one in five do not ultimately die from the disease: a much higher proportion of patients who have suffered mild heart attacks or strokes will die from a further deterioration of their condition. Pessimism about cancer prognosis is not confined to the lay public. Interviews carried out with British general practitioners by Jane Rosser and Peter Maguire in Manchester in 1982 revealed that some of them were deeply pessimistic, as these extracts from interviews with three doctors show:

> Unless you're lucky and get it early, it's still what I would describe as an undignified race, medicine versus the growth. It's still a question of whether you can kick it out before it kills the patient. Very unscientific really, isn't it, chasing round the body?

> It's very difficult for me to decide whether any cancers are cured by any kind of treatment, or whether those that are cured are not very malignant anyway.

> There is no doubt at all that there is some mystique about cancer; it's special, sinister ... maybe it's because of the way we handle it ... patients react better to coronary than cancer, it's a better prognosis. Myself, deep down, unreasonably, I think the same thing — I mean emotionally, not statistically. (Rosser and Maguire, 1982, pp.316, 317 and 316)

In fact, the prognosis for someone with coronary heart disease is frequently *worse* than for someone with cancer, even cancers of the more rapidly fatal sites.

Uncertain response to unpleasant treatment

The importance of uncertainty about the future cannot be underestimated in the daily life of someone who has had a cancer. They and their families must learn to live with a fluctuating anxiety, first about the success of initial treatment and then about the possibility of a recurrence.

Someone with cancer may die soon, or in several years time, or ultimately not from cancer at all.

> As far as the prognosis was concerned, we were desperate for information ... we really felt we were going from pillar to post — from doctor to consultant to radiographer — trying to get somebody to give us some concrete information.

> My doctor's fantastic really — because everytime I have an ache anywhere, if it's in my big toe or anywhere, I'll go down to him and think I've got cancer again. He tells me all what's wrong with me and it's nothing really but in my mind. If I have an ache anywhere, it's cancer.

Uncertainty about the outcome is, of course, not restricted to cancers; it is a pressing anxiety in many other diseases. However, people who have suffered a mild heart attack may comfort themselves that if they slow down, lose weight, give up smoking, and so forth, they will get better, whereas most cancer patients feel that the disease is taking its own course *regardless* of what they do. The longer the time since the last positive evidence of cancer, the more these considerations drift into the back of the mind, only to be reawakened by any sign of ill-health, no matter how trivial. As clinic day approaches most ex-patients get very jumpy.

> About three weeks before my tests, I start not sleeping and worrying and I get all these aches and pains which I never had before, but it's all in the mind and as soon as the doctor says you're alright, the aches and pains disappear. (Bob Champion, from an interview on Radio 4, broadcast in 1983)

Cancer as a source of shame

Cancer patients frequently experience a sense of shame, or at least stigmatisation. What is the source of these feelings? Although many people who are subsequently diagnosed as having cancer feel unwell for some time before the cause of their symptoms is identified, others appear to be 'struck down' by it when apparently in perfect health.

> It came as a terrible bombshell, of course. I think if I'd felt ill, it wouldn't have come as quite such a shock, but at the time I felt very fit and healthy and full of the joys of life, and for someone to suddenly tell you over the telephone 'Can you come in for a mastectomy, you've got cancer' — then obviously your whole world just sort of drops away.... I felt very much that my body had let me down and I couldn't count on it. (U205 TV programme, *A Cancer in the Family*)

Of course, this woman's response is typical of the way any

sudden attack of ill-health is received, but the fact that cancers may get to an advanced state before giving any sign of ill-health has generated a special kind of dread. How can a person be sure that they are safe from the 'hidden assassin waiting to strike at you' as poet W.H. Auden put it. Many people share a view of cancer as a secretive, purposive, invader that 'eats away' at healthy tissue and destroys the body from within. This imagery reflects the biological ability of malignant cells to spread (metastasise) to sites distant from their original location and multiply into a mass of cells that destroys normal tissues at its periphery.* A substantial percentage of people with metastatic cancer lose weight in the later stages of the disease, and appear to 'waste away', as if the cancer were 'feeding' on them (although actually loss of appetite is the principal cause of weight loss). (The name 'cancer' itself, from the Latin word for crab, reflects a belief dating back to Ancient Greece that cancer crept up 'sideways' on its unsuspecting victim and held on tenaciously like a crab holding onto a rock.)

> I just feel as if there's something the matter with me … I'm contagious, sort-of-thing. Once you tell anybody you've had it, they won't want to have anything to do with you anymore … this is how I feel. I never talk about it to anybody … I just cannot. Shall I tell you why? I feel dirty, you know, because I've had it.

This sense of being an outcast with a guilty secret affects individuals who feel no shame or revulsion about cancer: for example, this woman describing an incident with fellow patients:

> I certainly made them feel uncomfortable. I don't think I would have told anybody what I was in for, except on the very first evening some lady, who obviously wished she hadn't asked, was sort of going round the supper table asking everybody what they were in for, and it came to my turn and I just took a deep breath and said 'a mastectomy' — and she said, 'Oh dear, that sounds awful. What is it?' And I said, 'Well, they are going to remove a breast tomorrow', and of course there was absolute stunned silence round the table, and she didn't know what to do. Nobody else knew what to say — there were just sort of general mutterings of 'Oh dear' and 'How awful', and then they quickly switched the subject onto something else.

In summary, then, the fearful beliefs expressed by most people who have not experienced cancer for themselves are only partly supported by evidence. Cancers are a common cause of death in industrialised countries and more people nowadays live to an age when they are more likely to develop the disease. However, cancer rates are declining overall, and the average survival period following diagnosis with certain cancers is longer than most people expect.

Beliefs about causes

Another area of ambiguity, both lay and professional, is about the causes of cancers — whether biological, social or personal life history. The association of tobacco smoking and asbestos with cancer of the lung is well known, but what about the dozens of other organs and tissues in which a cancer may arise? A comprehensive answer to this question cannot yet be given, although almost everything we eat from yoghurt to tinned food has at one time been the subject of a 'cancer scare'. In the vacuum left by this lack of concrete knowledge, many people hold onto idiosyncratic beliefs about causes — burnt toast perhaps, or the brown scar on top of tomatoes where the stalk was attached. Some beliefs have achieved general rather than local popularity.

☐ Which of the following do you suspect may be implicated in the development of cancer? (If you have time, ask one or two other people for their assessment of the list, preferably choosing someone from a different generation. You may find suprising contrasts.)
(i)   smoking cigarettes
(ii)   a knock or a fall
(iii)   contact with someone who has cancer
(iv)   not keeping clean
(v)   loose living: that is, sexual promiscuity
(vi)   emotional stress, worry
(vii)   eating rich or spicy food
(viii) heredity: that is, cancer 'runs in families'
■ Compare your responses with Table 3.2, which shows the percentage of women in the 1973 Lancaster Study by Andrea Knopf who agreed with these suggested causes. The final column indicates whether the suggested cause is true or not.

In 1983 a British sociologist, Mildred Blaxter, asked women in Glasgow for their views about diseases.† Blaxter found that cancer was one of the most frequently mentioned diseases, but the women avoided detailed discussion of it and 'gave the impression of *preferring* to believe that cancer was quite randomly caused.'

Beliefs about causes that are false or only partly true (Table 3.2) are worth examining in more detail. Hereditary

---

*These terms and the cell biology of cancer are discussed in some detail in *The Biology of Health and Disease*. The Open University (1985) *The Biology of Health and Disease*, The Open University Press (U205 *Health and Disease*, Book IV).

†An article, 'The causes of disease: women talking', by Mildred Blaxter is included in the Course Reader. The section on cancer and tuberculosis refers to this survey. Black, Nick *et al.* (1984) *Health and Disease: A Reader*, Open University Press.

Table 3.2 Causes of cancers suggested to a sample of 756 women interviewed in Lancaster in 1973

Suggested causes	Percentage agreeing	Status of suggested cause
smoking	70.0	true
knocks, falls	27.7	false
living with someone who has cancer (contagion)	6.6	false
not keeping clean	23.5	partly true
bad living (sometimes called 'good living')	27.0	partly true
heredity	31.1	partly true
opinion that the cause of cancer is not yet known	79.0	true for most cancers

(Data from Knopf, 1974, pp.44–52)

and cancer rates are discussed in Chapter 4, but what of other beliefs? There is no evidence whatever that knocks or falls cause cancers (professional footballers, Judo experts, rugby players, and so forth, are no more prone to cancers than others), but this view persists, as these cancer patients testify:

> I couldn't understand it ... I hadn't had a knock or anything

> I would say to any women — old or young — if you get a little knock or scratch on the breast ... go and see the doctor.

These quotations are from interviews recorded in 1983. There are no current indications that the prevalence of this explanation for cancer has diminished in the ten years since the Lancaster study (Table 3.2). The notion that cancer is contagious also persists among a minority, but the incidence of the disease is no higher among staff working in specialist cancer treatment centres than in other sectors of the population. The belief that a person is somehow *contaminated* by cancer has much in common with the notion that 'not keeping clean' causes the disease. Although there is no general association with poor personal hygiene, skin contact over a prolonged period with certain chemicals or industrial products such as soots, tars and mineral oils is implicated in certain cancers. It is therefore possible that better washing facilities for people employed in such work might be beneficial — although measures to *prevent* exposure rather than washing afterwards, are obviously preferable.

In the English language the words 'dirty' or 'unclean' have come to mean sexually promiscuous, deviant, or lewd,

as well as unwashed. This double-meaning is exemplified by the debate over possible causes of cancer of the cervix. A woman in the Lancaster study had this to say about the association of promiscuity and cancer:

> I would say that she hadn't been looking after herself, you know. It could be she was having too much of a good time. There are people like that. They have very loose morals. (Knopf, 1974, p.30)

The lay view seemed to get professional backing in the 1970s when several epidemiological studies showed that women with cancer of the cervix had *on average* begun sexual intercourse at an earlier age and had more sexual partners than women free from the disease. The cohort data we cited earlier also showed increases in generations that experienced (among many other changes) a wider acceptance of sexual freedom. As nuns rarely get cancer of the cervix, and its incidence is reduced among women when barrier methods of contraception (such as the diaphragm or sheath) are used, the case for a sexually transmitted infection seemed proved. An unfortunate consequence of this research was that women with this type of cancer were sometimes assumed to have been promiscuous, or upset by questions about their sexual history. Gradually other aspects of the disease began to emerge. Rates of this cancer are very low among married Jewish women (whose husbands are usually circumcised). There is also a strong relationship to social class, working class women being most at risk.

□ Can you think of possible explanations for these observations?

■ One obvious interpretation reinforces middle-class stereotypes of the working classes as promiscuous, but there is no evidence that this is true. Another is to propose that men may be transmitting to their sexual partners a causative agent which is harboured beneath the foreskin — hence the relative freedom from the disease among Jewish women and those using barrier methods of contraception. By implication, working-class men supposedly are more at risk of carrying this agent.

Subsequent studies confirmed that women with cancer of the cervix were more likely to be married to men who had themselves changed sexual partners frequently. In other words, the charge of 'promiscuity' cuts both ways.

At the time of writing, attempts to identify a sexually transmitted virus as the proximal cause of this type of cancer have not been successful, but most people in cancer research are convinced that one will be found (possibly the same virus that causes genital warts). A virus infection, however, cannot easily explain the strong association with social class. The women most at risk were those married to

Table 3.3 The mortality (standardised mortality ratio) from cervical cancer in 1970–72 in married women aged 16–64 classified by their husband's social class and level of occupational exposure to soot, tar and mineral oils

Social class	Level of exposure		
	unexposed	moderate exposure	heavy exposure
I	46	61	—
II	65	73	—
III skilled non-manual	68	—	—
III skilled manual	103	128	94
IV	117	145	203
V	198	137	104

(Data from Zakelj *et al.*, 1984, p.510)

men in dirty or dusty jobs, such as miners, quarrymen, furnacemen, forge and foundry workers, and various other occupations including fishermen and members of the armed forces (Robinson, 1982). This raises the possibility that the introduction of certain chemicals or irritant particles into a woman's vagina by her partner's penis is a precondition for a subsequent viral infection to produce a malignant change, but the association between cervical cancer and husband's job is by no means proved. More recently, a study by members of the Epidemiological Monitoring Unit at the London School of Hygiene and Tropical Medicine (see Table 3.3) found a significant increase in mortality from cervical cancer associated with increasing levels of occupational exposure to soot, tar and mineral oils only in social class IV. The trend in class V was in the *reverse* direction.* The question remains open.

The debate about the causes of cervical cancer illustrates three general points. First, that 'old wives tales' may be at least partly true; second, that lay views about the causation of illness quite often 'blame the victim' and, third, that biological, social and personal-history factors interact in the causation of cancers, as they do with most other diseases.

The emphasis on personal history in lay beliefs about cancers comes out most strongly in the common view that grief, tragic loss or a certain type of personality cause cancers.

Well I think a lot of this is caused through stress, emotion. Well, I suppose it's allotted out to everybody what they're going to have, but I'd had a lot of emotional trouble beforehand ... my husband had gone off, and I was all right till then it seemed, and then I had all this trouble come on.

Despite the conflicting research findings†, some authors have made unequivocal statements on the matter. Take, for example, these quotations, the former from a radiologist and psychotherapist working in Texas, USA and the latter from a New York psychologist:

[Cancer patients have] a great tendency for self-pity and a markedly impaired ability to make and maintain meaningful relationships. (quoted in Sontag, 1983, p.55)

The basic emotional pattern of the cancer patient [is] a childhood or adolescence marked by feelings of isolation, the loss of the meaningful relationship found in adulthood, and a subsequent conviction that life holds no more hope. ... The cancer patient almost invariably is contemptuous of himself, and of his abilities and possibilities. [They are] empty of feeling and devoid of self. (quoted in Sontag, 1983, p.55)

☐ If the analysis of these quotations is accepted, what proportion of the population must be self-pitying, incapable of forming meaningful relationships, contemptuous of themselves and empty of feeling?

■ About a quarter, because one in four people in industrialised countries will develop a cancer, although only a fifth of the population will die from it.

Publicity for these unfounded beliefs has aroused guilt among some cancer patients that perhaps they 'brought the disease on themselves'. There may be conflict about whether to try to change their personality in order to stay alive, if that is possible. Consider this quotation from the diary of Sue Cartledge, who died in 1983:

... if I continue to despair I know I cannot live long — cancer or something else will kill me off. But I

*These terms refer to the Registrar General's classification of social class, which is discussed in *Studying Health and Disease* (U205, Book I).

†Some of these conflicting findings are discussed in *The Biology of Health and Disease* (U205, Book IV).

have found it hard, very hard to shake off the illness and the despair. Very likely I was far too optimistic in thinking I could recover so quickly from cancer and the operation, but I can't help feeling in some important way I have gone wrong. Have I allowed myself to become spiritually depleted? Have I got lazy? And what can I do about it? How can I drag myself out of the Slough of Despond when I have so little strength? Or is dragging myself out the wrong way to approach it? ... Perhaps I haven't got the will that it takes to fight for life? (from the Diary of Sue Cartledge, reprinted in *Spare Rib*)

There simply is not good evidence that personality makes a contribution to cause or to cure. The rise in popularity of 'alternative' treatments for cancer that claim to focus on the whole person rather than on the disease is testimony to the dissatisfaction some cancer patients feel with orthodox methods. Some people would prefer to be assured that they are *not* responsible for their own recovery and to leave it to medical science. Others find this offensive and deper-sonalising and believe they can make a vital contribution to the outcome. A few reject orthodox treatment altogether and embark on a course of self-discovery and self-healing — a subject to which we shall return in Chapter 5.

Objectives for Chapter 3

When you have studied this chapter, you should be able to:

3.1 Evaluate statements made about the incidence of cancers and mortality from cancers in the UK for different age groups.

3.2 Discuss the common fearful beliefs about cancers held by people in industrialised societies and possible consequences of those beliefs.

3.3 Illustrate the interaction of biological, social and personal-history factors in theories about the cause of cancers.

Questions for Chapter 3

1 *(Objective 3.1)* The *incidence* of cancers (taking all types together) rises with increasing age in both men and women, yet Figure 3.1 shows that the *percentage* of deaths from cancers falls dramatically after the age of 60 years in men, and 45 years in women. How do you account for this apparent paradox?

2 *(Objective 3.2)* Can you account for the fact that the average survival curve for women with cancers is better than those for men at all points up to five years after diagnosis (Figure 3.4)? Does this mean that women are less susceptible to cancers than men?

3 *(Objective 3.2)* What fearful beliefs about cancers are illustrated by the following quotation from a cancer patient's diary?

Cancer to me is like a person, a living breathing person with a mind and intelligence of its own. It enters secretly into most people in the part of you called the body ... It is the most clever sneaky disease ever, that is why it comes in so many shapes, forms and sizes. (Wellcome Foundation exhibition: Tell me, is it cancer?)

4 *(Objective 3.3)* Briefly summarise the interaction of biological, social and personal-history factors in the development of lung cancers.

4
Cancers: biology, epidemiology and politics

This chapter builds on and revises your knowledge of biomedical and epidemiological methods from Book I, *Studying Health and Disease*, and the biology of cancers from Book IV, *The Biology of Health and Disease*, Chapter 16. There are two Reader articles relevant to this chapter: 'Cancer and work' published by the General, Municipal, Boiler-makers and Allied Trades Union (Part 7, Section 7.7) and 'The national cancer chemotherapy program' by Emil Frei III (Part 7, Section 7.3).

The nature of cancer is perfectly understood ... For some unknown reason more new cells are reproduced than are required to replace those thrown off by wear and tear. The superfluous cells accumulate rapidly at the tumour seat. As the growth enlarges it destroys the healthy structures in its vicinity. Sometimes it reaches a vital part and so destroys life ... There seems to be no mode of depriving the cancer cells of their power to reproduce themselves. If we knew why they increased so, we should be within measurable distance of a cure for this terrible disease. (*Diseases and Remedies*, 1898, p.24)

The medical world of 1898 was optimistic in considering that the 'nature of cancer' was 'perfectly understood'. No biologist or doctor today would claim as much, despite the very significant advances of the 1980s. Since the turn of the century a very considerable research endeavour has been growing in the industrialised world, aimed at answering the question *why* do cancer cells multiply. Almost all of that research has flowed from two basic research methodologies: the reductionist approach of biological sciences, which focuses on the cellular, molecular and ultimately genetic features of cancers, and the 'top-down' approach of epidemiology, which seeks to clarify the causes of cancers by examining large popula-tions. In addition, there continues to be a huge expenditure on developing and evaluating new pharmacological preparations for use as anti-cancer drugs. In this chapter, we review the methods and contributions of biology and epidemiology to current knowledge of malignant disease. In the process, questions emerge about priorities for the future, which inevitably take us into the political dimension. Let us begin with biology.

Biological explanations for cancers
Scientific enquiry has tended to follow a reductionist path. The biological investigation of cancers began with the microscopic examination of malignant cells to compare them with normal ones. As equipment and knowledge

improved, research focused first on the molecules secreted or utilised by cancer cells and then on the genes.

☐ What other methods of investigation might a biologist use to discover what causes cancers?

■ The three principal avenues of investigation involve experimental animals. First, chemicals, radiation, infectious organisms, certain foods or living conditions can be tested on animals to see if they are carcinogenic (cause cancers). Second, the physiological state of the animals (for example, the concentrations of hormones and the activity of the immune system) can be altered to see if this affects the development of cancers. Third, the propensity of animals of slightly different genetic make-ups to develop cancers can be compared.

Using these methods a number of chemicals (for example, benzene and the vinyl chlorides used in some plastics) have been identified as carcinogenic and suspicion has·been cast on many others. (You may recall the 'scare' about the artificial sweeteners known as cyclamates because of disputed research findings that they might be carcinogenic in animals.) There is no dispute that certain types of radiation can cause cancers, as the experience of Hiroshima and Nagasaki tragically demonstrated, and as numerous animal experiments have confirmed.

There has also been a limited success in the search for organisms that cause cancers to develop, or at least make them more likely.* Bladder cancer is more common in people infested with schistosoma flukes and viruses have been implicated in a few human cancers, but the list is not long. It includes some skin cancers (including one called Kaposi sarcoma which is frequently found in AIDS sufferers), a cancer of the immune system called Burkitt's lymphoma (after the same researcher referred to in Chapter 2 as stressing the role of refined flour in causing appendicitis), which is mainly confined to Africa, a type of leukaemia that is rare outside Japan and a liver cancer that is associated with the virus that causes hepatitis. There is speculation that some other cancers of the immune system (leukaemias and lymphomas) may also involve viruses, and we have already mentioned the evidence pointing towards a virus as one of the factors precipitating cancer of the cervix. Note that in most of these cancers the virus *alone* does not seem able to cause the disease. A cluster of factors — for example, geographical location, or an individual whose health is already compromised (AIDS), or the additional presence of dust particles or certain chemicals — must coincide. Bacteria in the gut may also play a part

in digestive tract cancers by forming carcinogenic substances as waste products of metabolism.

The question of a hereditary predisposition to develop cancers has also yielded rather little to biological investigation. It has certainly proved possible to produce 'cancer-prone' strains of laboratory rats and mice by careful inbreeding, but no equivalent exists in 'wild' rodent populations. The proof that, in human beings, cancer does not normally 'run in families' was actually provided by epidemiological investigation — of which more later.

This extremely brief review of the biological contribution to discovering the *causes* of cancers may have left you with the feeling that biological research has not made much of an impact. This is broadly true — the precise chemical component of tobacco smoke that causes lung cells to become malignant has still not been identified — whereas epidemiological research established the causal link between tobacco smoking and lung cancers several decades ago. Given the myriad of different chemicals (natural and synthetic) in the world, it is easy to see, however, why so few of them have been fully tested. The *major* contribution that biologists have made to cancer research is in answering the question 'What *are* cancers?', rather than 'What causes cancers?' The quotation with which we began this chapter claimed that 'the nature of cancer is perfectly understood', but even in the past decade (1974–84) a profound shift has taken place in the way that biologists describe cancer cells. In 1983, Graham Currie, Director of the Marie Curie Memorial Research Institute, described it in these terms†:

Cancer research has in the past few years undergone a radical revolution in methods and ideas, and it is worth examining the kind of thinking about cancer which preceded this revolution and which has, I believe, been overthrown by it.

Perhaps the most noticeable theme was the assumption that cancer cells are very different from normal cells and that an exhaustive search for significant and consistent qualitative biochemical differences between normal and malignant tissues would eventually provide suitable targets for therapeutic attack.

It was assumed that a mass onslaught of biochemical expertise would uncover these differences, would identify novel aberrant metabolic pathways which could for example be blocked by suitable chemical compounds. The biochemistry of cancer, a somewhat random but extensive application of studies of cellular metabolism, after 60 years of

---

*The relationship of infectious diseases to cancer has been explored in *The Biology of Health and Disease* (U205, Book IV).

†The changes in cell biology in cancers are dealt with more fully in *The Biology of Health and Disease* (U205 *Health and Disease*, Book IV).

intense effort has failed to uncover any such consistent qualitative differences between normal and malignant.

Progress was essentially empirical, serendipity providing most of the modest advances in experimental and clinical oncology. Cancer was in general regarded as a condition characterized by *loss*; loss of differentiation, loss of organization and loss of growth control. This latter concept was and is particularly insidious. It presupposes the existence of a system of growth control, envisaged as a form of negative feedback evolved to cope with the innate mitotic exuberance of cells. Recent progress in molecular biology has, however, made this and other similar concepts quite obsolete.

Perhaps the most significant conclusion that can be drawn from recent studies of malignant transformation at the molecular level is that difference between normal and malignant cellular behaviour are the consequences of quantitative changes in gene expression. Cancer is now better understood as the consequences of the acquisition of proliferative autonomy, a *gain* rather than a loss.

The inappropriate activation of a range of genes encoding proteins responsible for various cellular behavioural phenomena involved in proliferation, differentiation, or embryogenesis could thereby result in the apparently complex series of phenomena known as malignant transformation. There is, after all, no feature of the behaviour of cancer cells which is not shared at one time or another by normal cells. (Graham Currie, 1983)

□ What are the principal differences in the behaviour of normal and malignant cells?

■ Malignant cells are characterised by their ability to divide more frequently than their normal counterparts, their enhanced mobility and their reduced adhesiveness to each other, resulting in failure to stop moving when in contact with other cells (contact inhibition). These factors enable them to grow into surrounding tissues. They also exhibit varying degrees of reversion to a less differentiated state (i.e. they look less and less like the normal specialised cells of the tissue of origin and more like the unspecialised cells of an early embryo).

□ What does Currie mean by the phrase 'innate mitotic exuberance of cells', and why does he consider this concept to be obsolete?

■ The phrase describes the notion, once prevalent in cancer biology, that cells have an 'inborn' or genetically programmed tendency to divide repeatedly (undergo mitosis) and are restrained from doing so by mechanisms that prevent further growth when the 'normal' number of cells has been achieved. According to such a view, failure of the control mechanisms exposes the 'innate mitotic exuberance', and cancers result. Current thinking presents cancer cells as having acquired 'proliferative autonomy' (i.e. the ability to go on dividing) by *regaining* faculties they once possessed (in the embryo) rather than by *losing* controls on their growth.

□ Currie states that malignant transformation is the consequence of 'quantitative changes in gene expression'. What does this mean?

■ A gene is said to be 'expressed' (rather than 'repressed') when the sequence of DNA bases that it contains is translated into a precise sequence of amino acids, linked together to form a particular protein — the so-called product of the gene. 'Quantitative changes in gene expression' refers to the theory that a number of genes that have been repressed since embryonic development become activated in cancer cells and that these genes are not *qualitatively* different from equivalent genes found in non-malignant cells. This is the so-called *oncogene* theory.

The revolution in biological explanations for cancers that Graham Currie describes has profound implications for the way in which all of us view the disease. As you saw in the previous chapter, there is a deeply held belief that cancer is a foreign, sinister, polluting and possibly contagious sickness that creeps through the body by stealth. It is curious that biological descriptions of the disease have hitherto borne a significant resemblance to the lay model. Cancer cells were routinely described by biologists as *foreign* (an adjective still used in immunology), which implies that malignant cells are qualitatively different from 'normal' cells in the body. It was confidently predicted that the immune system had evolved partly to destroy cancer cells as they arose and very considerable research effort was devoted to discovering the details of this apparently logical relationship. As long as cancers were seen as 'foreign invaders' possessing non-self molecules on their surface membranes and the immune system was regarded as a 'defensive armoury', the compelling symmetry of these military metaphors led to confident predictions that a so-called *immune surveillance system* that could recognise and hence destroy incipient cancer cells must exist. However, the new view is that cancer cells are best seen as reversions to less specialised, more embryonic forms — there is thus no longer reason to predict that bizarre molecules which would be recognised by the immune system will appear on their surface membrane. (In fact, some human cancer cells have surface molecules that are normally found only on embryonic cells and may therefore be used in diagnosis or treatment as 'identification labels' for the presence of certain cancers, even though they do not stimulate an immune response).

As can be seen from the following quotations, the new biological description of cancer cells is taking some time to filter through. Even in orthodox medicine, outdated explanations of malignant disease as foreign and subject to immune attack are still being taught in the mid-1980s. Equally, the alternative therapy movement has some rethinking to do because the rationale given for holistic methods, from vegetarian diets to acupuncture and psychotherapy, flow from the old metaphors. The methods *may* work, but the rationale is almost certainly wrong: for example, consider these two extracts from articles about cancer treatment.

Cancer cells are common to us all

Many people are not aware that each one of us continually produces cancer cells in our bodies; cells which, for the most part, are kept in balance by the body's immune system. ... If the body's own natural defence system can be brought back into action, healing will almost always follow. (Bristol Cancer Help Centre, 1983)

Meditation and cancer

It seems likely that a number of different psychophysiological responses are called into play by intensive meditation. The general reduction in the habitual level of anxiety reduces cortisone with consequent freeing of the immune system to act more effectively against the cancer. (Meares, 1982, p.1608)

Finally, it is worth noting that the dominant biological explanation for cancers inevitably influences the types of treatment deemed worthy of investigation. Orthodox medical treatment of malignant diseases has hitherto been in harmony with the military metaphors that symbolise cancers as growths to be attacked, cut out, bombarded with radiation, or poisoned with chemicals (some of which are actually derived from mustard gas developed for military use in the First World War). As new biological concepts have emerged, so novel and innovative treatment strategies have begun to be evaluated. One technique arises from the observation that when cancer cells from humans are injected into rats and mice they may evoke the production of antibodies. Immune cells from these rodents can then be induced to multiply in tissue culture and to 'churn out' quantities of antibodies that bind to human tumours. These antibodies can be linked to radioactive or poisonous molecules and *in theory* they can be injected into patients where they will be 'targeted' onto the cancer cells. The snag is that at the moment these antibodies bind to many normal tissues as well as to malignant ones (i.e. their specificity is low) and, because they are *mouse* or *rat* proteins, the

human patient's immune system soon begins to respond against them. Another technique aims to overcome the problem of repopulating the patient's bone marrow with normal immune and other blood cells after 'whole body' radiation treatment for widespread cancers has destroyed them. Before the radiation treatment a large amount of the patient's own bone marrow is removed, and the cancer cells it contains are destroyed by the mouse or rat antibodies described above, before being returned to the patient. In one method, the antibodies are linked to microscopic iron beads and after they have bound to the cancer cells, the bone marrow is 'cleaned up' by passing it over magnets.

These potential therapies are still reductionist: they aim to target a lethal agent onto the surface membrane of cancer cells so as to 'get inside' the malignant cells and switch off the genes that are causing them to multiply. The 'new biology', as much as the old, still promises molecular cures for cancers.

As you will see in a moment, epidemiological research has tended to be more concerned with prevention. The metaphors for cancers that biology provides may, however, have a powerful influence on the way we think about malignant disease. If we no longer think of cancer cells as 'foreign' — in some sense dirty, polluting, infective parasites in our bodies — we may be able to devise treatments that have less in common with the strategies of modern warfare and seek to *reverse* the malignant process rather than to attack its progeny.

The contribution of epidemiology

Epidemiologists have made little contribution to our understanding of what cancers *are*, but have made significant inroads into discovering the *causes* of cancers. Just as the methods of biological science are particularly suited to answering some questions and not others, so the methods employed by epidemiologists circumscribe a particular area of inquiry.*

☐ What methods might epidemiologists use to study the distribution of cancers in a population?

■ There are four principal methods.

1 *Descriptive studies.* These either measure the incidence of various cancers in populations and compare the rates for different countries, for different areas within countries and for different biosocial factors such as age, gender and social class, or estimate secular trends in incidence and mortality (that is, changes over time) and changes from one birth cohort to the next.

2 *Case-control studies.* These compare individuals who have the disease with controls matched for age, gender and class to elucidate whether the cases have

---

*These methods are discussed more fully in *Studying Health and Disease* (U205, Book I).

some common feature not shared by the controls.

3 *Cohort studies*. These compare cancer rates in individuals matched for all the usual biosocial variables but differing in a single parameter such as smoking, occupation, use of contraceptive pills, etc.

4 *Migrant studies*. These compare the incidence of cancers among migrants with the incidence among people in their country of origin and natives of their adopted country.

These methods have enabled epidemiologists to begin unravelling the thorny problem of how such diverse factors as age, nationality, occupation, diet, sexual behaviour and tobacco consumption interact in the development of certain cancers. The most clear-cut success has been to show the association of cigarette smoking with lung cancer, in very large measure due to the work of the British epidemiologists, Richard Doll, Bradford Hill and Richard Peto. Among many other studies, Doll and Peto (1976) published the results of a 20-year follow-up study of over 34 000 male British doctors, recording their smoking habits and mortality during this period. By comparing the health of smokers with that of non-smokers and those who had given up the habit, Doll and Peto were able to conclude that smoking was a direct cause of lung cancer, even when age and class variations were allowed for. Figure 4.1 charts the convincing 'fit' between the increase in cigarette smoking and lung cancer in the UK population as a whole this century. About one-third of all cancer deaths in the UK have some association with smoking because some cancers other than lung cancer also occur more frequently among smokers (e.g. bladder cancer).

If people stopped smoking it would drastically reduce mortality from lung cancer and from several other common causes of death such as bronchitis and ischaemic heart disease. Are *other* cancers also preventable? Doll and Peto estimate that over 75 per cent of cancer deaths in industrialised countries are *in principle* avoidable. The evidence for this stems from epidemiological data on the enormous variation in cancer rates in different population groups around the world, and across time. For instance, cancer of the skin is high in Queensland, Australia and low in Bombay, India; liver cancer is high in Mozambique and low in England; breast cancer is high in Canada and low among non-Jews in Israel. Sometimes rates in high-incidence areas are 200 or 300 times higher than in low-incidence areas.

☐ Can you think of two possible explanations for such variations?

■ Either these cancers arise as a result of exposure to one or more causative agents that occur more frequently in high-incidence areas than in low ones, or the genetic composition of different races produces variations in

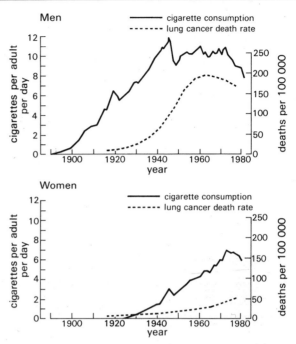

Figure 4.1 Cigarette consumption in the UK (average per adult per day) compared with age-standardized death rates from lung cancers for men and women aged 45–64 (Royal College of Physicians, 1977, Figure 4.1, p.53, and 1983, Figures 1.1 and 1.2, pp.1 and 4).

the propensity or resistance to developing cancers.

Migrant studies are ideally suited to testing the second hypothesis and have consistently disproved it. For example, breast cancer has a low incidence among Japanese women living in Japan, but those who migrated to the USA show rates of this disease rising in successive generations to reach the American rate. Similarly, black Americans of West African descent develop cancer of the colon as frequently as white Americans, but ten times as often as West Africans in their native land.

There are also significant variations in cancer rates for different parts of the same country as Figure 4.2 shows. Even when the mortality data are standardised to allow for regional variations in population size and age distribution (as here), striking differences emerge among different parts of the country and, occasionally (for example, bladder cancer), between the sexes.

Analysis of even smaller areas has enabled sources of carcinogenic substances to be located. For example, in 1965 two surgeons, Macbeth and Hadfield, proposed a causal connection between the 'clusters' of cancer of the nose and nasal sinuses in their areas and the presence of local factories manufacturing furniture. It has since been

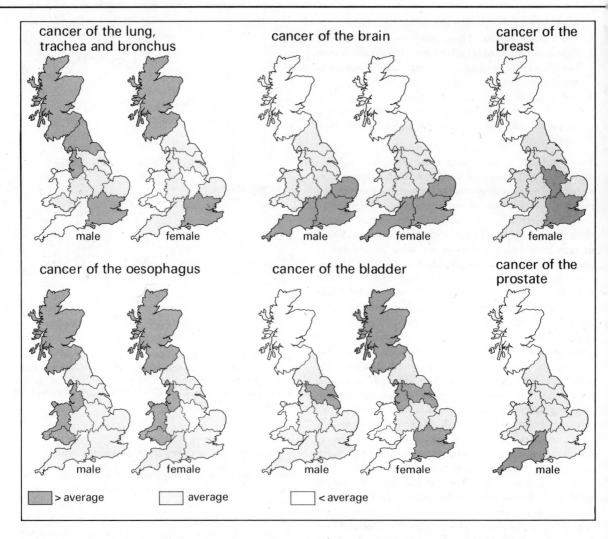

Figure 4.2 Variations in the distribution of deaths from certain cancers. The darkest regions have mortality rates above the national average and the lightest regions have lower than average rates. (Maps based on data from the Census Offices of England, Wales and Scotland.)

established that prolonged exposure to inhaled wood dust may lead to nasal cancer.

Such variations in cancer rates on such an international and local scale may be caused by differences in exposure to carcinogens. It is this which leads to the estimate that 75 per cent of all cancers could be avoided. There is, however, a considerable difference between these theoretical estimates and putting preventive measures into action. There are several reasons for this — some practical, others political. Let us begin by reviewing the practical problems.

The first difficulty is that relatively few substances have been reliably identified as carcinogens, as Table 4.1 shows, although there is intense speculation about many other substances. The second is that most cancers appear to

develop only after the cell has suffered several 'insults', possibly separated by many years. Thus for most cancers several factors must combine before a cell becomes malignant and disentangling their relative contributions from a mass of epidemiological data is exceedingly difficult. For example, consider a family in which a greater than expected number of cancers develop.

☐ Does this indicate that the members of the family have some genetic predisposition to develop cancers, or are there other possible explanations?

■ They may simply have shared the same 'carcinogenic' environment. They may all have lived in a certain house at some stage in their lives, or worked in the same

Table 4.1 Recognised causes of human cancers

Carcinogen	Reason for exposure	Site of cancer	Carcinogen	Reason for exposure	Site of cancer
aflatoxin	consumption of unprotected food in tropics	liver	isopropylene	manufacturing	nasal sinuses
			mustard gas	manufacturing	bronchus, larynx, nasal sinuses
alkylating agents: cyclophosphamide melphalan	medical treatment of cancers	bladder	nickel ores	refining	bronchus, nasal sinuses
anabolic steroids	medical treatment	liver	oestrogens (diethylstilbo-estrol, premarin)	exposure in utero medical treatment	vagina (adenocarcinoma) corpus uteri
aromatic amines	manufacture of chemicals, coal-gas, rubber articles	bladder	phenacetin	medical treatment	renal pelvis
arsenic	manufacture of pesticides, mining (some mines), medical treatment	skin, bronchus	polycyclic hydro-carbons	work involving exposure to combustion products of coal and certain mineral oils	skin, rectum, bronchus
benzene	work with glues, varnishes, etc.	marrow (leukaemia)	quid composed of mixture of betel and lime	chewing	mouth
bis (chloromethyl) ether	manufacture of ion-exchange resins	bronchus	tobacco smoke	smoking, particularly cigarettes	bronchus, mouth, pharynx, larynx, oesophagus, bladder, pancreas
cadmium	refining	prostate			
chlornaphazine	medical treatment	bladder			
chrome ores	manufacture of chromates	bronchus	ultraviolet light	exposure to sunlight	skin, including melanoma
ethanol (alcohol)	consumption	mouth, pharynx, larynx, oesophagus	wood dust	manufacture of hardwood furniture	nasal sinuses (especially adenocarcinoma)
immuno-suppression (azathioprine plus prednesol)	medical treatment	non-Hodgkin's lymphoma, skin (squamous carcinoma), various other rare sites	vinyl chloride	manufacture of PVC	liver (angiosarcoma)
			?	some industrial uses of rubber	bronchus
ionizing radiations	mining (some mines), use of X-rays, radium, medical treatment, luminous dial painting, nuclear warfare, nuclear reprocessing	all sites, but particularly leukaemias and lymphomas	?	some work in leather and shoe industry	nasal sinuses
			?	heavy urinary infection with schistosomiasis	bladder

(Data from Doll, 1980, p.2480)

industry, or even lived downwind of a source of industrial pollution. Equally, they may have adopted similar carcinogenic 'habits' (e.g. smoking, diet).

This is best illustrated by considering the 'risk factors' for cancer of the breast in women (men occasionally get it too!) as shown in Table 4.2, overleaf.

The table lists the risk factors, and describes the size of the risk involved. For example, the first line states that (i) age affects a person's chance of developing breast cancer (i.e. age is a risk factor), (ii) old people ('high risk') are more likely to develop the disease than young ('low risk'), (iii) old people are more than four times as likely to develop the disease as young people ('relative risk greater than 4').

□ What underlying causes are suggested by the risks associated with (a) socioeconomic status, (b) age at menarche, first pregnancy and menopause and (c) a first-degree relative (mother or sister) who has breast cancer?

■ (a) The association with higher social class suggests an underlying cause that is characteristic of 'affluent' living, possibly diet. (b) The reproductive 'milestones' indicate a hormonal factor at work. (c) There is an indication here of genetic predisposition to the disease.

The association with 'affluence' is borne out by the national distribution of breast cancer, which has a greater

Table 4.2 Risk factors for breast cancer

Factor	'High' risk	'Low' risk	Relative risk (high versus low)
age	older	younger	greater than 4
ethnic group (post-menopause)	white	black	less than 2
socioeconomic status	upper	lower	2 to 4 times
country of residence	North America, Europe	Asia, Africa	greater than 4
marital status	never married	ever married	less than 2
weight	overweight	thin	less than 2
age at menarche (first menstruation)	early	late	2 to 4 times
age at menopause	late	early	less than 2
age at first full-term pregnancy	older than 30	younger than 20	2 to 4 times
parity (number of full-term pregnancies)	none	several	less than 2
family history of cancer in both breasts before menopause	positive	negative	greater than 4
mother or sister with breast cancer	positive	negative	2 to 4 times
past history of benign breast disease	positive	negative	2 to 4 times
past history of cancer in ovary or uterus	positive	negative	2 to 4 times
exposure to ionising radiation (especially to the chest)	heavy exposure	light exposure	2 to 4 times

(Data from Kalache, 1981)

incidence in most industrialised countries than in the Third World. This has led to the notion that a diet rich in fats and sugars is to blame. Figure 4.3 shows the relationship between breast cancer rates for different countries plotted against the fat content of their diet.

☐ Does this prove that fatty diets cause breast cancer?

■ No. There are many other aspects of affluent living that could (in theory) be involved, for example, alcohol consumption, industrial pollution, oral contraceptives, etc. — all of which are less common in Third World countries.

In fact, similar scattergrams result if the sugar content of national diets is plotted against breast cancer rates, or the meat content against rates of cancer of the colon, or if the Gross National Product is plotted against deaths from all cancers combined. Even the number of telephones per head gives a reasonably good correlation with overall cancer rates! No-one knows precisely which aspects of a nation's way of life are responsible for enhancing or reducing cancer rates. The indications are that diets with relatively low fat and sugar content and relatively high proportions of plant fibre may be protective against certain cancers, particularly those of the digestive system and breast. Excessively salty, spicey or pickled foods may also play a part in stomach and colon cancers, if eaten daily.

We shall return to the subject of diet and cancers in a moment, but first we must conclude the discussion of 'risk' in relation to breast cancer. The association of hormonally

controlled events with this cancer has stimulated research into the incidence of breast cancer in women who have been long-term users of contraceptive pills. At the time of writing, nothing conclusive can be said on this matter, although there are signs that certain 'high-dose' formula-

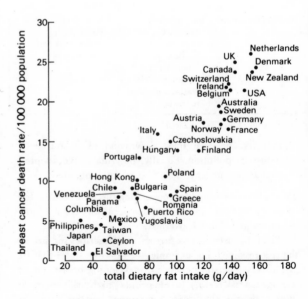

Figure 4.3 Animal and vegetable fat consumption in various countries and the risk of death from breast cancer in these countries. The data are adjusted for age. (Carroll, 1975, p.3374).

tions may increase the risk of breast cancer slightly if taken for a prolonged period by very young women. Finally, it is worth noting that breast cancer is one of the few cancers to show even a mild hereditary component; cancers do not generally 'run in families'. Thus a number of interacting factors make it unlikely that there will ever be a simple answer to the question, 'How can breast cancer be prevented?' Most other cancers have an equally complex aetiology and raise similar problems for preventive strategies.

Another practical problem facing those who would devise ways to prevent cancers stems from disagreements about the *relative* contribution of different categories of carcinogen to the overall mortality rates. If you turn back to Table 4.1 you will see that the most numerous entries are for substances involved in manufacturing and other industrial processes such as mining; the next most frequent category is medical treatment; there is only one entry for diet (food contaminated with aflatoxin — a tropical mould) and three for 'social drugs' — alcohol, tobacco and betel nuts. In fact, the greatest *proportion* of cancers attributable to a known carcinogen result from the consumption of tobacco (around 30 per cent of the total), and perhaps another 3 per cent result from the excessive intake of alcohol. Despite the numerous references to medical treatment in Table 4.1, this accounts for no more than 1 per cent of all cancers — paradoxically, carcinogenic drugs and radiation are most often used in the treatment of cancers! It is the remaining two categories — diet and industrial processes — that have proved contentious: there are those who attribute at least 30 per cent of cancers to diet; others claim the same rate for industrial processes. The main reason why these two apparently separate categories have proved hard to disentangle is that, at least in theory, they overlap.

Diets in industrialised countries contain many food additives such as synthetic colourings, flavourings and preservatives which are absent from Third World diets. There has been intense speculation that these additives, rather than the absolute fat or sugar content, are the cause of cancers. (However, artificial preservatives added to foods may have contributed to the *decline* in stomach cancer that has occurred in recent years.) The hypothesis has also been put forward that carcinogenic pesticides and fertilisers may contaminate our food, or that pollutants from industrial processes are the culprits. These may be taken into our bodies dissolved in dietary fats, particularly fats from cows grazing on polluted grassland. All this raises a problem for preventive strategies — should we concentrate as individuals on altering our eating habits, or should we be lobbying governments to legislate against food additives or certain industrial and agricultural chemicals? This same debate occurs even more strongly in other aspects of cancer

prevention where the causative agent is known. The problem of reconciling 'individual freedoms' to smoke cigarettes with the millions spent on advertising by the tobacco industry is the most obvious example. In other words, cancer has a political dimension, too.

The politics of cancer

As tobacco is the only proved cause of large numbers of cancer and other deaths each year, the political debate about preventing those deaths is more clear-cut than for other cancers. However, that is not to say that there is an easy solution. In the UK, it has been estimated that 30 million working days are lost each year as a result of absence through smoking-related diseases. There is a considerable additional cost in sickness benefits, and around £150 million is spent annually by the National Health Service on treatment. 101 billion cigarettes are sold annually in the UK, 80 per cent of the price going to the Treasury in tobacco duty — over £4 000 million sterling in a year. Although there was a fall of about 20 per cent in cigaret e sales during the 1970s, British tobacco consumption was showing signs of stabilising around 1983-84.

   ☐   What would be the main sources of *financial* gain and loss if the British government chose to ban cigarette sales altogether?

   ■   There would be a reduction in costs associated with the provision of medical services. Fewer working days would be lost. There would be a saving on sickness benefits, disablement pensions, insurance payments after fires, and less would be spent on cleaning public places such as trains, cinemas, etc. On the other hand, there would be a loss of revenue from tobacco duty, and job losses in the tobacco industry, including sales and advertising, would lead to an increase in the amount paid as unemployment benefit. The cost of retirement pensions would rise because large numbers of people would live longer. In addition, there would be complex effects on trade and the balance of payments, because all tobacco is imported into the UK.

This complex web of interactions illustrates the difficulty of reducing cancers related to smoking. In what sense are individuals genuinely 'free' to choose whether to smoke when tobacco is itself addictive, peer-pressure may be strong and advertisements create a free-and-easy sporty, sexy, or glamorous image for their products? Relatively little is spent on anti-smoking propaganda or on clinics, and the nicotine-chewing gum used to help people quit can be obtained only on private prescription. Governments generally confine their actions to limiting advertising, putting up prices by raising the duty, and having a health warning printed on packets and advertisements. To do otherwise might prove to be financial and political suicide.

Debates about who is to blame for the failure to prevent avoidable cancers have sometimes made a distinction between factors that an *individual* may be able to alter for themselves and those that require *government intervention*. The former (sometimes dubbed 'personal life-style factors') include smoking, the consumption of alcohol, diet and sexual behaviour. None of these factors can be seen as wholly personal, as illustrated by the pressures an individual faces when deciding whether or not to smoke. However, other possible sources of carcinogens in our environment come from industrial or manufacturing processes and are difficult for individuals to identify, let alone tackle. An extract, 'Cancer and work: guidelines for workers taking collective action over health hazards', from an advisory document published by the General, Municipal, Boilermakers and Allied Trades Union for their members, illustrates the extreme difficulties faced by employees in obtaining evidence of occupational exposure to carcinogens. The extract is included in the Course Reader, Part 7, Section 7.7.* Read it if you have time.

The dichotomy between 'personal life-style' and 'industrial' sources of carcinogens is partly spurious, but the phrases serve as convenient labels with which to analyse a significant controversy in cancer causation. In 1978 a book called *The Politics of Cancer* appeared, written by the American epidemiologist Samuel Epstein. It achieved wide publicity and was referred to in political debates on cancer causation. Epstein claimed first that cancer rates *other* than those related to smoking were *rising* at the rate of 1 per cent per year in the USA and, second, that 20 to 40 per cent of all cancers are caused by carcinogenic food additives, industrial pollution and agricultural chemicals. According to this analysis, 'diet' simply serves as a carrier for these substances, which it is claimed dissolve easily in fats. In 1983, a second book followed, *Cancer in Britain: The Politics of Prevention* by a group including Epstein and headed by sociologist, Lesley Doyal. The message was the same as for the USA: not only were employees of certain industries at risk, but the general public were as well, on a hitherto unrecognised scale.

That some industrial processes have exposed workers to carcinogenic substances has long been proved (as Table 4.1 documents), and on occasion carcinogenic emissions have affected neighbouring communities. For example, British Nuclear Fuels have accepted that more than thirty deaths from thyroid cancer resulted from a fire at their Windscale plant (now renamed Sellafield) in 1957, which released a cloud of radioactive iodine over a nearby village, and the question of whether the incidence of leukaemia around Sellafield is higher than the national rates is still contentious

*Black, Nick *et al.* (1984) *Health and Disease: A Reader*, Open University Press.

in 1984. But there has been a heated and at times acrimonious disagreement about the *relative* contribution of industrial carcinogens to the overall incidence of cancers. Epstein's interpretation of the epidemiological data was criticized most strongly in the UK by Richard Peto, who demonstrated convincingly that cancer rates overall were *falling* not rising, both here and in the USA. He also disputed Epstein's claim that 20 to 40 per cent of cancers were related to industrialisation and, with Richard Doll, put forward estimates that this figure is closer to 5 per cent. Doll and Peto's book, *The Causes of Cancer*, published in 1981, firmly asserts that the majority of cancers are due to smoking, alcohol, sexually transmitted viruses and certain aspects of diet. They point out, among many other strands of evidence, that Japan is heavily industrialised, yet has cancer rates that correlate closely with its low-fat, high-fibre diet (see Figure 4.3.)

☐ Can you see any adverse consequences arising from the polarisation of arguments about the causes of cancers into 'personal life-style' versus 'industrial'?

■ Emphasis placed on personal life-style may result in victims being blamed for their own disease; also industry may become complacent about the need to introduce controls over the escape of possible carcinogens, which might affect profitability. On the other hand, too much emphasis on industrial causes might lead to complacency on the part of individuals. Why stop smoking if cancer is all the fault of the factory down the road?

So far we have discussed some of the political implications of epidemiological data about the *causes* of cancers, but have neglected another important dimension. Epidemiology has also supplied the data on which *interventions* aimed at reducing cancer deaths or prolonging the lives of cancer patients are evaluated. Two examples with sharp political implications need to be considered briefly: screening for early detection of cancers and research aimed at developing new anti-cancer drugs.

Screening for cancers
National cancer screening programmes have always made a good impression on the public — something that governments consider carefully. As the rates of three cancers that kill large numbers of people (cancers of the lungs, cervix and breast) have risen there has been considerable pressure to initiate mass screening, and health services have often been keen to oblige. However, screening is only of value if an effective treatment exists — the abandoned screening programme for lung cancers testifies to this. But what about cancer of the cervix, where early treatment does reduce mortality? A comparison of the effects of cervical screening on UK and Scandinavian

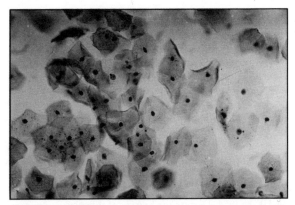

Figure 4.4 Cells from cervical smears (magnified about 300 times): (a) normal cells lining the cervix have a characteristic appearance — they are large polygonal, flat cells with small, regular nuclei;

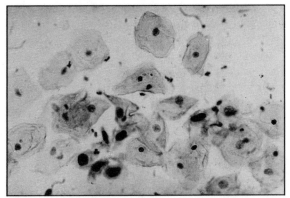

(b) a few cells in this smear look suspiciously like 'early' cancer cells — their nuclei are large, irregularly shaped and stain darkly;

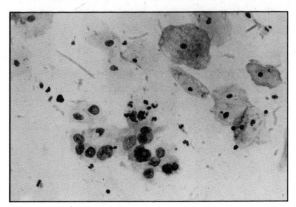

(c) the cells on the left of this smear are definitely malignant — they bear no resemblance to normal cervical cells.

mortality rates from this cancer illustrates a problem of interpreting the results. In Scandinavia, reductions of 30 to 60 per cent in mortality from cervical cancer occurred in the

10 to 15 years after screening by the 'smear' test was introduced. Figure 4.4 shows the signs of malignant change for which people are being screened. In the UK, mortality from cancer of the cervix has not shown much reduction in the past 20 years, even though 30 million smear tests have been performed. Indeed, in recent years rates of this cancer have even begun to rise. Of course, it may be that without those tests, mortality from cancer of the cervix would have risen sooner and faster, but it remains the case that the UK screening programme has not been as successful as its Scandinavian counterpart. How can this be explained, as the 'smear test' used is the same?

The answer seems to lie in the administration of the programme. In Scandinavian countries around 90 per cent of women are screened at regular intervals as a result of a nationally coordinated policy of personal invitations to women of all ages to attend a screening clinic. In the UK, attendance is much more haphazard. Although in some areas personal invitations have begun to be used, the majority of women who are screened are 'trawled' into the programme via Family Planning Clinics or by their general practitioners during consultations for contraceptive advice, prescription of the pill and devices such as the coil or cap. Women outside this group tend to be exhorted to attend mainly by advertisements or leaflets in doctors' waiting rooms, such as the one shown in Figure 4.5.

□ Can you see a problem with the usual method of bringing women into the screening programme in the UK?

■ Cancer of the cervix (like almost all cancers) increases in incidence with increasing age. The present method of recruitment predominantly reaches younger women during their reproductive years.

This problem was highlighted by an investigation into the screening history of 100 women diagnosed as having cancer of the cervix in 1983 in the South West Thames Regional Health Authority. The study (by Ruth Ellman and Jocelyn Chamberlain) revealed that 68 per cent of the women had never been screened, and 88 per cent of these were over 40 years old. An additional complication is that cancer of the cervix is more common among working-class than middle-class women. (The possible reasons for this were discussed in Chapter 3.) Working-class women are less likely to use the screening service than women from middle-class families, and hence another high-risk group slips through the net. Jocelyn Chamberlain has argued that: 'For the service to be effective we must take positive steps to recruit a higher proportion of older women into the screening programme, even if this means extending the interval between repeated smears offered to young women.' (Chamberlain, 1983, p.284)

Figure 4.5 *Mary Makes up her Mind* — a leaflet prepared by the Lancashire Health Authority (in collaboration with the Manchester Regional Committee on Cancer) as part of a public education campaign aimed at overcoming fear of having a cervical smear test (cytotest).

Thus, the *organisation* of a screening programme can undermine its effectiveness even if the available treatment is known to save lives.* It is also worth raising the question of emotional cost to the person being screened. How reliable are the tests? What about 'false' positive results, or the detection of premalignant changes that would have reverted to normal but which may lead to the treatment of women who do not have cancer? We must also ask does the screening test 'set the mind at rest' as the advertising claims, or are some people left in a state of anxiety about their health? This has been the subject of argument (but scant

*The economic and medical issues surrounding screening for cancers, among other diseases, are discussed in *Caring for Health; Dilemmas and Prospects*. The Open University (1985) *Caring for Health: Dilemmas and Prospects,* The Open University Press (U205, Book VIII).

research) in relation to cervical smears where only women whose test results are abnormal receive notification. The majority hear nothing and some women are distressed by this. It has also been argued that encouraging women to examine their own breasts every month for signs of breast cancer (see Figure 4.6) promotes a general fearfulness about the disease. Critics raise the spectre of a nation of women anxiously exploring their breasts and detecting lumps that for the most part are innocuous. Others think that self-examination helps women to regain power over their own health. At present there is no firm evidence that breast self-examination is effective in saving or prolonging lives, although a major controlled trial was being conducted in the UK in 1984. Despite the brevity of this discussion, you should be in no doubt that there are considerable difficulties in evaluating the effectiveness of screening — not only for cancers, but for other diseases too.

Finally, let us conclude this examination of the political dimension of malignant disease by considering research expenditure aimed at improving treatment.

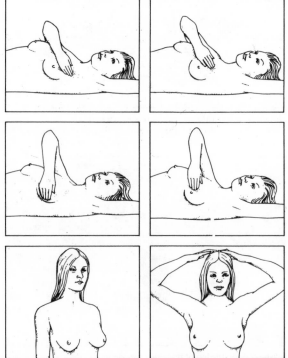

Figure 4.6 The method advised for carrying out self-examination of the breasts for 'early' detection of breast cancer. Each breast is examined with the flat of the hand while lying down and then the contour is checked in a mirror with arms raised and lowered. (Curling, 1981, p.1350)

Cancer chemotherapy

In 1980, the UK Department of Health and Social Security estimated that the total expenditure on drugs for cancer chemotherapy in that year was £40 million sterling. In some specialist cancer hospitals in Britain the drugs bill may swallow up 12–14 per cent of the hospital's annual budget, including staff salaries, running costs and the costs of treatments that are not based on drugs, such as radiotherapy and surgery. The problem is not so much the large numbers of drugs used to treat cancers as their enormous unit costs. The cost of treating a child for osteogenic sarcoma (a bone cancer) was estimated at £16 460 for the drugs alone at 1983 prices.

Why are the drugs used in cancer chemotherapy so expensive? Part of the answer lies in the very precise biological effects that they must produce. Malignant cells are very similar to other cells in the body, except that they divide more frequently than most (but by no means all) 'normal' cells. Anti-cancer drugs, like radiotherapy, exploit the fact that the DNA in a cell is most vulnerable to irreparable damage when the cell is in the act of dividing. Thus, the drugs used to treat cancers must be capable of inflicting damage selectively on dividing cells without harming 'resting' ones, even when the drug is dispersed throughout the body in the bloodstream. This is a tall order and drugs with this ability have proved to be exceedingly difficult to synthesise.

Cancers, however, are a major cause of morbidity and mortality in industrialised countries, so there is an enormous market for new anti-cancer drugs. Consequently, pharmaceutical companies have invested huge sums in cancer chemotherapy research. Investment has not only been by private companies: public funds have been allocated on a massive scale, especially in the USA. Around US $1 000 million is spent annually on biomedical research into cancer in the USA and at least US $100 million of this is devoted to the National Cancer Institute's programme of research into and development of new anti-cancer drugs. (Compare this with the £56 million sterling spent annually in the UK — £40 million of which comes from the various cancer charities.) This programme began in 1955 with the modest sum of US $5 million and its achievements since that time are described by Emil Frei III, from Harvard University, in an article 'The national cancer chemotherapy program' reprinted in the Course Reader, Part 7, Section 7.3. Read this article now and, as you do so, consider a question that Frei does not address — why are 'successful' drugs so costly?

Table 4.3 summarises the main types of substances screened by the National Cancer Institute in the USA between 1955 and 1982 as quoted by Frei.

☐ How many of these substances were considered to be sufficiently active anti-cancer drugs to warrant a

Table 4.3 Screening by the US National Cancer Institute for drugs with potential in cancer chemotherapy, 1955–82.

Type of substance screened	Approximate number of substances screened
synthetic chemicals	350 000
heavy metal compounds	2 500
fermentation products (mainly antibiotics)	200 000
plant extracts (from 35 000 species)	120 000
marine and other animal products and extracts	16 000
	700 000

clinical trial on patients, and how many of those proved to be effective?

■ 150 out of 700 000 substances were given clinical trials and of these, 40 were active in one or more categories of human cancer. (This represents 1/175 of 1 per cent of the total screened over a period of 28 years, and is the main reason behind the high cost of effective drugs.)

☐ One reason given why so few successful drugs have been developed is that some substances that were effective at damaging cancer cells proved unsuitable for use on patients. Why was this?

■ They were unacceptably toxic to normal organs and tissues, particularly those with 'a high rate of cell turnover': that is, those that share the key feature of malignant cells.

Toxicity is a significant problem, even with the drugs that are routinely used to treat human cancers, as Frei points out. Adverse effects range from hair loss and nausea, following damage to the rapidly dividing cells in hair follicles and the lining of the gut, to less common effects such as impairment of fertility, damage to the heart, and the development of certain cancers, particularly leukaemia. Advocates of cancer chemotherapy stress, as Frei does, that these more serious effects are uncommon and that nausea ceases and hair regrows when treatment stops. In his view 'cancer is a malignant disease and requires vigorous treatment'. In other words, the end justifies the means. Critics of this philosophy view cancer chemotherapy as a sledgehammer approach, and a rise in the popularity of so-called 'alternative' therapies has occurred on both sides of the Atlantic.

☐ In addition to the problem of toxicity and emotionally distressing 'side-effects', what other dilemmas does Frei mention when potential drugs are being tested on patients?

■ He mentions: (a) the 'spectre of human experimentation' — new drugs are tested for the first time on patients for whom there is no known effective treatment; (b) the problem of raising false hopes in patients and their families — a 'situation ripe for exploitation, as evidenced by the thriving, over-promising cancer quackery industry'.

The opposing views of orthodox and alternative practitioners have an obvious political dimension and the claims from both sides have occasionally spilled over into propaganda and mud-slinging. We shall come back to this debate from the viewpoint of patients and their *experience* of treatment in the next chapter. For the moment, we shall stay with the politics of research funding for cancer chemotherapy programmes such as the one Frei describes.

☐ What success for cancer chemotherapy does Frei claim?

■ He states that there has been a 20 to 43 per cent reduction in cancer mortality in the USA in the past 15 years in *younger* patients (i.e. those under the age of 45) and that this is a result of improved treatment, largely improved chemotherapy. He estimates that cancer chemotherapy now cures* 40 000 people per year compared with 10 000 annually a decade ago.

Frei's account is 'triumphal' in tone, and certainly the improvements he documents would be cause for modest optimism if there was not controversy over their accuracy. A later edition of the magazine, *Science* (which published Frei's article), printed a criticism of it by John Cairns and Peter Boyle of the Harvard School of Public Health. In their analysis of the National Cancer Institute's own mortality statistics for the USA between 1950 and 1977 they showed that the main decline in cancer deaths has been in those due to cancer of the cervix, stomach, colon and rectum. All of these cancers have been declining for the past 30 years in spite of the absence of any conspicuous advance in treatment — all are treated principally by surgery.

They estimate that the total number of American cancer patients now being 'cured' annually by chemotherapy at closer to 5 000 than 40 000, and conclude:

> ... when the time comes to pass judgement on a program that consumes more than $100 million a year, something more is required. During the period that the Chemotherapy Program has been using these vast sums of money to find out how to cure a few thousand patients each year, we have gradually reached the point where, each year, about 70 000 extra deaths from lung cancer are being added. Given numbers like these, it seems likely that some of the money spent on treating patients would have been better spent on a campaign to prevent cancer. (Cairns and Boyle, 1983, p.254)

This is the other great political debate within cancer research (as with so many other diseases) — prevention versus cure. Supporters of research into treatment strategies point out that most of the previously fatal cancers that are now curable for at least a sizeable proportion of patients, are cancers affecting children and young adults. (Frei makes this point in his article.) Thus, even if the *number* of lives saved is still relatively small, the *years* of life saved are considerable. According to this analysis, decades of costly research are worthwhile. Critics in the USA claim that success has been overestimated and hint that a 'media-hype' has been going on to justify the huge investment, for political and fiscal purposes.

---

*In this context 'cure' is taken to mean relapse-free survival for 5 years (and in some cases 10 years) after diagnosis and treatment.

Objectives for Chapter 4

When you have studied this chapter, you should be able to:

4.1 Summarise the shift in biological explanations for cancers that has occurred since the discovery of oncogenes, and explain how new theories conflict with metaphors for cancers that were previously common in biological descriptions.

4.2 Summarise the contribution of epidemiological research to an understanding of the causes of cancers, and illustrate the difficulties of using epidemiological data to identify carcinogens and develop preventive strategies.

4.3 Discuss some of the political issues raised by the early detection of cancers in mass-screening programmes, and the allocation of funding to cancer chemotherapy research.

Questions for Chapter 4

1 (*Objective 4.1*) Read the following quotations, (a)–(c). What shared biological explanations of cancers do they reveal, and how does this conflict with the most recent biological model of the disease?

(a) 'Some say that cancer is so called because it adheres to any parts which it seizes upon in an obstinate manner like a crab.' Paul of Aegina, seventh century AD.

(b) 'When we think of cancer in general terms we are apt to conjure up a process characterized by a steady, remorseless and inexorable progress in which the disease is all-conquering, and none of the immunological and other defensive forces which help us to survive the onslaught of bacterial and viral infections can serve to halt the faltering footsteps to the grave.' William Boyd, an eminent Canadian pathologist and bacteriologist, writing in 1966.

(c) 'Cancer can be likened to a power-crazy dictator — it is never satisfied with the territory it has and must spread.' *Nursing Mirror*, 1981 (from the leading article in a special issue devoted to cancer)

2 (*Objective 4.2*) A headline in a British national daily newspaper announced 'Breast cancer rises by 20 per cent among the pill generation' (*Guardian*, October 28th, 1983), implying a causal connection between hormonal contraceptives and the increases in the incidence of breast cancer during the past 15 to 20 years. Use the epidemiological data in Table 4.4 to evaluate this implied connection. (The pill became available in the UK in the early 1960s.)

3 (*Objective 4.3*) Consider the following quotation.

In theory, malignant disease seems an ideal target for early detection programmes, but, as in screening for so many other diseases, it is found in practice that there are disadvantages as well as advantages and the benefits need to be weighed up against the costs ... (Chamberlain, 1983, p.283)

If you were trying to assess the effectiveness of cervical cancer screening programmes (i.e. to weigh up the benefits and costs), what questions would you need to ask?

Table 4.4 Death rates from breast cancer in England and Wales per 100 000 population for women in different age-groups in 1961–65 compared with 1976–78.

Year of death	Age group/years				
	15–44	45–54	55–64	65–74	75+
1961–65	8.4	58.4	82.3	105.5	160.7
1976–78	8.1	66.6	95.9	121.3	178.7
% change	− 3.5	+ 14.0	+ 16.5	+ 14.9	+ 11.2

5
Cancers: truthfulness and treatment

This chapter requires you to study a 25-minute audiotape sequence, *Dilemmas in Cancer Treatment* (AC806, Band 5). The TV programme, *A Cancer in the Family* and its related audiotape sequence, *A Cancer in the Family* (AC806, Band 4) are also associated with this chapter.

In this final chapter about cancers we return to people's experiences of malignant disease and examine the attitudes of patients and their families, nursing and medical staff to truthfulness about cancers and dilemmas in treatment. These issues are, of course, by no means unique to cancers. Doctors are faced daily with the tasks of discussing diagnoses of disabling or potentially fatal diseases with their patients and juggling the costs and benefits of treatment strategies. Families caring for someone with chronic heart disease are under just as much strain. There are good reasons, however, for initiating this discussion in relation to cancers: there has been more public and medical debate about what to tell people who have a cancer than with any other disease and cancer treatments generate unusual apprehension.

These issues are discussed by two British specialists in cancer medicine in the audiotape sequence, *Dilemmas in Cancer Treatment* (AC 806, Band 5) — Tim McElwain, from the Royal Marsden Hospital, a specialist centre for cancer treatment in Surrey, and Peter Maguire, from Manchester, who is a specialist in psychiatric problems in cancer patients. We chose to give you interviews with doctors rather than patients at this point because they can give an overall view of the problems of truthfulness and treatment. Later in this chapter we shall discuss patients' accounts of their own experiences.

The doctors in the audiotape sequence are agreed that for most patients it is preferable to be truthful about a cancer diagnosis, the side-effects of treatment and, as far as possible, the likely outcome. This reflects a relatively recent shift in doctors' attitudes and, as both point out, it is more likely to prevail among staff in specialist cancer treatment centres than among those in general hospitals.

Play the audiotape sequence now.

☐ What reasons are given in the audiotape for concealing a cancer diagnosis?

■ The reasons mentioned are: (a) anxiety that the patient will not be able to cope with the diagnosis and will 'fall apart'; (b) inability on the part of the doctors to cope with their own emotions when faced with the responsibility of telling the patient; (c) ignorance of a patient's need to know, or failure to recognise cues that a patient wants to talk about the diagnosis; (d) lack of time to devote to the task — so it is not done at all rather than done badly in a short interview; and (e) acceding to the wishes of relatives who do not want the patient to know.

The emotional toll on doctors and nurses in the hospital setting can be severe and both McElwain and Maguire see the need for some form of support system for staff. Dealing with cancer may be even more distressing for general practitioners, who may know the patient with some degree of intimacy. It often falls to GPs to tell their patients they have a cancer, even when the diagnosis has been made elsewhere.

Some GPs see this as cowardice on the part of hospital colleagues, whereas others see it as much better for the patient than getting the news from a stranger. Either way it is a hard task.

> I always try to tell, except sometimes I chicken out; I always at least try to face my patients up to the truth. ... It's very hard to accept that you cannot actually cure something. And if you actually have to go and talk to somebody about your failure to cure them ... it takes time, and it does burn me up, and I always come away exhausted. (in Rosser and Maguire, 1982, p.316)

☐ In the view of Maguire and McElwain, what are the possible adverse consequences of concealing the truth?

■ Patients can become bewildered and suspicious when tests or treatments are carried out without explanation.

Previously supportive relationships with family members can become strained by the stress of deceit.

The patient usually finds out eventually and thereafter may lose faith in other statements from their doctors and family.

Relatives may feel prolonged guilt and regret about the deception if the patient dies.

There is no opportunity to 'put affairs in order' and make arrangements that might be a source of comfort to the patient or of financial benefit to the family.

For a few patients and their families these adverse consequences are still preferable to the truth, but many patients are kept in the dark needlessly. Many discover the truth only when they are referred to a specialist cancer centre for treatment, and as Peter Maguire puts it, 'psychologically all hell lets loose'. Less often the truth is learned through a careless remark by staff who are unaware

of the deception as in this quotation from an essay by Robert Millington.

> 'You're the boy with leukaemia, aren't you?' the nurse asked as she routinely took my TPR (temperature + pulse rate). These seven words hit me like a blunt instrument. (from an essay by Robert Millington who died in 1980)

The adverse consequences of deceit for family relationships have been described most eloquently by Lawrence Goldie, a consultant in psychological medicine at the Royal Marsden Hospital, London:

> A surgeon may tell a spouse not to use the word cancer to the patient and urge a pretence that it is something else by using words like 'lump', 'ulcer', 'abscess', 'blockage' .... This may mean, for example, a patient knows that his wife knows, but they do not speak of it to each other! ... couples instead of growing together, wither in each other's arms. (Goldie, 1982, p.128)

What do we know about the wishes of patients in these circumstances? Several studies have attempted to assess the outcome of telling patients that they have cancer. All have tended to confirm the results of the classic early work of Jean Aitken-Swan and her colleagues at the Christie Hospital in Manchester in 1959, summarised in Table 5.1.

Three of the reactions reported are typical:

> I asked the doctor — I looked him straight in the face and I asked "Is it cancer?" and he said "Yes". Well, I'd rather know the truth — it's better than imagining all the time. ... If I'm ill I'd rather know what I'm suffering from, because you don't die any sooner for knowing about it.

> It took the use of my legs when he told me. But I'd much prefer to know, and then you know what you're fighting. ... Don't you think people can fight things better if they know?

Table 5.1 Patients initial reaction on being told a cancer diagnosis*

Reaction	Percentage of total
approval	66.2
denial that they had been told	19.0
disapproval	7.4
inconclusive	7.4

* Patients were interviewed between a week and a month after being told the diagnosis. (Data from Aitken-Swann and Easson, 1959, p.780)

He said it was a simple cancer of the skin. It was a terrible shock — I went all dizzy. I had never thought of such a thing. Well, it is the *word!* I've had diarrhoea ever since and haven't slept at all, thinking about it and imagining things. ... It has upset me so much. He could have said it was a cyst or something. (Aitken-Swan and Easson, 1959, pp.779, 780 and 781)

Almost one fifth of patients in this study 'forgot' that they had been told that they had cancer — some doctors have cited this as evidence that all patients should be told since those who cannot cope with the information will simply suppress it. Others, however, like Maguire and Goldie, think that the mode of telling is to blame. Patients may be unable to cope because the news is delivered bluntly by a doctor who does not stay to witness the consequences.

So the consensus from these doctors is that the truth is preferable to deception. The doctor's task is to identify whether the patient wants information and what he or she wants to know. Compassion and sensitivity must accompany the telling. This takes time — to let the news unfold gradually, to assess how well the patient is able to cope with it and 'tailor' the pace and content to the patient's response, and to answer questions in terms that a lay person will understand. This approach minimises the risk of telling people who do not wish to know and withholding the truth from those who do. Thus, the dilemma in cancer management has not been, 'What *is* the truth?', but whether or not the 'truth' should be told.

Treatment

Remedies without number continue to be brought forward as cures for cancer — all kinds of drugs, electricity, compressions ... etcetera. Count Mattei's electro-homeopathic remedies will occur to many, and how they have been found by an investigation committee to be absolutely worthless. All such remedies are serviceable only in as much as they keep the patient interested, and so direct his mind from his terrible affliction and render his sufferings less hard to bear. ... Various forms of diet have been brought forward from time to time as capable of curing cancer. A purely vegetarian diet is asserted to cure, by enthusiasts of the vegetarian school, but experiments have found it wanting. ... There is but one recognised treatment for a malignant tumour, and that is its early removal by the knife. (Diseases and Remedies, 1894, pp.24–5)

Since the turn of the century, debates about remedies have continued in much the same tone. Cancer treatment within orthodox medicine still relies heavily on 'the knife', but the use of radiation and anti-cancer drugs are now standard practice for cancers in many sites. These techniques have raised many anxieties.

For certain cancers, and particularly those that affect children and young adults, progress in the past 20 to 30 years has been significant. Some cancers that were once almost always fatal are now predominantly curable. Although there has not been equivalent success with the most common cancers (such as those of the lungs, breast and colon), treatment may result in a better quality of life for the patient than was hitherto possible.

The three main orthodox treatments currently available set ever widening circles of intervention around the primary cancer and detectable secondary growths. Surgery seeks to remove them entirely, together with a relatively small amount of the surrounding healthy tissue, to be 'on the safe side'. Radiotherapy casts the net wider and treats a significant area into which malignant cells may have spread. With chemotherapy the whole body is involved by introducing drugs into the bloodstream to search out metastases* from multiple locations. Radiotherapy and chemotherapy both exploit the fact that the DNA in a cell is most vulnerable to the irreparable damage caused by ionising radiation and certain drugs when the cell is in the act of dividing. These treatments have attracted far more concern than surgical interventions.

Cancer chemotherapy is never a pleasant experience, and for some patients it may be so distressing that they contemplate giving up. Peter Maguire describes this in the audiotape. In a study of general practitioners' attitudes to cancer, Jane Rosser and Peter Maguire found that three-quarters of them expressed some reservations about the use of cytotoxic (cell-poisoning) drugs. A few were more critical: 'The hospital pretend that chemotherapy is marvellous, will cure, which I think is just deception, it's perjury. ... I'm not knocking it, it may extend life, fair enough, but it causes side-effects.' (in Rosser and Maguire, 1982, p.319).

A study of 50 patients who had received chemotherapy, however, found that 60 per cent were glad they had been given the treatment and 74 per cent would recommend it to a friend with cancer. This was despite the disruption in their lives which they attributed to cancer chemotherapy and which are shown in Table 5.2. Note that as many people reported improvements in family relationships as reported disruption.

Although the physical side-effects of radiotherapy are usually less distressing than those associated with cancer chemotherapy, the equipment used (see Figure 5.1) can arouse particular fears.

*This term is defined in Chapter 16 of *The Biology of Health and Disease* (U205, Book IV).

Table 5.2a The effects of cancer chemotherapy on patients' lives

	Percentage reporting	
Area investigated	disruption	improvements
marital/family relationships	24	24
sexual relationships (marked change)	17	0
financial burden (significant)	54	0
attending work	60	0
general life style	60	0
normal activities	38	0

Table 5.2b The effects of chemotherapy on patients' well-being

Side-effects on patient	Percentage reporting
fatigue	96
nausea	88
anxiety	62

(Data from Meyerowitz *et al.*, 1978, p.359)

It was awful because once you go in there, they put you under this machine and they put sandbags round you. ... And you know you can't move because if you move about the radium will go where it shouldn't do. ... I've got a vivid imagination and I used to think all the molecules or whatever it was used to be bombarding my body, and if they didn't get it in the right place, they're gonna kill some really good cells in there. (Interview with Course Team member)

Some research by J.A. Parsons and colleagues in 1961 into the effects of *sham* radiotherapy found that more than 75 per cent of people still developed symptoms such as nausea and fatigue even though the equipment was not switched on. The use of distressing and toxic treatments such as radiotherapy and chemotherapy pose a significant dilemma of balancing profit and loss, as this general practitioner states: 'There's nothing good about treatment; treatment for all cancers is horrible. If they're cured then obviously the price was worth paying. But if they're not cured, this has contributed to the misery of their disease.' (in Rosser and Maguire, 1982, p.319).

This dilemma is possibly at its most acute in the treatment of children with leukaemia. About 250 children die from leukaemia each year in the UK, so it is a rare disease, but it still accounts for about half of all childhood deaths from cancers and almost 10 per cent of all deaths below the age of 15 years. In acute leukaemia, the normal white blood cells in the circulation are replaced by huge numbers of abnormal ones that cannot fight infection and clog up blood vessels causing the failure of vital organs. Blood-clotting mechanisms also break down and patients

who survive infection may die from internal bleeding.

Recent advances in treatment for childhood leukaemia involve the use of intensive chemotherapy and radiation to the head and spinal cord, where metastases are commonly

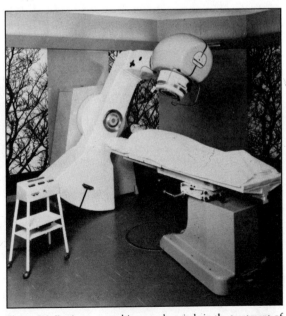

Figure 5.1 Equipment used in some hospitals in the treatment of cancers by radiotherapy. The patient must keep perfectly still and the beam of radiation is directed onto a very precise part of the body. Lead panels or sandbags may be used to shield other body areas. Treatment usually lasts only a few minutes. (Photograph, courtesy of T.E.M. Instruments Ltd., and the Oldchurch Hospital, Romford.)

harboured. Between 1970 and 1980 this 'aggressive' approach cut deaths among children between the ages of 3 and 12 years by over one-third and at least 50 per cent of children now survive more than five years. A significant proportion of these children are believed to have been cured in the sense that they are expected to live on into adulthood.

The question of whether or not to treat a leukaemic child in this intensive way has no straightforward answer because the chances of success are so finely balanced. The doctor may feel no hesitation in recommending a calculated gamble, but what of the child's parents? They must watch their child suffer the unpleasant side effects of the treatment, including the embarrassment of losing their hair, and hope that the outcome will be worthwhile. If the child dies they may feel guilty that their child's last months were marred by the rigours of treatment and hospitalisation.

Mastectomy

Although radiotherapy and chemotherapy for cancers has attracted most anxiety, the surgical treatment of some cancers has also caused controversy. In 1894, W.S. Halsted, a surgeon working at the John Hopkins Hospital in the USA, published details of an operation 'for the cure of cancer of the breast' which involved the removal of not only the entire breast but also the muscles of the chest wall that overlie the ribs and extend under the armpit as far as their attachment points beneath the shoulder blade. All available

lymph nodes in the area were also removed and several blood vessels and nerves involved in the normal function of the arm were 'sacrificed'.

For the next 70 years, Halsted's operation, known as a *radical mastectomy,* was the recommended treatment for breast cancer. Sometimes even more extensive interventions were involved, for example splitting the breastbone, detaching the first rib and elevating the collarbone to get at lymph nodes inside the chest cavity. This is one of the most clear-cut examples of a surgical innovation that became standard practice without any form of evaluation. During the 1960s, the tide began to turn away from such disfiguring and disabling surgery. Surgeons began to wonder if their patients might survive just as well if less tissue were removed and trials began to be performed comparing the radical operation with one in which the breast and lymph nodes under the armpit were removed, but the underlying musculature was left intact. This is known as a *total mastectomy.* Figure 5.2 shows the result of a total mastectomy after the scar has healed and the cosmetic effect of wearing a synthetic breast (a breast prosthesis) inside a brassiere.

No difference in survival between patients given radical mastectomies and those given total mastectomies has been reported and a few trials have attempted to establish whether even less extensive surgery could be as effective if combined with chemotherapy, or with radiotherapy to the breast and armpit. The so-called 'lumpectomy' with

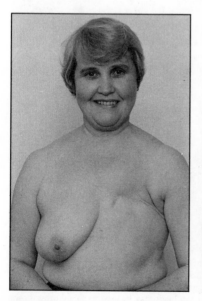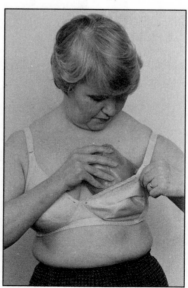

Figure 5.2 Several years ago this woman had a total mastectomy, including removal of lymph glands beneath her armpit. The breast prosthesis that she usually wears is one of several different types available from a range of shapes, sizes and weights to ensure a perfect match with her natural breast.

radiotherapy may or may not prove to be as good at preserving life as more disfiguring operations. If it *is*, another dilemma could arise. There may not be adequate radiotherapy facilities to enable every suitable case to be treated in this way and some women might still have to suffer the loss of a breast as a consequence. Women with breast cancer are rarely given the choice between alternative treatments, perhaps because such a choice is an awesome responsibility.

Living with a cancer in the family

Even if the decision about what treatment to opt for is not at present faced by most patients, they and their families must carry considerable burdens during treatment — both emotional and practical. One of the practical problems is meeting the unforeseen expenses that are incurred, especially during the initial period of intensive treatment. More than half the families interviewed for the study summarised in Table 5.2 reported significant financial strain. The cost of travelling to and from the hospital is responsible for a large part of this. One of the drawbacks of specialist treatment centres for *any* disease is that there are so few of them that most people who attend them live far away. This can be particularly difficult when the patient is a child because parents generally try to visit once or twice a day and a study in 1980 found that for such families financial difficulties were common (Table 5.3). It shows that nearly 25 per cent lose direct income.

Travelling back and forth continues to be a problem for patients in the later stages of treatment. For example, radiotherapy may require three or four visits a week to an out-patient clinic over, say, a four-week period. Ambulance transport can sometimes be arranged but some patients dislike the long roundabout journey picking up people from all over the area. The alternative is to make your own way.

With all the pressures of treatment, travelling, worries about money, strain on family relationships *and* the ever-present fear of dying, it is perhaps not surprising that cancer patients are particularly prone to severe emotional difficulties*. As Peter Maguire says on the audiotape, his research has shown that as many as one in four suffer from depression or anxiety that is serious enough to warrant psychiatric treatment.

In one of Maguire's studies (Maguire *et al.*, 1980), women were offered counselling following mastectomy and showed a marked reduction in psychiatric illness from 39 per cent with such symptoms shortly after the operation to 8 per cent 18 months later. A control group who received

---

* The emotional consequences of mastectomy for women and their families are the subject of a U205 TV programme, *A Cancer in the Family*; there is also a related audiotape sequence with the same title (AC 806, Band 4).

Table 5.3 Reasons for financial difficulties among families who had a child with cancer.

Reason	Percentage of families reporting
travelling to and from the hospital	55
loss of time at work	36
extra expenses associated with the child's illness (e.g. extra heating, special food)	19
having to give up employment	17
dismissed from work as soon as diagnosis known	7

(Data from Clark and Malpas, 1980. Private communication)

no counselling showed far less alleviation of their symptoms. Forty-three per cent were severely distressed after the operation and after 18 months this figure had fallen to only 35 per cent.

Measures aimed at alleviating the distress felt by many people with a cancer, and their families, are rare in the UK at present. Just as funding for research into cancer prevention has been scarce, funding for treatment has focused on treating the *disease* rather than treating the *patient,* and preventable sources of anxiety and misery have been neglected or ignored.

In recent years there has been something of a backlash against orthodox treatment methods, not simply because surgery, radiotherapy or chemotherapy may have distressing or toxic effects, but also because 'scientific medicine' tends to make some patients feel like a 'feather in the wind', as Tim McElwain puts it on the tape. Note that other patients *prefer* to have the doctor take responsibility for the treatment, and then 'leave it up to the cancer' to decide whether they live or die. For an increasing minority of cancer patients, however, the orthodox approach to treatment leaves them feeling that they have been reduced to a vehicle for their disease, a collection of symptoms that only the experts can alleviate. In this climate, alternative or complementary therapies have flourished.

During the 1960s and 1970s the most popular alternatives were themselves 'magic bullet' preparations — mirror images of orthodox medical treatments in which the person who has cancer need do nothing more active than 'take the medicine', albeit not one that orthodox medicine recognised. There have been fashions for many products, including laetrile (a substance extracted from apricot kernels), garlic, the roots of the May apple, tea made from the leaves of the creosote bush, and coffee enemas.

The majority of these compounds have never been subjected to a clinical trial and the few that have been assessed, for example laetrile, have showed disappointing results. Pharmaceutical companies faced with millions of chemical compounds to test as anti-cancer agents have been quick to isolate compounds from folk remedies and a few have proved to be the starting point for useful synthetic derivatives. The 'old wives' were not always wrong.

More recently, attention has switched to what are described by their advocates as 'holistic' remedies, that is treatment regimes that address the whole person and attempt to involve the individual in a measure of responsibility for his or her disease.* In Britain clinics such as the Bristol Cancer Help Centre have attracted widespread attention and royal support. A range of therapies are offered including acupuncture, herbalism and osteopathy, but the twin cornerstones of the holistic approach are diet and spiritual awareness.

Dietary treatments for cancers have a long history. The grape diet was prescribed as long ago as 1556 and advised the eating of nothing but grapes to 'facilitate elimination of wastes that cause disease'. This emphasis on 'cleansing' survives to the present day — the Bristol diet begins with a three-month cleansing period of raw vegetables, fruit and grain, with little fat, no salt, no refined sugars, tea, coffee or milk. Small amounts of fish, chicken and eggs may subsequently be allowed. Vitamin supplements are taken, some in large doses, together with certain minerals and enzymes.

The spiritual dimension of self-help is encouraged through meditation, relaxation techniques, psychotherapy, hypnosis and faith-healing. A technique known as *imaging* is also widely used, in which the person with cancer is asked to imagine their cancer cells as vividly as possible and then imagine elements of their own healthy tissue attacking and destroying the malignancy. Drawings of these imaginary encounters (see Figure 5.3) often reveal terrifying battles between symbolic representations of good and evil.

For many people who commit themselves to the holistic approach, there seem to be significant improvements in the 'quality of life'—a feeling of having something positive to contribute to the outcome of your own disease may markedly enhance such unmeasurable qualities as happiness, well-being and sense of self-worth.

> I felt I knew why I'd got cancer — but nobody wanted to talk about that. All they wanted to do was cut off my breast. I saw my cancer as a symptom, and knew I had to take charge and treat the cause myself. ... The whole experience has altered me profoundly. I am a much stronger person. I act rather than react. More than that, facing death concentrates your mind wonderfully on living. I see and feel with an extra intensity. And I mean it when I say that having cancer

*You should note that the word 'holistic' is used here in a different sense from the way in which we have used it elsewhere in this course. See, for example, the discussion in *Studying Health and Disease* (U205, Book 1).

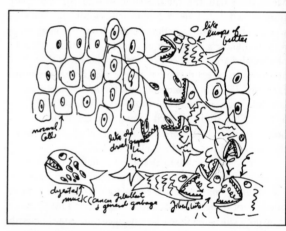

Figure 5.3 Drawings made by people with cancer who were asked to imagine the cancer cells in their body being attached by some healthy vital force that is powerful enough to overwhelm the disease. (Simonton *et al.*, 1978, pp. 142 and 151).

has actually strengthened my marriage. (Penny Brohn, Bristol Cancer Help Centre 'graduate')

For others, the road has an unforeseen pitfall — if you accept that you are 'responsible' for your disease, then you must also be implicated in the fact that you developed cancer in the first place. And if the disease does not regress, does this mean that you are not 'trying hard enough' or 'doing it right'? This may have some bearing on the 50 per cent drop-out rate reported by the Bristol Centre. In addition, the self-discipline required by the dietary regime and the expense of the vitamin and mineral supplements has proved too demanding for some.

> I have decided to give up the diet, the injections and the Bristol treatment altogether. What happened was

that after feeling increasingly miserable with the diet and less and less like eating or drinking anything I was allowed, plus distaste for the carrot juice and vitamins and *having* to get them down, plus fed up with all the work involved for ever in preparing these and cleaning up the machinery, I saw the two consultants — Kings [College Hospital] and the hospice — on successive days. They both said the same thing — that my cancer was growing, that this would be a matter of months (rather than years or days) and that the Bristol treatment, while they did not oppose it, seemed essentially irrelevant from the implications of what they said. It wouldn't lead me to discourage other people from trying the Bristol method, it may be that it works better for some kinds of cancer or some kinds of people than for others.
(from the Diary of Sue Cartledge, *Spare Rib*, November 1983)

Alternative therapies seem to offer a pointer to a basic fault in orthodox methods — that too often patients are kept in the dark and made to feel that they have nothing to contribute to the outcome of their disease. This is by no means confined to cancer patients, but nothing to do with cancers seems straightforward and, as you have seen in these three chapters, we are still a long way from knowing what causes these conditions or how to escape the 'grey fog' of dread that most people feel about them. Honesty seems to help, likewise a sense of humour. The geneticist J.B.S. Haldane, who died from cancer of the bowel and rectum shortly after writing the poem with which we end, sums it all up in his ironic and spirited account.

Cancer's a funny thing

I wish I had the voice of Homer
To sing of rectal carcinoma,
Which kills a lot more chaps, in fact,
Than were bumped off when Troy was sacked.
   I noticed I was passing blood
(Only a few drops, not a flood),
So pausing on my homeward way
From Tallahassee to Bombay
I asked a doctor, now my friend,
To peer into my hinder end,
To prove or to disprove the rumour
That I had a malignant tumour.
They pumped in BaSO$_4$
Till I could really stand no more,
And, when sufficient had been pressed in,
They photographed my large intestine.
In order to decide the issue
They next scraped out some bits of tissue.
(Before they did so, some good pal
Had knocked me out with pentothal,

Whose action is extremely quick,
And does not leave me feeling sick.)
The microscope returned the answer
That I had certainly got cancer.
So I was wheeled to the theatre
Where holes were made to make me better.
One set is in my perineum
Where I can feel, but can't yet see'em.
Another made me like a kipper
Or female prey of Jack the Ripper.
Through this incision, I don't doubt,
The neoplasm was taken out,
Along with colon, and lymph nodes
Where cancer cells might find abodes.
A third much smaller hole is meant
To function as a ventral vent:
So now I am like two-faced Janus
The only* god who sees his anus.
I'll swear, without the risk of perjury,
It was a snappy bit of surgery.
My rectum is a serious loss to me,
But I've a very neat colostomy,
And hope, as soon as I am able,
To make it keep a fixed time-table.
   So do not wait for aches and pains
To have a surgeon mend your drains;
If he says 'cancer' you're a dunce
Unless you have it out at once,
For if you wait it's sure to swell,
And may have progeny as well.
My final word, before I'm done,
Is 'Cancer can be rather fun.'
Thanks to the nurses and Nye Bevan
The NHS is quite like heaven
Provided one confronts the tumour
With a sufficient sense of humour.
I know that cancer often kills,
But so do cars and sleeping pills;
And it can hurt one till one sweats,
So can bad teeth and unpaid debts.
A spot of laughter, I am sure,
Often accelerates one's cure;
So let us patients do our bit
To help the surgeons make us fit.
J.B.S. HALDANE

*In India there are several more
With extra faces, up to four,
But both in Brahma and in Shiva
I own myself an unbeliever.

Written by J.B.S. Haldane, *The New Statesman*, 21 February, 1964. Reproduced by kind permission of the publishers.

Objectives for Chapter 5

When you have studied this chapter, you should be able to:

5.1 Summarise the difficulties faced by doctors in discussing a cancer diagnosis frankly with a patient, and the possible consequences of telling the truth or concealment.

5.2 Discuss dilemmas related to cancer treatment under the following headings:

(a) balancing side-effects with possible cure or extended survival;

(b) financial implications for patients and their families;

(c) the advantages and disadvantages of specialist treatment centres.

5.3 Discuss the strengths and weaknesses of orthodox medicine versus alternative therapies for cancer.

Questions for Chapter 5

1 (*Objective 5.1*) Consider this quotation.

If I see a man who I know has a fatal illness, what right have I — on the basis of a very brief acquaintanceship — to give him that dreadful news? So I tend to compromise by, perhaps, breaking the news to a close member of the family — a wife, or a son or daughter. Now you'd be surprised how very frequently the reaction of the family is 'No, I don't want him to know'. (Hospital clinician interviewed in TV programme 3 of the OU Course E263, *Language in Use*)

What do you think are the considerations on which this doctor is basing his decision not to tell the patient the diagnosis?

2 (*Objective 5.2*) Summarise the advantages and disadvantages of specialist treatment centres for cancer that were discussed in the audiotape sequence *Dilemmas in Cancer Treatment*.

3 (*Objective 5.3*) List three criticisms that a practitioner of orthodox cancer treatment might give of alternative therapies, and vice versa.

In this chapter we leave the clearly biological diseases such as cancer behind to enter the troubled and uncertain terrain of the so-called mental disorders. To begin this study, you are asked to listen to a 30-minute audiotape sequence, *Mental Distress and Disorder* (AC807, Band 1), on which patients in a mental hospital discuss their feelings with their psychotherapist. Some extracts from the tape are included in the text.

We shall draw on ideas about brain function discussed in Chapter 6 of *The Biology of Health and Disease* (U205, Book IV) and you should refresh your memory of this material before you begin to read this present chapter.

6

Experiencing and explaining mental distress and disorder

Everyone experiences mental anguish at some time in their lives. Everyone feels — and describes themselves as feeling — depressed, anxious, even 'paranoid' or 'schizophrenic'. Sometimes these terms to describe common feelings come out of everyday language (e.g. 'depressed' or 'anxious'), but they have also taken on specific clinical meanings as well. Sometimes, the reverse happens: for example, 'paranoid' and 'schizophrenic' are clinical terms that have come to assume a broader meaning.

How and when do these feelings come to be considered problems appropriate for doctors to try to alleviate or cure? When does mental distress become mental disease or mental disorder? What causes the disease or disorder and what are the appropriate treatments for it? Let us begin by considering some case studies of people talking about their own condition and state of mind and feelings, and the clinical descriptions of these cases.

First, it is necessary to define our terms. A great range of terms is used to describe the states of distress, disease and disorder that we touch upon in these chapters. 'Psychiatric illness' or 'psychiatric disease', 'mental illness' or 'mental disease' or 'mental disorder' and 'mental handicap' are among those used by doctors, psychiatrists and other professional groups. Lay terms vary from the straightforward 'mad' or 'simple' through circumlocutions such as 'a bit touched' or 'not all there' to the street language of 'loonies' and 'nutters'. Throughout this and the succeeding chapters we are going to use the slightly cumbersome term *mental distress and disorder* to describe conditions classified medically in a variety of different ways. In a way, this phrase, too, is a circumlocution. We have chosen it deliberately, though, first because 'distress and disorder' describes something of the *range* of problems we shall be discussing and, second, because we do not want to prejudice discussion of either the *causes* or the *treatments* of these states of mind.

Mental distress and disorder must be distinguished from mental handicap. A mentally handicapped person suffers

Norris in Bedlam 1812.

from a limitation of intellect, or limitation of the capacity to use that intellect to survive successfully in the world. Mental distress and disorder does not imply a loss of intellect, but a sense of personal anguish or incapacity to relate successfully to the natural and social worlds around the sufferer.

The study of the mind and its manifestations is the field of *psychology*. Mental distress and disorder is referred to as a *psychiatric* illness and *psychiatrists* are those medically qualified to treat it. By contrast, *psychotherapists* are not necessarily medically qualified (though a few are), but have generally had particular types of training in the theory and practice of counselling to people suffering mental distress or disorder. There are many schools of psychotherapy. One which is well known is *psychoanalysis*, which refers to a system of explaining and treating mental distress and disorder based on the theories of Sigmund Freud and his followers — and rivals — in the early part of this century. *Behaviour therapy* aims to change a person's behaviour by rewarding 'desirable' behaviours and discouraging undesirable ones by witholding rewards or even offering punishment. In *group therapy*, people are encouraged to meet and discuss their problems in a small group led by a therapist. Finally, another specialist category is *neurology*. *Neurologists* are concerned with the study of brain function and, in the instance of *clinical neurology*, with disorders of brain function. The relationship between brain function and mental distress and disorder is a question we shall be concerned with in some detail in Chapters 7 and 8.

Now listen to the audiotape sequence, *Mental Distress and Disorder* (AC807, Band 1), in which four patients — Mrs Jean Arthur, Mrs Ann Bailey, Mr Paul Davis and Mr Frank Harris — who are suffering from various types of mental distress and disorder talk to their psychotherapist. Try to identify the similarities and differences in the descriptions these people give of their symptoms and the diagnoses given by the therapist.

Mrs Arthur and Mrs Bailey are both diagnosed as suffering from depression. If, however, we compare their descriptions of their symptoms we find considerable differences. The most striking of these is that Mrs Arthur does not complain of feeling physically unwell, but of being in despair about life and about her lack of feeling what she believes to be real emotions of love and affection. As the therapist explains, Mrs Arthur herself was denied affection — she suffered physical and mental abuse as a child. In contrast, Mrs Bailey regards herself as physically unwell, weak and unable to walk. She believes that there must be something the matter with her that a thorough medical examination might reveal, enabling physical treatments to be offered to her.

Mr Davies too suffers from depression. He describes how, as well as being depressed, he believes at times that he has been an agent for an extra-terrestrial force. In the audiotape sequence, you can hear the tone of his voice change as he discusses this period. Mr Davies's depression has been interspersed with periods when he has been manic. The therapist diagnoses this as a case of manic-depressive psychosis. Mr Harris also believes he is possessed by an alien other, an (evil?) goddess who is directing his thoughts and making him behave badly.

□ How does Mr Harris's description of his experience differ most strikingly from those of Mrs Arthur and Mrs Bailey?

■ Mrs Arthur blames herself for her problems and for Mrs Bailey, too, it is a question of her own illness, or of some personal weakness.

It is probably easier to understand and sympathise with the problems of Mrs Arthur and Mrs Bailey. The depressions they suffer from are examples of what psychiatrists would tend to classify as neurotic disorders. (We shall have more to say about this classification in the next chapter.) They seem to experience the same real world as 'normal' people, but they are unable to respond to it and to reach it in the way that they would wish, or to overcome their adversity — or sensation of adversity. In contrast, Mr Harris — and Mr Davies in his manic moments — seem to be describing private worlds that make sense to them, but are hard for the outsider to understand. For this reason both Mr Davies and Mr Harris would be regarded by psychiatrists as suffering from psychoses. (Again we shall have more to say about the significance of these types of classification in the following chapters.)

Now consider this account of Calvin Johnson, a man of Caribbean origin living in South London with his wife, Alice, and daughter, Victoria.

Calvin Johnson

Three years ago Calvin had saved enough to be able to go on his first visit back to Jamaica. While he was there he had a strange experience: he heard a voice from God which told him to read certain verses in the Bible. With divine inspiration he was able with some difficulty to interpret their meaning. Having learnt that meat was sacred food reserved only for the saints, he became a vegetarian. At the same time he became a Rastafarian. On returning to London he began to have doubts about the whole business, but he now thinks these doubts were prompted by the Devil.

Later in the same year he went to his local post office with his daughter Victoria to cash a postal order — advance payment for a job he was to start later that week, replacing some floor boards in a near-by house. Disturbed by Victoria's latest school report and an argument he had had with her teacher, Calvin was feeling rather irritable and tense: after some weeks without work the offer of a job was particularly important. He signed the form, but after examining it the cashier told him to wait and went behind a partition. A quarter of an hour later he re-appeared with three policemen who rather abruptly asked him how he got the postal order. Humiliated and angry, Calvin tried to walk out of the post office with his daughter, but was pulled back. Completely losing his temper, he lashed out, hitting a policeman more by chance than intention, and was promptly arrested. Victoria, the cashier and a small group of bystanders watched silently. While struggling, Calvin took out of his pocket and waved a 1966 shilling which he always carried with him: 'The sun was shining on it as if the lion would step out. I began to sing "The Lord is My Shepherd". The police said, "You black bastard — you believe in God?" They took me to a mad-house — Oh God, since when are we religious mad?'

After some weeks in a psychiatric hospital the charge was withdrawn and Calvin went home; the postal order had been cleared but the job was now lost. In the course of the next year his relationship with the local police was tense. He was arrested for assaulting his two cousins while he himself pursued an unsuccessful case against the police for assault with the help of a community legal aid centre. Calvin became well known at the local magistrates' court and his quarrels with the police became a vendetta.

While remanded on the assault charge he was seen by the prison psychiatrist: 'This man belongs to Rastafarian (*sic*) — a mystical Jamaican cult, the members of which think they are God-like. This man has ringlet hair, a goatee straggly beard and a type of turban. He appears eccentric in his appearance and very vague in answering questions. He is an irritable character and he has got arrogant behaviour. His religious ideas are cultural. He denies any hallucinations. He is therefore not schizophrenic at the moment. He came to England in 1961 but he has obviously been unable to adjust to the culture of this society. He tells me that he would like to be repatriated to his homeland and I am of the opinion that this certainly would be a most desirable outcome because if he continues to live in the United Kingdom there is no doubt that he will be a constant burden to society.' [Not long after, Calvin was admitted to hospital under Section 136 of the 1959 Mental Health Act.] Using this provision, the police can take anyone they feel to be in need of psychiatric attention from a public area 'to a place of safety', which usually means a psychiatric hospital. This time the trouble had started after Calvin had been smoking cannabis and arguing with Alice. Normally it had little effect on him apart from inducing a mild euphoria, but 'This time round I let it all out. I told my probation officer I would do something. I knew what I was doing but I

couldn't stop. I wasn't mad.' The police were called by neighbours after he had thrown the family pans and an oil stove out of his window. Seven policemen eventually got him to the local hospital, where the doctor on duty noted: 'He was lying in the lift with two policemen on top of him. The patient was unkempt with long matted hair, talking in broken English and was difficult to follow. He frequently mentioned Christ and lions. There were ragged lacerations on his hands where he had been handcuffed. Probably a relapsed schizophrenic. Observe carefully. (Littlewood and Lipsedge, 1982, pp.14–16)

Now consider a further case-history told by a neurologist:

Peter Franklin

I first met Peter Franklin about two years after he had suffered his stroke. He was a tall, distinguished-looking man in his early sixties, immaculately groomed, with a neat handle-bar mustache, clear hazel eyes, and an infectious grin. Sitting near him in a waiting room, one would have detected no physical infirmities. Yet he displayed a slight limp when walking, he carried himself in a stiff manner, and there was a degree of weakness discernible in his left arm. Mr Franklin had come to the Aphasia Unit where I work in order to be evaluated and to receive language therapy. He shook my hand firmly, carefully removed his jacket, and crossed his legs as we began to talk.

"How are you today?" I asked.

"Fine, fine," he replied, at first smiling, but then displaying some slight misgiving or discomfort, I was uncertain which.

"Can you tell me what brought you here to the hospital?" I asked.

"What's that?"

"Excuse me," I said (this time speaking more slowly). "How did you get sick? What's wrong?"

"Oh, I see. Now, listen here. Now listen here. Well, I'll tell you. I said, sit down, strewn with clothes, sit, sit down, thank you, thank you. Oh, goodness gracious, goodness gracious. Mrs Hope, thank God, Mrs Hope, going to bed. Sleeping. All right, all right. Seconal, seconal [a sleeping pill]. And by the way Victoria Hospital, Maine. I said and, by the way. Dead. Dr Hope, psychiatrist. Brilliant. All right and two days. Sick. Piss and bewildered. I can't remember. And doctors, doctors. Boys, boys, tip fifty dollars, tip, tip, boys."

"Right," I said. I had reviewed Mr Franklin's medical charts and so was able to interpret what he had said. I knew that he had spent the summer of 1971 on a small lake in southern Maine, living by himself in a cabin, in close proximity to a long-time friend, Natalie Hope. Both the Franklin and Hope families had vacationed for many years in the Lake Carson area and, even now, after Mrs Hope's husband had died, and Franklin was estranged from his wife, they returned annually to this spot.

Although the medical charts were not precise on this point, I gathered that Mrs Hope and Mr Franklin had dined out together the night of the stroke. Mr Franklin had complained that he was rather tired and had a slight headache, and so had retired early. Unable to rest, he took some sleeping pills. The next thing he remembered was lying on the floor, with clothing strewn about him; he somehow dragged himself out of the cabin, where Mrs Hope spotted him walking about, bathrobe half on, drooling saliva, generally dishevelled and confused, about nine o'clock the following morning. She had called the local police, who arrived in the company of a doctor about fifteen minutes later. Mr Franklin had been rushed to the local Victoria Hospital, where he had recuperated for a few weeks before returning to his home in Pennsylvania. In the last sentence quoted above he was apparently alluding to a few youths from a nearby village who had assembled his belongings when he vacated the cabin.

As Mr Franklin had not referred to the reason for his current hospitalization, I attempted a more direct approach to this sensitive area. "Could you tell me what's bothering you now?" I asked.

Suddenly Mr Franklin's even demeanor changed and, shaking his fist, he lashed out at me: "Now listen here. Irritate. Irritate. Irritate, irritate, irritate, irritate, irritate, irritate! Questions, questions. Stupid doctors. No good, no good. Irritate. Irritate. Dean, dean, yes sir, yes sir. What's this, what's this. Wall, wall, door." He pointed at various objects around the room and gave vent to several oaths. "That's all, that's all, forget it, forget it." With these last words, Mr Franklin calmed down somewhat. He then said, as if issuing instructions to himself, "Calm calm down, calm down, it's all right, it's all right." Eyeing me for the first time in several moments, he said, "Sorry, sorry." (Gardner, 1977, pp.6–8)

> □ What is the main difference in the type of diagnosis given to Calvin Johnson and to Peter Franklin?
> ■ Mr Franklin's erratic speech and apparently random comprehension is ascribed to the aftermath of a stroke, to the destruction of particular brain cells as a result of a clot of blood in the cerebral blood vessels which starves the nerve cells of oxygen, thereby killing them. Mr Johnson is not assumed to be brain-damaged, but to be suffering from a disorder of behaviour the reason for which was unknown — perhaps the condition known as schizophrenia.

Frank Harris was also diagnosed as suffering from schizophrenia. Here is an extract from his explanation of his suffering, as given to the therapist:

> If you've been wronged by a woman, say, or a

woman's being wronged by a man, then a person who's been wronged, if they're thinking about that person and they're hurt by them, well God will bring themselves to life in the other person without them knowing, and have a part of them, an emanation from them. And that's one of the ways that physical illness occurs, because that person will live inside another body . . . she can change her shape you see, that's another thing that's hard to believe for people who don't know, haven't experienced it. But Kali is the Indian Goddess of mutilation. Men who end up in hospital are very often put there by someone who, it's not a single person I hope, but it's only one woman . . . she has to ask God if she can hurt this person, she has to ask . . . the person she is inside, and she tries to make the habits of the man bad, so making him eat too much food maybe, or make him stop brushing his teeth, or making him aggressive to someone . . . against someone, and then she can sort of legally, legally entitle them to damage some part of his body inside you . . . that's what I think happens.

> □ From what you know of Mr Harris and have read about Mr Johnson, what would you say are the similarities and the main differences between their situations?
> ■ The speech behaviour and actions of both men are connected with their religious beliefs. Calvin Johnson's religion, however, is a public one — one he shares with many other black British people. His actions *may be* explicable in terms of the beliefs of this religion and the hostility that both the religion and its black adherents experience in Britain today. Frank Harris's religion seems to be a much more personal affair — like that of Paul Davies, a matter between him and the strange being that occupies him and for whom he serves as an agent. However, it clearly fits into a system of beliefs about the world that, to him at least, is logical and apparently draws on certain eastern religions.

These accounts, then, begin to reveal some of the problems of deciding when a person's conduct is acceptable and appropriate and when it is to be regarded as unacceptable and liable to attract a medical diagnosis.

Mind and brain

So far, all the people we have discussed were suffering from what outside observers at least would describe as mental distress or disorder. Clinical diagnosis offers categories of disease, psychiatric or neurological, into which the sufferers could be grouped, but the individuals did not always describe themselves as suffering from a disease. To some of them their conduct appeared to be rational and appropriate, it was the rest of the world that was out of step. Our task in this and the next few chapters is to discuss one of the most vexed questions about our own and other people's health and disease: to what extent is mental distress an issue of medical concern and to what extent, therefore, are medical and social interventions that are designed to alter a person's state of mind and emotion either possible or appropriate?

These questions mask a deeper one: to what extent can we explain a person's mental distress or disorder in terms of abnormalities, problems or crises in their personal biological make-up?*

If understanding the workings of the brain and interpreting the functioning of the mind are among the hardest tasks faced by biological sciences, explaining the *mal*functioning of either brain or mind is perhaps the hardest task for the medical sciences. To begin with, it is even less clear where the medical task begins and ends in the domain of mind than for clearly biological diseases. Calvin Johnson — to cite but one of those cases we have discussed already — certainly has a problem, but is the problem inside his head, or is it generated by the racism of the white majority culture in which he lives? Or is it both? If the problem is inside his head, is he criminally violent — to be treated by the law, or mad — to be treated by doctor or psychiatrist, or is he just religious? As we shall see in the material that follows, time and again dilemmas of interpretation precede those of treatment. Is the extent of mental distress and disorder to be regarded as a medical problem, or as a statement about the mode of diagnosis used, or a statement about some crisis in our social order?

Surgical treatment of the brain is one of the oldest medical operations known — signs of trepanning, or opening the skull, presumably to relieve pressure after brain injury, are said to be observable in prehistoric skeletons. The role of medicine in the wider domains of mental distress and mental disorder is much newer. Distress and depression such as that evidenced by Jean Arthur and Ann Bailey may cause you to wonder whether, in an earlier time or in another culture, such distress would not have been discussed with a priest (rather than a doctor) from whom consolation would have been sought. When Frank Harris spoke of having the spirit of Kali inside him, would a different culture have regarded him as possessed by a holy (or an evil) spirit rather than as being schizophrenic? After all, Joan of Arc claimed to hear voices instructing her to crown the Dauphin King of France. The French saw her as a political inspiration. The English and their allies regarded her as a witch and burned her at the stake. Today, would she too be diagnosed as schizophrenic?

We are not saying that cultures other than modern Western ones do not recognise categories of mental distress and mental disorder. They do, and many offer complex treatments for it, but not all cultures seek to explain mental distress and disorder in terms of some type of brain dysfunction. It is also uncertain how other cultures classify and distinguish what in industrialised societies are diagnosed as neuroses or psychoses. However, several comparative studies show, as we shall discuss later, that when Western criteria are used to diagnose schizophrenia in Third World countries such as India and some African nations, the incidence of the disorder is found to be similar to that in Europe or the USA. This may reflect no more — and no less — than that the Western medical model is now generally accepted by psychiatrists working in these countries.

An important aspect of this model is that it takes a *materialist* view — that all phenomena may be described in terms of the properties of the physical world of matter. Of course, this materialist outlook is not the exclusive property of the Western medical model. Let us explore how a materialist approach to the relationship between mind and body could develop. The point is that the state of a person's being, their state of mind and emotion, their thoughts and intentions at any time — what might be summed up in the term their *existential state* — must, in any materialist account, be related in some way to the state of their body's biology at that time. A person's hormonal balance seems to be related to their mood, but above all, the brain is that region of the body, that organ, most directly concerned with the phenomena of thought, emotion and consciousness. Direct intervention into the functioning of the brain — changing its electrical activity, or interfering with its neuro-transmitters chemically with drugs — affects a person's thoughts, emotions and consciousness. Conversely, it must be assumed that affecting a person's thoughts, emotions and consciousness by talking to them or changing their experience — for instance, by putting them in alarming or exciting environments — will change the state of electrical and chemical activity of the brain. So a materialist theory of the relationship of the properties of a person's brain to that person's existential state may be phrased as follows: for every 'brain state' that may be studied by neurology there is a corresponding 'existential state' that may be studied by psychology. Reciprocally, to every existential state there corresponds a particular brain state.

Such a description speaks only of the present, yet a person's existential state is, as everyone knows from their own experience, shaped not merely by present events but by what has happened in the past.† So to our description of the

---

*The broad outlines of the biological workings of the human brain are introduced in *The Biology of Health and Disease* (U205 Health and Disease, Book IV). Some questions about the relationships between our understanding of the phenomena of brain and mind are also raised there.

† This was described in *Studying Health and Disease* (U205, Book I) as a personal life-history explanation, which we contrast with biological (or reductionist) and social explanations for current events.

correspondence between a person's existential state and their brain state we must add a past history in which a person's experience during their life affects their brain state. Their experience is stored, either generally, or specifically in the form of memories. Memories stored in the mind correspond to particular patterns of nerve pathways in the brain, particular modifications of synapses, connections and circuits. We summarise this relationship in Figure 6.1.

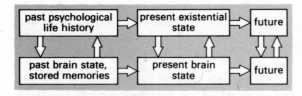

Figure 6.1 The relationship between mind states and brain states.

This materialist description of the relationship of existential state to brain state implies a complex understanding of the idea of the cause of any sort of mental distress and disorder. Mental distress and disorder is not *caused* by a particular brain state, but is *the same as*, identical to, that particular brain state.

This is, of course, only one of several competing theories. There are some who believe that the 'mind' is virtually autonomous and quite separate from a person's biology. There are others who believe that the goal of biology should be to eliminate all such terms as 'mind' and 'existential state', and reduce them all to descriptions in the biological language of nerve pathways, cells and chemicals. (Open University, 1981, *Biological Bases of Behaviour*; Rose, 1982.) As you will see, especially in Chapter 9 in which we discuss *treatment* of mental distress and disorder, the theories people hold about the relationship between a person's existential state and their brain and body affect not merely the way in which they *explain* mental distress and disorder, but also how they try to *alleviate* or cure it.

In any event, we assume in this book that, if it is possible to describe a person's behaviour in the language of mind, using terms such as 'anger', 'distress' and so forth, there must be a corresponding set of descriptions we can offer in the language of brain. What, can then, be said about events in the brains of Jean Arthur, Ann Bailey, Paul Davies, Frank Harris, Calvin Johnson and Peter Franklin that may help our understanding of their mental states?

The human brain and mind has evolved as a system that enables humans to interact with, respond to, and control and modify their environments. It is a vital aspect of the human capacity to survive in the world. If people no longer respond effectively to their environment — and in their various ways the people whose experiences we have recorded were not, or were no longer, responding effectively — then the question is what, if anything, is different about, or wrong with, their brains that prevents them from responding effectively? Or is it perhaps a problem of something wrong in the environment which is generating the response? This is the question we shall begin to address in the next chapter.

Objectives for Chapter 6

When you have studied this chapter, you should be able to:

6.1 Give examples of the range and complexity of mental distress and disorder that doctors and psychiatrists are called upon to treat, classify and explain.

6.2 Discuss the relationship between mental distress and disorder and brain function in terms of a materialist account of the relationships of mind, brain and environment.

Questions for Chapter 6

1 (*Objective 6.2*) In the audiotape sequence you heard Paul Davies talking about his states of depression and his 'manic' moods. According to the materialist theory of the relationship of brain states to existential states discussed in this chapter:

(a) Would you expect Mr Davies' brain state to be different when he was depressed from what it was when he was manic?

(b) When Mr Davies is depressed would you expect his brain state to differ from that of other men of his same age, class and ethnic background?

(c) If his brain state did change under such circumstances, would you conclude that his changed brain state is the cause of his changed existential state?

7

Studying
mental distress
and
disorder

In this chapter we discuss the diagnosis and classification of mental distress and mental disorder, and raise questions about how the causes of mental distress and disorder can be studied. We assume knowledge of brain structure as discussed in Book IV, Chapter 6 and of methodology as discussed in Book I.

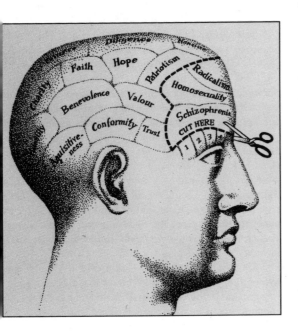

In the previous chapter we discussed the experience of mental distress and mental disorder and, in doing so, raised questions of the problems of defining a condition as one of medical concern. This in turn made it necessary to stop to consider the relationship between a person's behaviour and state of mind — their existential state — and their biology, in particular, their brain state.

The case histories showed clearly that there were some conditions, such as stroke, in which the problem in the person's functioning with respect to the outside world could clearly be related to the faulty development of the brain or damage to it. In other cases, there was no evidence of damage or faulty functioning that could account for the mental state. The medical distinction that is generally made is between *neurological* (or organic) *disorders*, in which damage to the brain is evident, and *functional* or *psychological disorders*, in which there are no *obvious* biological correlates of the mental state.

Although this distinction is found in standard psychiatric textbooks, the problem is that it implies a sort of *dualism*, a belief that the world can be divided up into two sorts of causative process, one biological, the other mental. Mental causes may themselves be ascribed to personal life history, or to the social order that surrounds the individual. More compatible with the biologically based reductionist philosophy that runs through most medical explanations, however, is the assumption that there must be at least *something* biological, which may one day be measurable in the brain and body of a depressed or schizophrenic person, that 'marks' the distinction between them and 'normal' persons. It seems plausible that such differences must exist and might be measurable, though as we shall see later, they are extraordinarily elusive and may be of little help in either explaining or offering treatment for the distress.

Perhaps a better distinction to consider is that a functional disorder is one in which an individual's personality or sense of their own individuality is affected, whereas in a neurological disorder a person's capacity to perform particular tasks or actions is impaired. This enables one to accept an intermediate category of diseases in which there is obvious brain damage *and* the sufferer's personality and existential sense are affected. These are the so-called 'organic psychoses', which may result from senility, or from alcoholism, or some other form of poisoning. Clearly, Peter Franklin's state left him with a biological impairment that produced a speech deficiency, but as a result of the stroke, or perhaps as part of the impatient reaction of an intelligent and vigorous man to the limitations imposed upon him by the speech deficiency, his interview also shows him as irascible and erratic, which suggests damage to his personality and existential sense. This complexity indicates some of the difficulties of interpretation and categorisation faced in the study and diagnosis of brain dysfunction and mental distress and disorder. At any event, we do not wish to suggest that there is a hard and fast distinction between biological and functional disorders.

It is relatively easy to see how brain damage can affect a person's existential state as well as their behaviour. On the other hand, when there is no obvious brain damage, it is much harder to disentangle the relationships of cause, effect and diagnosis. It is with this latter category of conditions of mental distress and disorder that we are primarily concerned. In this chapter we ask: first, how it can be diagnosed and classified; second, about its epidemiology; and third, how the causes of mental distress and disorder might be studied.

Even when there has been relatively clear-cut damage or disease of the brain, the effects on a person's behaviour or existential state may be diffuse or unpredictable. As Peter Franklin's case showed, this uncertainty underlies the problems of classifying and diagnosing those conditions of mental distress and disorder without clear-cut accompanying brain damage — the functional disorders.

Jean Arthur, Ann Bailey, Frank Harris and Paul Davies were all diagnosed as suffering from one or other form of functional disorder. Although there was no obvious brain damage, their existential state and their relations with the outside world were regarded by the doctors who saw them (if not by the individuals themselves) as manifestations of depression or schizophrenia. It is time to look a little more closely at the implications of such diagnoses. Clearly, the borderlines of what is considered a psychopathological state are hard to draw. Alcoholism, for example, is obviously a severe condition which can require medical attention — but is a *propensity* to alcoholism a sign of some underlying psychopathology? Clinical opinions may vary on this; some psychiatrists cast the net of their concern very wide, others more narrowly.

The earliest task of psychiatry was to attempt to classify mental illness and 'insanity' — a task tackled energetically from the mid-nineteenth century on. Hard and fast classifications present problems of their own, however, and more recently it came to be realised that many psychiatric conditions are not so much actual 'diseases', but statements about particular people's reactions to situations they find difficult or stressful. Today, modern textbooks offer a broad distinction between two types of illness, *psychosis* and *neurosis*. The psychoses are regarded as the disease entities which in their full form involve insanity and include for instance, schizophrenia and manic-depressive psychosis. The psychotic patient experiences life in a disturbed way owing to delusions, hallucinations or misinterpretations. The neuroses have come to be seen as minor illnesses in the sense that the patient experiences only such mental symptoms as anxiety or tension that are not in themselves outside the realm of normal experience. These conditions are regarded as unrelated to insanity, but as arising as an exaggerated response to difficulty or stress.

Psychoses

As we have seen, however, some clearly neurological conditions give rise to types of behaviour that could be classified as psychotic. Some psychiatrists therefore make a further distinction between 'organic psychoses' and 'functional psychoses'. Schizophrenia and manic-depressive psychosis fall into the category of functional psychoses.

Schizophrenia literally means 'split mind'. The classic picture of a schizophrenic is of a person who at the depths of their suffering feels in some fundamental way cut off from the rest of humanity. Often unable to express emotion, or to interact normally with others, or to express themselves verbally in a way that is rational to others, schizophrenics may appear blank, apathetic, dull. They may complain that their thoughts are not their own or that they are being controlled by some outside force (e.g. Frank Harris's 'Kali'). Dramatically ill schizophrenics appear not to be able to, or wish to, do anything for themselves. They take no interest in food, sexual activity, or exercise. They experience auditory hallucinations and their speech seems rambling, incoherent and disconnected to the casual listener. (Most people trying to follow Frank Harris's account of the reasons for his mental distress would experience this incoherence — as indeed did the doctor trying to understand Calvin Johnson's Rastafarian speech.) Some examples of writing and pictures done by schizophrenics are given in Figure 7.1. Periods of acute schizophrenic withdrawal are often followed by periods of lucidity and some psychiatrists doubt whether schizophrenia is a single entity at all, or speak of 'core' schizophrenia and a wider range ('spectrum') of schizophrenia-like symptoms. We should thus perhaps refer to 'the

Figure 7.1 Writing and pictures produced by patients suffering from schizophrenia.

schizophrenias' rather than to 'the' disease as a single entity. The idea of a single 'disease' of schizophrenia may be a hangover from the nineteenth-century description, developed by Kraepelin. Although we shall continue to refer to it in the singular here, as schizophrenia rather than schizophrenias, you should recognize that the diagnosis of schizophrenia in a person with a given set of symptoms can vary between doctors and cultures.

In manic depressive psychoses (sometimes called bipolar manic depression) of the type evidenced by Frank Harris in Chapter 6, the manic, or excited, phase may lead to grandiose (but false) ideas, such as about being possessed of great wealth or of being a historically important person, like Napoleon. By contrast, in the depressed phases there may be beliefs of impending ruin, death and destruction.

Neuroses

Although neuroses may be very disabling, they are benign illnesses in the sense that they are not associated with such grave developments as the psychoses and distortions of content do not appear.

There are many ways of subdividing the neuroses. Perhaps the simplest grouping is to consider them in two broad categories. One group are the *affective disorders*. *Affect* is the term used in psychology and psychiatry as a way of describing a person's responses — of emotion, attention and so forth — to events in the world around them. The affective disorders include, for instance, *depression*, which is characterised by a variably depressive mood, but without the manic phase of a psychosis, and *anxiety*. The condition discussed as hysteria in Book II would today probably be grouped along with depression and anxiety among the affective disorders.*

The other broad category of neurosis may be described under the general heading of *personality disorder*. It includes conditions such as obsessional neurosis, in which a person's thoughts are constantly interrupted by involuntary thoughts or impulses which cannot be willed away. It also includes *phobias* — 'irrational' fears such as agoraphobia (fear of being in open places), claustrophobia (fear of being in enclosed spaces) and many others.

Sometimes the whole group of conditions that we have described here as psychoses and neuroses are referred to in the catch-all term *psychopathology*, or disease of the mind. Indeed, the whole history of the development of psychiatry over the course of the century has been characterised by debates over whether the different conditions are mainly different manifestations of a single disease, or a small number of underlying diseases, or whether, on the other hand, there are really a multitude of different diseases that are quite distinct in aetiology, despite closely related symptoms.†

One of the problems, of course, is that of definition. Obviously, the definition of 'abnormal' depression or 'easily provoked or long lasting' anxiety that characterise such diagnoses depends on making judgments about what is *normal* behaviour or a normal response to a stressful situation. This involves comparing an individual's behaviour with that of people in similar situations, or a person's behaviour today with that on some previous occasion. It then becomes clear that definitions of what is

*Hysteria is discussed in *Medical Knowledge: Doubt and Certainty* (U205, Book II).

†The complex problems of the definition of 'disease' are discussed in *Studying Health and Disease* (U205, Book I) and again in *The Biology of Health and Disease* (U205, Book IV) in relation to what might seem much more straightforward conditions than the complex states of mental distress and disorder we are discussing here.

normal are themselves to some extent bound to time and culture, as you saw in the discussion of Calvin Johnson and Joan of Arc.

What are appropriate 'adaptive responses' to the world? If, for example, a man is cast into an apathetic despair about the likelihood of the world surviving a nuclear holocaust through the 1980s, or a woman is afraid to go out of her house at night for fear of being raped or murdered, how is one to judge that these are 'inappropriate' responses compared with those of the less sensitive majority? What the clinician or therapist attempts to do is to ask if the response is part of an overall pattern, or syndrome, that is preventing the sufferer from engaging effectively with the world within which he or she is embedded. The task then becomes one of trying to help sufferers to regain some control of their own destinies.

Let us consider the case of depression. When a clinician diagnoses depression, it is common to go on to attempt to distinguish between what are called *exogenous* (or 'reactive') and *endogenous* depressions. Exogenous depressions are supposed to be precipitated by the events in the world outside the individual — maybe a bereavement or loss of job. Conversely, endogenous depressions are said to be without obvious external precipitants and may occur cyclically at regular intervals. Sometimes they alternate with periods of heightened emotion or activity, in which case they are supposed to belong to the category of manic depressive disorder or psychosis. Depression is often associated with important transitions in a person's life, such as the birth of a baby (postnatal depression) or the menopause.* It is, of course, not the event in the abstract that is so important, but the context in which it occurs. What is important in the onset of depression is the meaning the event has for the individual and the way it affects their lives. The birth of a baby affects its mother differently if she is living in poor housing conditions and economic insecurity than if she is living in good conditions with a secure income and support in bringing up the child. Even depressions apparently triggered by seemingly specific events do not, however, necessarily simply go away if the crisis which generated them is resolved.

Mrs Arthur, Mrs Bailey and Mr Davies, whose experiences you heard on the audiotape, were diagnosed as suffering from depression — in Mr Davies' case a cyclic manic-depressive disorder. These diagnoses were made on the basis of extended interviews with a psychotherapist in a mental hospital. The textbook neatness of these distinctions between types of depression is, as we will see

*The mental states associated with postnatal depression and the menopause are discussed in *Birth to Old Age: Health in Transition.* The Open University (1985) *Birth to Old Age: Health in Transition*, Open University Press (U205, Book V).

in the next chapter, relied on extensively by clinical scientists in trying to explain a disorder biologically. The likelihood is, for most sufferers, that the distinctions between different types of depression, and even between depression and anxiety, are rather unclear. The distinctions may also be unclear to the people directly concerned with treating them, at least in the first instance. In the clinical practice of most family doctors, who form the 'front line' of prescribers of drugs to alleviate suffering, rough-and-ready diagnostic criteria, in the six minutes worth of consultation time that is on average likely to be available, do not allow for much of the subtlety and neatness of distinction that researchers on mental distress and disorder and its brain correlates like to make.

The extent of mental distress and disorder

How much mental distress and disorder is there in the United Kingdom today? In 1982, the total in-patient population in psychiatric hospitals was 90 000 (with also a further 47 000 in-patients for various types of mental handicap). This is considerably fewer than in 1959, when the figure was 240 000, partly because the Mental Health Act of that year committed Britain to a policy of community psychiatric care. Policy has thus directed patients out of the hospitals and, at the same time, there has been a steady introduction of new and more powerful drugs and treatments that have helped to open the locked psychiatric wards of hospitals.

The figure of 90 000 is for patients in hospitals at any one time and, as terms of stay are now generally short, the number of annual admissions to hospital is about twice the in-patient figure. Mental handicap admissions are about 16 000 a year. The story is not all one of 'success': the decline in first admissions to hospital has been accompanied by a steady increase in readmissions. A significant percentage of the post-1959 in-patient population has been termed the 'new long-stay', those who stay in for more than two years. No psychiatric hospital has closed in Britain over the period.

Another way of looking at the figures is to note that 1 in 12 men and 1 in 8 women in the UK will enter into hospital at some time in their lives to be treated for some type of psychiatric illness, although as you will see shortly the chance of being diagnosed as suffering from such illness is very unequally distributed across class, gender and ethnic lines. Eight per thousand of the population are hospitalised for mental illness or confined in institutions for the mentally handicapped or severely 'subnormal'.

It is worth contrasting these figures for hospital admissions for mental illness in the UK with the situation in Italy where, in 1961, there were 113 000 patients in mental hospitals, with an average stay of 15 years. In 1978 legislation was passed in Italy to phase out all mental hospitals in order to treat patients in general hospitals or 'the community'. By 1982 there was a mental hospital population of only 36 000 with an average stay of 15–20 days.

Hospital in-patients are of course only the tip of the iceberg of psychiatric casualties using medical services. In the UK in 1980 there were 1 691 400 out-patient appointments for persons suffering mental distress or mental disorder and it has been estimated that 23 per cent of patient consultations with their general practitioners are for advice on 'emotional and social problems'. Many other consultations, ostensibly for 'physical' illnesses, may be not unconnected to such 'emotional and social problems'. On the other hand, GPs may tend to regard patients (especially women) consulting them for what the patient regards as physical ailments as 'really' being about emotional problems. Thus the picture that is obtained from counting hospital admission figures or GP consultations can give only a partial measure of the scale of mental distress and disorder in the UK today. Certain questions need to be asked before such figures can be interpreted. For instance, a good deal of attention must be paid to the nature of the diagnoses that are being made. On what basis are people being diagnosed? How good are the criteria which enable particular labels to be placed on a person's behaviour? Global figures about the numbers of people diagnosed as suffering from particular types of disorder or disease must be broken down by geographical distribution, by age, class, gender and ethnicity before their implications can be fully understood.

An attempt to provide an estimate of the scale of psychopathology in North America and Europe was made by Bruce Dohrenwend and his collaborators in the US. They collated, in all, 27 different studies carried out between 1950 and the late 1970s (Dohrenwend *et al.*, 1980). The median estimate for psychopathology in the adult population below age 65 was 21 per cent, but the range was enormous.* One study estimated the figure to be as low as 0.6 per cent and the highest estimate was an astonishing 69 per cent. For Europe, where the median was 21 per cent, the range was between 4 per cent and 56 per cent. Table 7.1 gives the medians and ranges for a number of the conditions we have described. Not all of the studies used exactly the same diagnostic criteria, obviously, and this will account for some of the variations. It means that the median figures given in the table must be treated with caution.

It is possible, however, to make some internationally standardised attempts at diagnosis, the most substantial of which was that attempted for schizophrenia under the

Table 7.1 Medians and ranges of rates of disorder for various types of psychopathology in Europe and the USA

Type of diagnosis	Median (per cent)	Range (per cent)
psychoses	1.6	0 to 8.3
schizophrenia	0.6	0 to 2.7
manic depressive psychoses	0.3	0 to 1.9
neuroses	9.4	0.3 to 53.5
personality disorders	4.8	0.1 to 36.0

(Data from Dohrenwend *et al.*, 1980)

leadership of John Wing at the Institute of Psychiatry in London for the World Health Organization in the early 1970s (World Health Organization, 1973). These studies found that the estimated rate at which schizophrenia could be expected to appear in the adult population during the years of highest risk (16–45) was between 0.5 and 1 per cent. The British first-admission rate is about 15 new cases per year per 100 000 of the population, but the US rate is higher, perhaps because a broader definition of 'schizophrenia' is used in the USA than in the UK.

Dohrenwend and his colleagues went on to look at the class and gender distribution of psychopathological diagnoses. On the basis of 21 studies conducted between 1950 and the late 1970s, the prevalence rate in the USA, the UK and the rest of Europe is about 2.5 times greater in the 'lower' social classes than in the 'higher' social classes. Although definitions of social class vary from country to country the ratios were remarkably similar in all countries. Those ratios applied to all types of psychopathology. Table 7.2 shows what happens if they are broken down into different diagnoses.

☐ What is the most striking feature of this table?
■ Psychoses are more than twice as prevalent in 'lower'-class people than in 'upper'-class people, but there is no apparent difference between social groups in the prevalence of neuroses.

These studies also found that the severest disorders are, on average, twice as common in the lowest class as in the highest class. Manic depressive psychoses are not

Table 7.2 Prevalence of different types of psychopathology in 'low' classes compare to their prevalence in 'high' classes

Type of diagnosis	Average ratio 'low' class : 'high' class
psychoses	2.06
neuroses	no trend
personality disorders	1.77
all psychopathology	2.59

(Data from Dohrenwend *et al.*, 1980)

*'Median' is defined in Chapter 4 of *Studying Health and Disease* (U205, Book I).

Table 7.3 Prevalence of different types of psychopathology in women compared to men

Type of diagnosis	Average ratio women:men
schizophrenia	no trend
manic depressive psychoses	2.96
neuroses	2.86
personality disorders	0.66

(from Dohrenwend *et al.*, 1980)

excessively diagnosed in 'lower class' groups and most of the difference between classes is due to the greater prevalence of schizophrenia in the lowest classes. Again, the figures are averaged for a variety of studies, but they begin to indicate the questions that must be asked if we are seeking for a causal explanation of the incidence of mental distress or disorder.

Table 7.3 analyses the diagnoses according to gender. There are no gender differences, on average, in the diagnosis of schizophrenia, but there are striking differences in disorders like manic depressive psychoses and neuroses, where women tend to be diagnosed nearly three times as frequently as men. By contrast, the personality disorder diagnosis is only two-thirds as common in women as men.

□ Look at Tables 7.2 and 7.3 and compare the breakdown between psychoses and neuroses for different classes and for different genders. What is the most striking difference between them?

■ Diagnoses such as schizophrenia show class differences, but do not show gender differences. Diagnoses such as neuroses show gender differences, but do not show class differences.

The final type of classification which can be attempted is that by ethnic grouping. An attempt to study this was made by a social psychologist, R. Cochrane, working in Birmingham. He analysed age-adjusted hospital admissions in England and Wales in 1971 for men and women aged over 15, broken down by country of birth. Look at Table 7.4. In doing so, bear in mind that, in 1971, none of the immigrant groups constituted more than 1 per cent of the population and therefore, of all admissions in 1971, 91 per cent were for people born in England and Wales. Within some of the immigrant groups there were big disparities in the numbers of men and women living in England and Wales — for instance, 72 per cent of all Pakistanis living in the UK at the time were men. This reflected the pattern of immigration and immigration legislation of the period. The figures have been 'age

Table 7.4 Admissions to mental hospitals in England and Wales in 1971 per 100 000 of the population over 15 years old standardised for age.

Country of Birth	Schizophrenia	Manic depressive psychoses	Neuroses	Personality and behaviour disorders
1 Males				
England and Wales	87	45	48	43
Scotland	90	42	56	100
N. Ireland	96	78	121	201
Irish Republic	83	69	88	139
West Indies	290	30	19	27
India	141	31	33	36
Pakistan	158	22	36	18
Germany	99	35	41	58
Italy	71	35	22	30
Poland	189	63	42	27
USA	76	32	30	54
2 Females				
England and Wales	87	92	88	41
Scotland	97	99	111	67
N. Ireland	160	147	172	111
Irish Republic	254	174	165	114
West Indies	323	91	67	46
India	140	57	64	29
Pakistan	103	38	103	55
Germany	130	59	98	48
Italy	127	61	67	33
Poland	301	119	139	40
USA	133	122	78	98

(Data from Cochrane, 1977)

adjusted' to compensate for the fact that the immigrant population may well have been much younger, on average, than the native English and Welsh population.

Finally, you should note that the number of hospital admissions is, of course, only one measure of the scale of mental distress and disorder. There could be different consultation rates among the groups and many other features could account for such differences.

☐ If you compare schizophrenia and neuroses for men and women born in England and Wales, what is the most striking feature?

■ There is no sex difference in the schizophrenia admission rates, but women are nearly twice as likely as men to be admitted to hospital suffering from neurosis.

☐ Now look at the figures for schizophrenia and neuroses for men and for women born in the Irish Republic and compare them with those for people born in England and Wales.

■ There is nearly a two-fold increase in the neurosis rate among Irish men and a similar increase among Irish women. Women of Irish origin are three times as likely to be admitted with a schizophrenia diagnosis as are women of English or Welsh origin.

☐ Now look at the figures for the West Indies.

■ The figures for admissions of men of West Indian birth for neuroses are very low — lower than those for men born in England and Wales. The same is true for West Indian born women. The schizophrenia figures for people of West Indian origin, however, are very high, without much difference between the sexes. If you were born in the West Indies and living in England and Wales, you were, during the 1970s, 3.5 times as likely to be admitted to a mental hospital suffering from schizophrenia than one of the 'native' population.

What do these differences indicate? Could there be a different *biological* propensity to become schizophrenic rather than neurotic in the different groups?* This is improbable given the fact that social definitions of ethnicity do not map onto biological ones. (We shall consider the genetics of schizophrenia in the next chapter.) Is there something socially different about the cultural backgrounds of immigrants to England and Wales that makes them more or less liable to suffer from neuroses or schizophrenia compared with the indigenous population? Or is there something about the experience of being an immigrant in a society that is certainly not free of racism? Like other ethnic groups, the English have stereotypes of

how they expect non-English people to behave, whether Irish, German or Pakistani. You may recall how, in Calvin Johnson's case, his religious belief, Rastafarianism, was considered to resemble schizophrenia by the doctor who made case notes on him. Perhaps doctors expect people who are presented to them with mental distress and disorder to fit into certain stereotyped categories?

Studying the causes of mental distress and disorder

The previous sections have raised some of the issues that must be discussed in the context of diagnosing, classifying and measuring the extent of mental distress and disorder. They have also given you some of the statistics of psychopathology. Given the epidemiological pattern that we have just discussed, how can you explore the *causes* of mental distress and disorder?

☐ What three types of causal explanations might you set out to study?

■ Social causes, personal life-history causes and biological causes.†

How might you explore possible biological causes? As this biological study is of human beings, certain sorts of possibly useful information could be achieved simply by collecting personal data from the depressed individual or schizophrenic patient.

☐ If you were a research psychiatrist investigating the causes of depression among patients, what types of question would you want to ask any individual sufferer diagnosed by their clinician as depressed?

■ You might begin by considering the person's life history. Was there anything in their immediate past which could explain their present suffering? Was there anything in their social and physical circumstances, or anything in their childhood history? You would probably go on to consider their family. Did other brothers or sisters suffer from the same condition? Parents or grandparents?

☐ What would these last questions point to?

■ A family trait — did the condition 'run in families'?

You could then draw up a 'pedigree analysis' showing the family history for the trait.‡ Such a pedigree analysis is not a very practical possibility for depression or schizophrenia.

☐ Why not?

■ Pedigree analysis requires a psychiatric diagnosis

---

*You should bear in mind the distinction between biological and social definitions of ethnicity discussed in *Studying Health and Disease* (U205, Book I).

†These three types of causal approaches and the general methodology of the following pages are discussed in *Studying Health and Disease* (U205, Book I).

‡Pedigree analysis is discussed in *The Biology of Health and Disease* (U205, Book IV).

on individuals running through several generations. It would be necessary to rely on clinical case notes on members of a family, as it would often not be possible to interview parents, grandparents, etc. As definitions of psychiatric illness have changed much more markedly over the course of this century than have those for more obvious types of 'physical' illness, the reliability of such records would be a serious problem.

□ Think again about the case of Mrs Bailey, discussed in Chapter 6. If you found that her sister, or even her parents, had also been diagnosed as suffering from depression, could you conclude that the condition was genetically transmitted?

■ Families share similar genes, but also a similar environment, so you could not distinguish a genetic involvement in this way.

□ There are people who share *identical* genes. Who are they?

■ Identical or monozygotic twins.

□ Suppose Mrs Bailey had an identical twin sister who was also depressed (i.e. Mrs Bailey and her sister were *concordant* for depression). Could you then conclude that the depression had a genetic cause? (Note that you would also need to check whether their depression had occurred in similar circumstances and had shown a similar clinical pattern.)

■ It might seem quite a strong possibility, but remember that identical twins also share a common environment during their development and childhood. Indeed, it is likely to be more similar than that of ordinary siblings.

The way round this, the 'ideal' *twin study*, would be to find pairs of twins who had been separated at birth and reared apart. As all they have in common is their genes, it might seem that all the difference between them in the chance of being diagnosed later in life as depressed, schizophrenic, or whatever, was due to their different environments. Such studies have been made, as we shall see, but in practice such 'ideal twins' are few and far between and as the features of their childhood environments that might contribute to a psychopathological diagnosis later in life are unknown (though they may be guessed at), the implication of twin studies tends to be very uncertain. An alternative approach, which has been used in the study of schizophrenia, is a sort of twin study in reverse, called an *adoption study*. In such studies the incidence of a particular psychopathological diagnosis in *adopted* children is compared with the incidence of the same diagnosis in the *biological* children of their adopted parents and in other children of their own biological parents.

□ What is the assumption being made in this kind of study?

■ The assumption is that the adoptive and biological children of particular parents share a common environment. If the adopted child shows psychopathology, it can then be asked whether the child shared that psychopathology with its biological siblings — in which case the assumption is that there is a probability of some mode of genetic transmission — or with its adopted brothers and sisters — in which case the family environment offered by the adopted parents may be held responsible.

There is an example of this type of study applied to schizophrenia in the next chapter, but again we must caution against simplistic assumptions that the apparent neatness of such an approach can ever be matched in the richer reality of the world of adoption. For instance, the age at which children are adopted varies and the parents' relationship with their adopted child is likely to differ from that with their biological child. This depends, in part, on when their biological child was born — before or after the adoption. Parents' reasons for adoption differ and adoption agencies do not assign children to be adopted randomly, but try to screen potential families. Thus selective placement of adopted children occurs. We shall see all these difficulties in play in the case study.

The genetic studies that we have been discussing are designed to answer the question: is there a genetic propensity to a particular psychopathological condition? Whether or not there is such a propensity, the biologically minded psychiatrist would want to know whether it was associated with particular observable changes in the structure or chemistry of the brain.

How can such questions be approached? Almost by definition, there are going to be no gross brain abnormalities associated with 'functional' disorders or they would long ago have been moved on to the category of 'organic' disorders. In functional disorders, post-mortem study of brain tissue does not reveal obvious damage. New scanning techniques enable 'snapshots' of living tissue — including the brain — to be made. The use of these techniques has been the basis for — as yet unconfirmed — suggestions that there are abnormalities to be found in the shape and size of certain brain structures in people diagnosed as schizophrenic. Most studies, however, work from the assumption that the abnormality, if it occurs, must lie in the biochemisty, not the structure of the brain.

The detection of any such abnormality raises acute methodological problems. To start with, there are many hundreds of thousands of different chemical substances present in the brain, including at least 30 000 different proteins. The function of only a tiny number of them is known with any degree of certainty and new substances are being isolated and studied all the time. It is no good simply cataloguing everything present in the hope of finding one particular different substance. There have been claims, from time to time, that 'unique' substances are present in body tissues from individuals suffering from schizophrenia, but no such claim has ever stood up under rigorous analysis.

Hence, we must start with some hypothesis about the type of chemical or process involved. Many such hypotheses have been made, generally influenced by the biochemical fashion of the moment and we shall review some of them below. Having made a hypothesis, we must then extract the body tissue in which to study it. One possibility is to use tissue derived from post-mortem samples of the brains of patients suffering from the disorder.

□   What difficulties might this present?
■   There is the obvious practical difficulty of obtaining tissue fresh enough to make biochemical analysis of unstable substances possible. There are also other difficulties. You need to compare the amount of some substance in the tissue derived from the patient with the amount present in 'normal' controls. The people from whom such samples are taken need to be matched for age, diet and sex of the patient and something must be known of the comparative medical histories of both the patient and the control. For instance, if the patient had been on drugs, traces of the drug and its metabolites may be found, which would be of strictly iatrogenic origin. Obviously, it would be an advantage to work with material taken from a living person.

□   What types of material might be available from living people?
■   Urine, blood and cerebrospinal fluid (the fluid which bathes the brain and spinal cord, CSF) can be obtained for analysis, the first two readily. Much of the biochemical approach to mental disorder reduces to the exquisitely sensitive chemical analysis of such samples. The assumption is that any abnormal metabolism in the brain will result in the production of unusual substances that will be secreted into the cerebrospinal fluid or the blood and, ultimately, will be filtered by the kidneys into the urine.

□   What is the flaw in the assumption that if an abnormal substance is found, then it must be the *cause* of the disorder?
■   Any abnormal substance produced might be a *consequence* of the disorder rather than causally related to it. For example, someone with a cold secretes

excessive nasal mucus, but the mucus does not cause the cold, it results from it.

A further approach to the biochemistry of mental disorder and distress is pharmacological. It is based on the study of drugs known to affect the condition. The argument is that if (a) a particular drug is known to affect the symptoms of the disorder, either by alleviating or exacerbating it, and (b) the biochemical sites of action of the drug are known, then (c) the disorder may be associated with a biochemical abnormality at that particular site. This form of reasoning thus argues backwards from the *effects* of a medical intervention to infer a basic biochemical *cause* for a disorder. Although this method is widely used, it is subject to a fundamental logical difficulty.

□   What is this difficulty? (Think about the relationship of aspirin to toothache)?
■   A drug can attenuate the symptoms of a disorder without having any effect on its cause. Aspirin alleviates the pain of toothache, not because it interacts with the abscess or dental caries generating the pain, but because it affects the nerve cells in the brain which respond to inputs from pain fibres.

In many types of disease a resource open to biologists is the use of experimental animals: infections, the effects of hormones and many drugs, the onset and consequences of cancers, can all be readily followed in rats or mice. Such a resource is almost ruled out in the study of mental distress and disorder simply because of the lack of any convincing animal model. The outsider knows that a person is suffering from distress primarily by what they say about themselves, by their communication, but non-human animals cannot, of course, communicate in this way. True, dogs and cats may behave in ways which those who know them well might regard as neurotic. 'Aggressive' or frightened behaviour can be induced in many animals by drugs or severe handling regimes. Monkeys can be worried into ulcers, for instance. Some people might well argue that the conditions under which most laboratory animals are held are enough to make them neurotic!

The search for *animal models* in which to study the biology of psychiatric disorders is very limited. One approach is to administer drugs that may produce behaviour in the animal that appears analogous to that in the human disorder. Thus the effects of certain drugs on the behaviour of dogs or monkeys might lead one to assume that the animals were hallucinating, or anxious, or frightened. The pharmacological method of arguing backwards can then be applied, without some of the ethical considerations which limit experiments on humans. The area of human mental distress and disorder is, however, much richer than can be tapped by exploring the behaviour of animals in such ways. Animal models of the human condition are always impoverished and can lend themselves to the most hazardous extrapolations.

Faced with such a formidable array of problems in the way of a successful biological approach to studying mental distress and disorder, you may well wonder why people have tried. Yet the sheer scale of the problem that the epidemiological figures reveal makes the effort to explain the symptoms of mental distress and disorder, in order to alleviate or cure, of major importance. Hence, medical and biological sciences are under pressure to 'do something about it'. In the UK, for instance, the study of the human brain, its function and dysfunction, is a priority area for the Medical Research Council, which funds biological research. The powerful reductionist strand of thinking which dominates orthodox medicine and biological psychiatry makes the biological approach seem the most powerful. Finally, but by no means least importantly, exploring the *biochemical correlates* of mental disorder leads to the development of new pharmacological agents and it is in the field of psychiatry, above all, that the pharmaceutical industry finds its most ready users, as you will see in Chapter 9.

Nonetheless, it will not surprise you to learn that there is no consensus, even among biological psychiatrists, on any unique biochemical abnormality that can be unequivocally associated with any specific condition of mental distress and disorder, despite several decades of energetic research and many tens of millions of pounds of government and industrial funding.

Objectives for Chapter 7

When you have studied this chapter, you should be able to:

7.1 Discuss the definitions of 'functional' ('psychological') and 'organic' ('neurological') disorders, give examples of each and appreciate the ambiguities involved in these distinctions.

7.2 Distinguish between psychoses and neuroses.

7.3 Comment on the problem of interpretation of gender, class and ethnic distribution of psychopathology diagnoses in the United Kingdom.

7.4 Discuss the limitations of the techniques available for the study of the biological correlates of functional disorders.

Questions for Chapter 7

1 (*Objective 7.1*) What distinguishes a psychological from a biological disorder?

2 (*Objective 7.2*) (a) Would an otherwise fit individual with an important letter to post, who felt she could not mobilize enough energy to walk the 50 metres to the post box, be likely to be diagnosed as suffering from a neurosis or a psychosis?

(b) Would an otherwise fit individual with an important letter to post, who felt it was dangerous to go out of doors because he was likely to be followed by malevolent two-foot high Martians, be likely to be diagnosed as suffering from a neurosis or a psychosis?

(c) How sure should you be of your answers to (a) and (b)?

3 (*Objective 7.3*) Look at the data from the Cochrane study reproduced in Table 7.4. There were differential admission rates for Irish-born men and women, English and Welsh-born men and women, and US-born men and women for personality disorders in England and Wales in the early 1970s. In particular, men born in Northern Ireland were admitted to hospital for personality disorders nearly five times more frequently than English or Welsh-born men and almost twice as frequently as women born in Northern Ireland. Can you conclude from this:

(a) That men have a genetic predisposition to personality disorders?

(b) That the Irish have a genetic predisposition to personality disorders?

4 (*Objective 7.4*) What would be the main limitation of the study of post-mortem samples that were derived from the brain of an individual diagnosed as depressive in order to try to locate the biochemical 'cause' of depression?

8

Explaining depression and schizophrenia

In this chapter we consider the various types of explanation offered for the causes of depression and schizophrenia. You are asked to read two articles from the Course Reader: Erving Goffman's 'The insanity of place' (Part 5, Section 5.1) and George Brown's 'Depression: a sociological view' (Part 2, Section 2.4). We make reference to concepts about the brain from Book IV, Chapter 6 and methods of study discussed in Book I.

There are four broad types of explanatory principle around which attempts to account for depression and schizophrenia are organised and we shall consider each in turn. They are:

1 Depression and schizophrenia do not exist as specific disorders 'within' an individual, but are ways of describing certain kinds of relationships between individuals, either directly (as in 'games people play' with one another within a family, say) or indirectly between individuals and the power structures of society.

2 The disorders do exist, but must be explained as occurring as a consequence of pressures on individuals derived from their recent and present experiences.

3 The disorders exist in adults as a consequence of formative experiences in very early childhood.

4 The disorders exist in adults as reflections of disordered brain biochemistry, itself possibly a consequence of specific genetic abnormalities.

These types of explanation are not necessarily exclusive and, in trying to simplify the complex understandings of most researchers, clinicians and therapists, we have stated them baldly. These simplifications do, however, enable us to look at the arguments and evidence for apparently competing explanations. We shall discuss these four approaches in relation to both schizophrenia and depression because the types of evidence and argument involved are rather similar in each case, but you should always bear in mind that the two conditions are quite distinct in terms of the existential state of the person diagnosed as depressed, on the one hand, or schizophrenic on the other.

Expressions of social relationships

At this stage, you should read the article in the Course Reader on 'The insanity of place' by Erving Goffman, a sociologist who worked in Philadelphia in the USA.

☐ How does Goffman characterise mental disorder?

■ He sees it as a form of *social deviation*. Although he is far from explicit about this in the article, he appears to argue that the individual *chooses* to show symptoms of mental disorder as a way of avoiding or counteracting the demands of other people with whom the mentally disordered person lives and interacts.

☐ What does Goffman see as the consequence of initiating disordered (depressive and manic) behaviour?

■ Depressive people affect the mental balance and functioning of the family. The manic individual, ignored by his family, seeks to promote himself in the family hierarchy by adopting particular modes of disruptive behaviour and is 'someone to be watched'.

Goffman's views came to prominence during the height of what became known as the *anti-psychiatry* movement of the 1960s and early 1970s. The movement was at the forefront of the campaign to *deinstitutionalise* mental patients by arguing that madness was not a question of a failure in the brain or psychology of the individual, but a product of a socially unjust society, a society that *chooses* to define certain types of behaviour as unacceptable and therefore to be controlled by medical treatment. Individuals who showed such behaviour were, anti-psychiatry argued, *labelled* as mad. We have already referred to one consequence of this campaign — the legislation passed in Italy to close mental hospitals.

Although there were many strands to the anti-psychiatrists' arguments, we can summarise these at two levels. The focus of mental distress was seen on the one hand, as in the Goffman article you have just read, as located in the family and, on the other, in the power of the state. Sometimes anti-psychiatrists themselves oscillate between the two levels of explanation. The anti-psychiatry thesis itself varies between arguing that madness is 'merely' a label and, alternatively, that people are mad as a result of the injustice of a society in which there are gross disparities in status, wealth and power.

To take the family first, consider the approach to schizophrenia developed by the British anthropologist Gregory Bateson in the US, and the Scottish psychiatrist R.D. Laing, working in Britain and the US. Bateson, and later Laing and his colleagues (in books such as *The Politics of Experience and the Bird of Paradise*, Laing, 1967), argued that schizophrenia is essentially a *family disorder*: it is not the product of a sick individual, but of the interactions of the members of a sick family. Within this family, locked together by the 'nuclear' style of living of contemporary society, an individual — normally a child — comes to be 'picked on'. The child is always at fault, never able to live up to parental demands or expectations. Thus the child is in what Laing calls a *double bind*. *Whatever* he or she does is wrong. Under such circumstances, the retreat into a world of private fantasy becomes the only logical response to the intolerable pressures of existence. For Laing, in the last analysis, in a mad world, only the mad are sane. Schizophrenia is thus a rational, adaptive response of individuals to the strains of their life.

Treatment of the schizophrenic by hospitalisation or drugs is, therefore, not seen as a liberation from the disease, but as part of that person's oppression. Schizophrenia itself is seen as almost benign, a 'breakthrough' rather than a 'breakdown'. Laing claimed, for instance, that a proper analysis showed that schizophrenic speech, far from being jumbled and incoherent, revealed an inner logic and rational account of the schizophrenic's life and problems, which, granted a supportive, therapeutic community, could be resolved. Laing's views were given prominence in the early 1970s in a film about schizophrenia, *Family Life*.

Doubts about the validity of the explanations being offered, and about the therapeutic outcome of his methods, grew during the 1970s. Laing was unable to produce clear evidence of the validity of his theoretical framework either in understanding how schizophrenic people actually spoke or behaved, or indeed, in treating them. Today the 'pure' Laingian position is no longer held by Laing himself, though many of his followers still maintain it. Laing's views are, however, clearly compatible with the account of madness given by Goffman. In fact, these views have an interesting echo 'from the other side', as it were. Here is a description by John Pringle, one of the founders of the British-based organization, The Schizophrenia Association, of the problem of having a schizophrenic in the family.

Living with schizophrenia

One of your adolescent children begins to behave oddly. At first he just moons about. But many adolescents moon about. He or she takes to lying on the bed, presumably day-dreaming. He or she becomes moody, bad-tempered, slovenly, 'difficult'. But many adolescents day-dream and are moody or difficult.

To you, as a sensible parent, such behaviour is well within the limits of the normal growing-up process and no attention is paid to it. He or she will 'grow out of it', you say. But time goes on and he or she does not grow out of it. A crisis occurs when some wild display of aggression, truancy, or merely bizarre behaviour, drives you to seek expert help.

. . . your home, in an atmosphere of simulated normality, a determined show of ordinary living, is rapidly becoming preoccupied by the sick member: the ups and downs of his moods, his unpredictable vagaries of behaviour.

Reactions of brothers and sisters may differ widely and their resentment may be deep if the sick one is not handled according to the ideas of each: affectionate concern; or alternatively, jealousy over the attention he is getting;

irritation at the sufferer's 'laziness' or 'selfishness'; rejection; guilt for past teasing or bullying (shadowing the omnipresent and inescapable parental guilts); refusal to accept that he is ill at all, but only 'being himself', 'doing his own thing', that it is not he or she but 'society' which is 'all wrong' — 'What he needs is to get away from those damned hospitals and live among normal people'. . . .

Opposite pressures, reflecting the ambivalencies of your situation, will be exerted on you by the fears of social embarrassment and 'stigma', both in the post-diagnosis stage and earlier.

There are the material anxieties: how is the disabled one to be given a livelihood? None of these fears is irrational or imaginary. Try finding a sympathetic employer for *your* schizophrenic. Try getting digs where the landlady will not quickly make some excuse for getting rid of him. Try just listening in the background as he or she is floundering in front of some social security clerk who suspects he is work-shy or fiddling his 'benefit'.

Protests from neighbours

As regards stigma, *your* family has to live in the world as it is — a world in which the popular press and TV 'image' of a schizophrenic is mostly of a rapist or child-murderer, in which a hostel cannot be established in a 'better class' district without protests from the neighbours that their wives and daughters won't be safe. (Useless for families of schizophrenics to reflect that *their* poor, frightened lad wouldn't hurt a fly. . . .)

Some members of your family may never accept the diagnosis and will quarrel with the parent who tries to implement it. You then have a divided and part alienated family on your hands, if you haven't one already — to say nothing of the cases where once happily married parents are themselves driven apart because one rejects or partially rejects, which the other cannot forgive.

The sheer disruptive power of schizophrenia over a family is fully intelligible only to those who have been through it. But a few of the worst effects, could, I think, be avoided if the *medical* problem of communicating with the family were tackled at an earlier stage, and firmly. And not only with the parents, but with *all* the family who matter, collectively. I do not know how this is to be done, only that it ought to be done. (Pringle, 1972)

☐ Compare Pringle's view of the origins of schizophrenia with those of Laing and Goffman.
■ For Goffman and Laing, the disorder originates as a *response* by the individual to the problem of family life. Pringle is primarily concerned with the problems of the rest of the family trying to *respond* to the schizophrenic member of the family and the disruption generated in their lives. Thus, for him, the original and

primary disorder lies in the unprovoked odd behaviour of the adolescent.

☐ Are these interpretations necessarily incompatible?
■ No, they are not. Both descriptions could be true, in which case the individual sufferer and their family would enter a declining spiral of relationships. Each would learn to expect certain types of behaviour and response on the part of the other. Indeed, Goffman makes just this point and a number of psychiatric treatments are based on the idea that mental distress and disorder are in this sense *learned behaviours*. You will see the significance of this idea for at least one type of therapeutic approach in the next chapter.

Goffman and Laing are essentially working within the qualitative tradition of social science methodology.* How far can their ideas on the ways in which personal interactions between patients and the people they live with be tested quantitatively? As we have already said, Laing himself has not presented substantive evidence concerning his patients, apart from the few famous cases described in his early writings. An attempt to be more precise about the nature of the relationships between sufferers from schizophrenia and the relatives they live with has been made by a group of research psychiatrists led by Julian Leff at the Institute of Psychiatry in London (Leff *et al.*, 1982). They measured what they describe as the level of 'expressed emotion' in the relatives of schizophrenics, noting particularly the number of critical comments made by relatives and the amount of 'hostility' and 'over-involvement'. Of course, if you found a high level of 'hostility' and other forms of 'expressed emotion' in terms of critical comments made by people living with a schizophrenic patient who showed the sort of behaviour described by Pringle, you could consider three possible explanations for the relationship between the patient's schizophrenic behaviour and the hostility expressed by relatives.

☐ Suggest what these might be?
■ First, the behaviour of the schizophrenic person is so disruptive that it caused the hostility. Second, the hostility pre-dated the schizophrenic's behaviour and precipitated it. Third, there is no direct causal relationship, but a complex interaction between the behaviour of the schizophrenic person and the relatives.

The first explanation is suggested in the extract by Pringle, the second by Laing's 'double bind' type of analysis. Goffman's position is, perhaps characteristically, ambiguous. In fact, Leff and his colleagues claim that, by

---

*The qualitative methods of the Social Sciences are described and discussed in *Studying Health and Disease* (U205, Book I).

the use of statistical procedures, they have been able to rule out the possibility that the patient's disturbed behaviour is directly responsible for their relatives' high levels of expressed emotion. Further, they have developed an interactive therapeutic strategy based on attempts to change the relative's behaviour by educational programmes and group discussion. As you will see in the next chapter, such a strategy does diminish the rate of relapse among schizophrenic patients living with relatives.

Goffman, Laing and the theorists of learned behaviour are concerned with the micro-world of the family and its relationships. There is, however, a bigger stage on which the theory of anti-psychiatry has been played out. Writers such as Thomas Szasz in the US and Michel Foucault in France have seen madness as the terrain of larger social institutions. Szasz, in numerous books published in the 1960s and 1970s, has said that madness is 'manufactured' by something he calls *institutional psychiatry*. Individuals, according to Szasz, either have something organically wrong with them — properly the province of medicine — or they must be regarded as responsible for their own actions. As he seems to believe that there are no brain changes in madness (including schizophrenia and depression) then it is merely the power of an institutionalised state psychiatry that denies people the right to be mad, by compulsorily submitting them to treatment by drugs or to hospital confinement. For Szasz, such a psychiatry is a 'speciality not of medicine, but of mythology'. His solution is a return to the concept of private, individual psychiatry. Any person should have the right — if they can afford it — to consult a private psychiatrist about their problems: no one should have the right to prescribe treatment against the will of the individual patient. Everyone is answerable for their own actions: no one has 'diminished responsibility' (Szasz, 1977).

Szasz's views seemed to be given substance by a famous experiment carried out by David Rosenhan and his colleagues in California in 1973. Rosenhan's group of experimenters presented themselves individually to doctors, complaining of 'hearing voices'. The results varied, of course, but many were admitted to hospital. Once inside, according to the strategy of the experiment, they declared that their symptoms had ceased. Some were released quite soon, others were not to find it so easy. Their claims to normality were disregarded. They found themselves treated by doctors and nurses as mere objects and were only released after considerable periods. A 'pseudo-patient' who took notes in hospital, for instance, was described by nurses as showing 'compulsive writing behaviour'. Even more revealing, perhaps, was the drop in hospital admissions for schizophrenia in the area after Rosenhan circulated doctors with the results of the first experiment and warned them that they might be visited by further pseudo-patients in the future, although none were actually sent (Rosenhan, 1973).

Rosenhan's account produced a strong counter-attack from more orthodox psychiatrists, who argued that the patients had been properly admitted to hospital and humanely treated there. Peter Sedgwick (1982), a British political scientist, has pointed out that the concept of pseudo-patients has had a bizarre aftermath. In the trial of Peter Sutcliffe, the 'Yorkshire Ripper', in the UK in 1981, the defence psychiatrists endeavoured to prove that Sutcliffe was schizophrenic and therefore 'not responsible' for his actions. The prosecution cited the Rosenhan experiment as an example of how pseudo-patients can 'fool' psychiatrists and the jury refused to accept the plea of diminished responsibility.

The most comprehensive expression of the thesis that mental distress and disorder is a problem created by defining particular people in particular ways, in a sense, labelling them, has come from the work of Michel Foucault and his school in France over the last two decades (e.g. Foucault, 1971). Foucault has argued that the entire category of mental disorders is to be seen, in a certain sense, as a historical invention, an expression of power relationships within society manifested within particular families. It is not that the behaviour society *calls* 'mad' does not exist, but that it can be understood only in terms of the way in which it is socially regarded. Foucault claims that all societies require a category of individuals who can be dominated or made into scapegoats and, over the centuries since the rise of science, and particularly since the Industrial Revolution in the nineteenth century, the 'mad' have come to fill this category. In medieval times, he says, houses of confinement were built for lepers and madness was often explained in terms of possession by demons or spirits. Similarly, epilepsy was, for many years, regarded as an indication that the epileptic, while in a fit, was capable of communicating with other worlds. According to Foucault, the idea of institutionalising the mad developed during the eighteenth and nineteenth centuries, after the clearing of the leper houses left a gap for new scapegoats to replace the old ones.

In this view, madness is not so much a property of the individual, but instead, a social definition wished by society on a proportion of its population. As we have said, theorists who take this position differ as to who has the power to make these social definitions. Is it the state, or the dominant class and gender within society, or does it arise within the relationships of the family? All agree, however, that to look for correlates of madness in the brain becomes a meaningless task, for madness is not 'located' in the brain, or in the individual at all. It is an expression of a *relationship* between the individual and society.

Arguments based on Foucault's framework became popular in Britain in the late 1970s and early 1980s and they do point to the relationship between definitions of madness and the ideology of the society that makes such definitions. Consider, in this context, the history of hysteria. One explanation of the way in which the label 'hysteria' was applied is that its diagnosis was mainly by male doctors to female patients as an expression of disapproval of certain types of female behaviour and, above all, as a way of asserting and establishing control.* An alternative thesis is that women's hysterical behaviour was a *response* to their subordinate role. Certainly, one is left in some doubt as to whether a condition called 'hysteria' existed at all outside the context of the power relationship between male doctors and female patients. Similarly, Goffman sees mental illness as being developed by the patient in order to achieve changes in the balance of power and being exacerbated by the attempts of members of the family to keep the balance as it is.

That describing people with inappropriate behaviour, morals or views as mad and incarcerating them in asylums — psychiatric hospitals — can and does occur is undisputed. We shall consider the wider implications of this in Chapter 13. Nonetheless, to dismiss the existential suffering of a schizophrenic or depressed person, such as those whose cases you met in Chapter 6, *merely* as a problem of social labelling by those who have power over those who have not, is an inadequate response to a complex social and medical problem. Despite the enthusiasm shown for Foucault's views, both in Britain and France, and their emergence at the crest of the wave of 'anti-psychiatry' in the 1960s and 1970s, the accuracy of his historical account of when and how 'asylums for the insane' arose has been seriously questioned by, for example, Peter Sedgwick. Even more important, by locating the phenomenon of madness entirely in the world of social relations, this approach, in its most extreme form, cuts madness completely adrift from the individual and so fails to take account of a person's own individual biology. It is as if people cease to exist except as the 'bearers' of particular sets of power relationships. It fails to explain how or why drugs or other therapeutic treatments work and is, of course, incompatible with the ideas on the relationship between 'brain state' and 'personal existential state' discussed in Chapter 6.

Social and economic problems

You should now read the article in the Course Reader 'Depression: a sociological view' by George Brown, a medical sociologist working in London.

Brown's position on the origin of depression as expressed in the article is unequivocal, though you may have noted that

*'Hysteria ... the *furor uterinus*' is discussed in *Medical Knowledge: Doubt and Certainty* (U205, Book II).

he is more cautious about schizophrenia. Brown himself would probably agree that he was deliberately stating the case in a very strong form in this article: 'I believe', he says, 'that depression is essentially a social phenomenon'.

☐ Summarise the evidence offered by Brown, and also cited in Chapter 7, on which such a claim is based.

■ From Chapter 7 you will recall that women are diagnosed as having depression much more frequently than men. Brown, in conjunction with Tirril Harris, studied women in the inner London suburb of Camberwell. He found that at least 25 per cent of the working-class women with children, when interviewed, appeared to be depressed to an extent that would invite a clinical diagnosis had they visited a psychiatrist. In contrast, middle-class women showed such depression at only a quarter of the working-class rate.

The depressed women tended to have suffered from some serious or life-threatening event in the recent past — a 'provoking agent' — and were more likely to become depressed if, for instance, they had three or more children under 15 at home, or were unemployed. These are what Brown calls *vulnerability factors*. Some of these factors relate to events in the individual's more distant past, such as losing her mother before the age of 11. These factors combine, Brown believes, to produce a condition of 'low self-esteem' resulting, in the depressed condition, in a general sense of hopelessness. As Brown points out, this sense of hopelessness is not unrealistic: 'the future for many women is bleak', he says.

You can feel this sense of hopelessness in the words of depressed women:

In spite of having my children, the feeling that I couldn't go on battling with life any longer remained. Each time I attempted suicide I admitted defeat. All I wanted was peace of mind and death was the only way I could think of in which I might find it. (*Chris*, quoted in Nairne and Smith, 1984, p.5)

Depression ... well, you just feel you can't do anything, you can't do anything right and it doesn't seem to matter how hard you try you just can't seem to get to where you want to get ... you try and you try and you try ... you have fits of tears and just feel utter despair. (*Elizabeth*, quoted in Nairne and Smith 1984, p.5)

I remember the first time I felt depressed. It was when I was hanging out the washing one day, just before my eldest daughter went away to college. I suddenly thought 'I'm not going to have anyone to talk to when she goes'. I realised that I hadn't been able to talk to my husband for years and that I did not have any friends I could talk to either. (*Penny*, quoted in Nairne and Smith 1984, p.120)

After reading these quotations and listening to Jean Arthur and Ann Bailey (Chapter 6), and reading Brown's article, there seems to be little space left for that textbook distinction we cited in the last chapter between endogenous depression and exogenous or reactive depression. Is that distinction to disappear? Brown's view is that it is at least not nearly as clear cut as some psychiatrists have held in the past and that the distinction cannot really be made in symptomatic terms. It is clear, however, that there *are* people who become depressed without obvious external precipitating factors. There are depressive states which people experience which seem quite 'out of proportion' to the apparent precipitating cause, or which continue long after the immediate precipitating cause is past.

> I suppose everybody's got to find peace of mind in their own way. Someone like me, where do I find it?
> I really do believe that some of us are born to go through life in the same way.... (*Chris*, quoted in Nairne and Smith 1984, p.13)

A sizeable proportion of sufferers from depression show regular cyclic changes in mood, be it a cycle of days or months. Sometimes their mood swings between 'normality' and depression (sometimes called unipolar depression).

> Depression is a funny thing. One minute you will be wallowing in its depths and the next you are miles away from it. (*Marie*, quoted in Nairne and Smith 1984, p.13)

Sometimes a person's mood swings between manic states of hyper-excitement and hyper-activity and, on the other hand, depression (called cyclic manic depressive psychosis or bipolar depression). Paul Davies, who is interviewed on the audiotape, suffers swings of mood of this sort. It is this type of cyclicity that leads many clinical psychiatrists to feel uneasy with a 'purely' social explanation of the phenomena of depression. Nonetheless, it would be a brave biological psychiatrist who would wish to argue that all of Brown's depressed working-class mothers in Camberwell shared a similar biochemical abnormality.

In his article, Brown, while stating the case for a 'social' explanation for depression, makes no such claim for schizophrenia. Why is this? True, as you saw from the epidemiological data in Chapter 7, schizophrenia is diagnosed equally among men and women, at least for the native population of England and Wales. It is, however, more often diagnosed in working-class people than in upper-class people and, in England and Wales, it is clearly disproportionally diagnosed in certain groups of immigrants. This *might* suggest that there was something

about the experience of being working class or an immigrant that made it more likely for these people to attract the diagnosis. Yet the complexity of arriving at such a conclusion is shown by considering one of the earliest attempts to make an epidemiological study of schizophrenia, that by Faris and Dunham in Chicago in the 1930s (Faris and Dunham, 1939). This study indicated that the incidence of schizophrenia was highest in derelict inner-city regions and lowest among people in middle-class occupations living in the suburbs. The most obvious interpretation is that schizophrenia results from exposure to certain stressful types of living and working conditions.

☐ Can you suggest other explanations to account for the observed incidence of schizophrenia?

■ There are several that may have occurred to you, but here are three: First, people with a tendency to schizophrenia or with a history of schizophrenic illness may not be able to hold down middle-class jobs and, therefore, may drift 'down' socially and move into inner-city slums.

Second, the full-blown schizophrenic symptom takes time to manifest itself. If, as is indeed known to happen, middle-class people tend to consult their doctors more frequently and earlier than working-class people, especially over 'mental' rather than 'physical' disorders, the disturbance may be diagnosed and treated earlier in middle-class patients, before it is given the label 'schizophrenia'.

Third, eccentric behaviour may be more acceptable or differently labelled in middle-class people. (There is, for example, a class difference in the diagnosis of children's disorders. Middle-class children tend to be more frequently diagnosed as 'autistic' or 'dyslexic', while working-class children are more frequently diagnosed as 'educationally subnormal').

These different ways of accounting for the results of studies such as the Chicago one are not, of course, mutually exclusive. They may, indeed, all be contributing factors in accounting for the differential distribution of the schizophrenia diagnosis. Perhaps all schizophrenic people 'drift' socially downwards and this may be the most important factor in explaining class differences in the schizophrenia diagnosis. It is, however, difficult to account for the differential diagnosis of immigrants in the same way. The general pattern of Faris and Dunham's findings has been repeated in the UK, but both in the UK and in the USA most psychiatrists and sociologists now feel that the 'obvious' interpretation of the data is not correct.

Early childhood experience
In a sense, this category overlaps with the previous one. For example, there are elements of this type of explanation to

be found in both Brown's and Goffman's articles — though both of them concentrate on the immediate past and present of the person. Brown, for instance, includes among his vulnerability factors aspects of childhood experience. In an important sense, the past must be a key to the present. If you are born to working-class parents you are more likely to be working class yourself and suffer from the disorders, psychiatric and bodily, which tend to go with that class position.

There is, however, a type of psychiatric explanation that is more individual in its orientation. Laing, in looking to the family as the site of schizophrenia, was following a tradition set by Sigmund Freud and subsequently found in many other types of explanation and theory. We cannot discuss them in detail here, but we should emphasise their common theme, of locating the origin of a person's present mental distress and disorder in events that occurred very early in life.

The exact period of the 'window' of experience held to be most important varies from theory to theory. For instance, in primal therapy the nature of a person's birth itself — easy or painful, with forceps or by Caesarean section — is believed to give a series of clues to their present mental state: anxiety may come because of frustration felt by the infant in banging its head against the wall of the birth canal during delivery; depression because of the feeling of rejection by the mother immediately after birth and so forth. Pregnancy and birth experiences are thus held to carve channels in people's lives, forcing them into certain types of compensatory behaviour which inevitably deepen the channel. Therapy, according to this model, consists of 'reliving' the birth process (real or imagined), thereby in some sense starting again.

More conventional psychoanalytic theories also attribute important consequences to crucial, formative, very early childhood experiences. The model of development that such analytical theories espouse is one of *stages* through which the child must pass to become an adult.* Psychoanalytic theories concern themselves with stages in the development of emotions, relationships and conceptions of the self separated from mother, as distinct from the non-self environment. Melanie Klein and her followers saw the process of weaning the baby from the breast as an important stage. According to Freudian theory, oral and anal stages come later, and if they are not properly transcended during development, reappear as psychoses or neuroses later in life. In Freudian psychoanalysis childhood development is seen in terms of sexuality, the initial differentiation of the child who recognises that it is an

entity, but also a sexed entity, possessed of penis if male, of 'penis envy' if female. For Freudian analysts the source of much adult anxiety and neuroses is to be found in the difficulties experienced in passing through the stages of emergent sexuality to fully mature sexual activity 'appropriate' to what Freudians see as the proper male and female roles in society.

Although the orthodox psychoanalytic tradition finds it relatively easy to account for neuroses within such an explanatory framework, like Brown, its adherents have tended to draw back from treating schizophrenia and other psychoses in quite the same way. It was left to Bateson, Laing and their followers to endeavour to bring schizophrenia within a psychoanalytical framework in which childhood experiences shape subsequent behaviour. For this school, however, the age at which the child was placed by its family into a 'double bind' was not seen as crucial; the 'double bind' was seen as a continuous process developing through childhood and adolescence.

The extent to which you should take stage theories at face value, rather than seeing them as attempts to impose theoretical order on much more complex and interactive processes of development, is debatable, but the importance of adding a personal-psychological-historical dimension of causality into the framework of social and biological explanations cannot be denied.

☐ To what extent are such personal-psychological-historical explanations of mental distress and disorder compatible with theories based on social relationships?
■ They are incompatible with the extreme form of relational theories espoused by Foucault, who denies that the condition is located in the individual at all. They are, however, partially compatible with social explanations. Brown's 'vulnerability factors' might include those childhood experiences discussed by the psychoanalytic tradition, although Brown sees these problems of interpersonal relationships within the family as being imposed by some external accident, such as death or economic insecurity. Within the psychoanalytic tradition, whether Freudian or Laingian, such external contingencies are supposed to be largely irrelevant — the economy, job security, adequate housing, all are almost taken for granted. In so far as personal life-history explanations are concerned with the remote, rather than the immediate past, and lead to the conclusion that therapeutic intervention demands the recovery of that past, they are incompatible. When Brown notes that the future for many women *is* bleak he clearly does not hold out much hope that if the depressed woman relives her birth experience, or comes to terms with her penis envy, then she will transform her future prospects.

---

*Stage theories are discussed briefly in the chapters on children's development in *Birth to Old Age: Health in Transition* (U205, Book V). There, the emphasis is on transition in the acquisition of skills and abilities.

☐ To what extent are personal-psychological-historical explanations compatible with biological ones?

■ On the surface, they seem to bear no relation to biological explanations at all. Psychoanalysts and psychotherapists rarely discuss, or are concerned with, an individual's biology. Yet, in fact, the incompatibility *is* only on the surface. If childhood experience affects future behaviour, this may be because of the way in which that experience has shaped nerve pathways and patterns of activity in the brain.

It is interesting that Freud himself sought a biological 'grounding' for psychoanalysis in a theory of nerve-cell action within the brain. Newer therapies, such as primal therapy, constantly seek a 'biological' validation by attempting to show that the therapeutic process changes the body's biochemistry.

Personal life-history explanations are thus compatible with some sorts of biological explanations, provided they are not *genetically* based, which is often taken to mean that they are largely independent of a person's life history. As you will see shortly, however, it is precisely in the direction of genetics that most biological explanations drive.

Biological phenomena

As we said in Chapter 7, biological attempts to explain mental distress and disorder fall into two broad classes. The first, nowadays, is largely biochemical in approach and seeks to find an abnormality in the brain that 'causes' the disorder. The second type of explanation asks about the predisposing biological factors within the individual — are they genetic or environmental? Both approaches are, of course, fundamentally reductionist.

Biochemical approaches

So far as the first approach is concerned, the problem is where to look. How this is decided depends on three things: the current state of the biochemical art (i.e. what can be measured); present views about which of the myriad chemicals of the body are important (i.e. what the present biochemical fashion is); and how biologists think the brain works (i.e. what the present fashion in theories is). The whole approach is therefore a bit like that of the drunkard looking for his doorkey under the lamppost, where the light is better, even though he probably lost it somewhere quite different. These days, the main biochemical research effort is based on the effect of drugs. The logic of this approach is to argue backwards on the basis of the therapeutic effects of the drugs to the underlying biochemical system believed to be abnormal. This is not surprising, since so much research is sponsored by the pharmaceutical industry.

Apart from some early speculations about the presence of abnormal substances in the bloodstream, urine or sweat of schizophrenics (and sometimes depressives), most research has focused around the belief that the problem is not the presence or absence of a specific molecule, but whether there are higher or lower concentrations of a particular substance in the brain of the schizophrenic person. For the past twenty years or so, most attention and theories have revolved around the idea that any variations in concentration are likely to be among the class of molecules which serve as neurotransmitters.

☐ How do neurotransmitters work?

■ Nerve impulses travel down a nerve axon to the synapse, the point at which the axon makes contact with the next cell in the sequence, or with an effector organ such as a muscle. At the synapse, the electrical nerve impulse triggers the release of a chemical, the neurotransmitter, which diffuses across the synaptic junction to the post-synaptic nerve cell or muscle. There, it acts as a signal for electrical activity in the nerve cell or for contraction in the muscle cell.*

There are many neurotransmitters working within specific nervous pathways — perhaps thirty or more different types. These include amines, such as dopamine, serotonin and noradrenalin, and the class of substances related to morphine — the peptide group called endorphins, sometimes regarded as the body's natural pain killers. If the chemical process of transmission is interfered with, nervous pathways become blocked.

Interference with neurotransmitters may therefore result in subtle changes in the working of the brain and, hence, in a person's existential state and behaviour. Obviously, if the neurotransmitter involved is one that carries messages between nerves and muscles, such as the muscles of the lung, the consequence of interfering with it may be speedily fatal. What might happen if there were interference — overproduction or underproduction — of neurotransmitters in the brain in pathways concerned with analysing sensory information? The result might be jumbled messages in the brain, experienced as hallucinations. Suppose the neurotransmitters were in the pathways in the brain concerned with what is called 'affect' or emotional state, or with processes of arousal or attention? The results *might* be the characteristic symptoms of anxiety, depression or manic depressive psychoses.

Evidence pointing in this general direction has accumulated over the past twenty years or so. To begin with, there was just fragmentary data. In the case of schizophrenia, for example, it was noted that agents that

*Neurotransmitters and how electrical nerve impulses are transmitted are discussed in *The Biology of Health and Disease* (U205, Book IV).

produce hallucinations in normal subjects — drugs such as LSD — both mimic some of the experiences of schizophrenia and are chemically related to a particular group of neurotransmitters, the amines. The evidence got stronger when research to develop a drug to alleviate the symptoms of a quite different condition, Parkinsonism, came up with what, for a period, was regarded as a new 'miracle drug'. Sufferers from Parkinsonism show tremor of their hands when attempting to grasp objects. This tremor results from a malfunction of some of the nerve pathways that regulate the activity of motor output nerves from the brain. These pathways involve a particular amine neurotransmitter, the substance dopamine. Parkinson patients began to be treated during the early 1970s with L-Dopa, a drug chemically related to dopamine. This drug, at least when patients first take it, alleviates the symptoms of Parkinsonism such as motor tremors. With prolonged use, however, other consequences of taking the drug become apparent. Depending on the drug used, patients can experience disorientation, hallucination and existential distress comparable to that of schizophrenics. Researchers soon began to suggest a link: perhaps disorders of dopamine metabolism were related to schizophrenia.

Post-mortem studies of tissue from patients diagnosed as schizophrenic or depressed began to produce claims that there were altered levels of dopamine and other neurotransmitters, such as noradrenalin, in specific regions of the brain. As further evidence has accumulated, the claims made during the 1970s and early 1980s, that there were altered dopamine and noradrenalin levels in these tissues, have not, however, been verified.

Another line of argument leading to the idea that neurotransmitters are involved came from the systematic exploration of the biochemical effect of drugs used in the treatment of neuroses and psychoses. Many of these drugs seem to bind on chemically to the enzymes and other proteins involved in the mechanics of neurotransmitter function at synapses, especially in those regions of the brain known to be involved in regulating emotion or, in more formal language, with 'affect'. Substances that act as anti-depressants and tranquillisers, such as benzodiazepines (like Valium) and imipramine, seem to bind to specific nerve cells in these regions of the brain. Hence, the pharmacological argument points to the involvement of these cells and their neurotransmitters in 'causing' the existential state that the drugs modify.

Despite a multitude of biochemical and pharmacological research publications, and some widely publicised claims, there is no clear consensus about which neurotransmitter systems might be involved, or how. Different research groups have published conflicting experiments and hypotheses, and many of the experiments can be criticised for poor design or inadequate controls.

□   Think about the problems of relating the biochemical effect of a drug to its effect on the mood of a sufferer from depression. What criteria need to be met before a change in mood can be related to the biochemical effect?

■   You might have thought of the following:

1 The same dose of a drug should produce both changes in mood and a biochemical effect. For instance, suppose a dose of a drug produces an effect on mood, but no biochemical effect is apparent until ten times that dose are administered. It would therefore be unlikely that the biochemical changes could explain the changes in mood.

2 The timing of the biochemical effect and the effect on mood should be related: if the drug has an immediate biochemical effect, it should also have an immediate effect on mood, and vice versa.

3 Drugs that are more effective at modulating mood should have a correspondingly greater biochemical effect and vice versa.

4 Patients who do not respond to the drug with a change in mood should also show no biochemical effect. (There are always some people who do not respond to drugs of this sort.)

5 People who are not depressed should show a biochemical reaction to the drug that is different from the reaction of depressed individuals.

6 A depressed person in remission should show a different biochemical response to the drug from the one they showed when they were in a depressed state.

Unfortunately, it is very hard to meet these criteria and very few research programmes with particular drugs manage it. A particular problem is the second criterion. Many antidepressants take some weeks to build up to their full effect, while the biochemical changes that have been studied seem to occur rapidly after the drug has been administered.

A similar pattern of claim, counter-claim and practical evidence exists for schizophrenia. From the 1950s, a series of competing hypotheses for 'the' biochemical basis of schizophrenia have been proposed. Almost every neurotransmitter has at one time or another been suggested as abnormal in schizophrenia. The list includes neurotransmitters such as dopamine and noradrenalin, as well as acetylcholine, serotonin, endorphin, several different amino acids and more. In each case the evidence has been based on a combination of post-mortem and pharmacological studies, drug experiments with animals, measurements of enzyme levels and 'pharmacological' reasoning. There have also been dietary, immunological and viral hypotheses. It is not unfair to say that despite the wealth of hypotheses and reported positive findings, not a single molecular 'mechanism' for schizophrenia yet commands majority assent among the small army of researchers on the biochemistry of schizophrenia. It remains to be seen whether this failure is simply because research has so far been looking at the wrong molecules or biochemical processes, or whether there is a more fundamental flaw in the experimental procedures and logic being adopted.

Genetic approaches

The biochemical studies discussed in the previous section have problems both of methodology and of distinguishing between cause, consequence and correlation, but because genes do not change with the day-to-day state of the sufferer, the study of genetic differences is not fraught with the same types of problem. The driving force behind the biochemical study of depression and schizophrenia has been the search for new drugs; the thrust of the hunt for genetic explanations, however, cannot be seen as therapeutic, for even if it were proved that there is a genetic predisposition to the condition this would not provide a base for developing therapy. Instead, the search for genetic explanations must be seen in the wider framework of a reductionist science.

It would seem at first sight a reasonable goal to try to investigate the role of genes in the causation of schizophrenia or depression. Certainly the belief that mental distress and disorder is 'in the genes' has at least a century of psychiatric adherence behind it. The literature of genetic psychiatry is peppered with emphatic assertions that disorders of intellect and will, along with alcoholism and moral weaknesses of many sorts, are fixed in the human genes.

In Chapter 7 we discussed the available ways of 'sorting out' the effects of genes from the effects of shared environment, in particular, methods based on noting the extent of the disorder in the family of the sufferer. These methods are those of kinship correlation and pedigree analysis.

So far as depression is concerned, despite a variety of elaborate research programmes, neither kinship correlations nor pedigree studies reveal anything more than a slight tendency for depression to 'run in families'. The best evidence for a genetic 'predisposition' to mental disorder comes in schizophrenia and it is certainly well established that there is a tendency for schizophrenia to run in a family. The chance is that among parents of schizophrenics some 4 per cent are themselves schizophrenic. For brothers and sisters of schizophrenics this figure is 8 per cent and for the child of someone who is schizophrenic, 12 per cent — well above the overall rate of incidence of schizophrenia in the general population of 0.6 per cent. Of course, such observations would fit R.D. Laing's family 'double bind' theory just as well and they would be compatible with the idea that there was some common environmental factor, whether social or chemical, that the family shared.

As you will recall from Chapter 7, twin studies offer a more rigorous approach and there have been a number of such studies conducted over the past twenty years. The most substantial, made by the American biological psychiatrist Seymour Kety and his colleagues, are based on the twin registers kept for the entire population in Denmark, although the research concentrated on Copenhagen. Such studies suggest (Rosenthal and Kety, 1968) that the concordance for schizophrenia is higher for monozygotic (i.e. identical) twins than for dizygotic (i.e. nonidentical) twins. The concordance for monozygotic twins ranges from 14 to 65 per cent, but the more recent the study, the lower the concordance. In general, the older studies were less well controlled than the more recent ones. For instance, it is necessary to be sure whether the twins are really monozygotes or not. Simply asking people, which used to be all that was done, is not enough. There could obviously be good reason for a person whose twin was schizophrenic to deny that they were identical, hence the discordance among dizygotic twins would be artificially magnified. To be sure whether a twin is really monozygotic, it is necessary to do blood tests and not just rely on appearances. In three studies conducted in the late 1960s and early 1970s, the concordance figures are 14 per cent, 24 per cent and 25 per cent for monozygotic twins, as opposed to 4 per cent, 10 per cent and 7 per cent respectively for dizygotic twins. Even these newer figures, however, cannot be taken quite at face value: the monozygotic twins, for example, tend to be treated more similarly than dizygotic twins and this seems likely to affect the results by increasing concordance in monozygotic twins.

□ How would you test this possibility?
■ You could compare the concordance of dizygotic twins with the concordance between non-twin brothers or sisters.

□ If the concordance between dizygotic twins were the result of genetic effects, how would you expect it to differ from the concordance between non-twin siblings?
■ There should be no difference. Genetically, dizygotic twins are no more alike than are non-twin siblings. Monozygotic twins differ from both dizygotic twins and ordinary siblings by being identical genetically. Of course, dizygotic twins tend to be treated more similarly than ordinary siblings, so if there are family environmental factors involved, concordances between dizygotic twins should be higher than those between ordinary siblings. This indeed is the case. The same studies that find high rates of concordance for monozygotic twins also find higher rates of concordance for dizygotic twins than for ordinary siblings — a

difference of the same order as between monozygotic and dizygotic twins. Thus the higher concordance found for monozygotic twins could be explained as being a result of their having been treated even more alike than the dizygotic twins.

The final type of study is based on adoption (Chapter 7). Again, the major studies have been those of the joint Danish-American team led by Seymour Kety (Rosenthal and Kety, 1968; Kety, 1978). These studies are often taken as the best evidence for a genetic factor in schizophrenia. They are based on locating adults who have been diagnosed as schizophrenic and who were adopted as children. The incidence of schizophrenia in the adoptive and biological relatives of these patients is then compared with the incidence in matched non-schizophrenic individuals (the controls) by assessing the diagnostic records of the relatives (where they can be traced). Of thirty-four schizophrenic adults who had been adopted as children, 8.7 per cent of the biological relatives showed schizophrenia, compared with 1.9 per cent of the biological relatives of the controls. This difference between 1.9 and 8.7 per cent is the remaining evidence for the genetic basis of schizophrenia. As has been pointed out by the American psychologist Leo Kamin (Rose, Lewontin and Kamin, 1984) and by the psychiatrists Theodore Lidz and Sidney Blatt (Lidz and Blatt, 1983), even these figures tend to dissolve on closer inspection. So few were the actual cases of schizophrenia located among the relatives of *either* the schizophrenics or the controls, that it was necessary to widen the definition of schizophrenia to include an entire spectrum of related personality disorders or 'psychopathology'. Double blind procedures, in which researchers were asked to assess the people in the control groups for schizophrenia, showed that many of the *controls* were regarded by the researchers as schizophrenic. Because they expected that some of those they were rating were *likely* to be schizophrenic, the researchers erred on the side of 'over-diagnosis'. (Recall the Rosenhan study discussed above.)

The conclusion is that, despite extensive studies over half a century, there is still little unequivocal evidence for a marked genetic basis for the disorder. This is not to say that everyone has an equal genetic predisposition for schizophrenia. It may well be that, in a given environment, certain genotypes are more predisposed to schizophrenia

than others. The point is that all the studies to date — and perhaps any that could be made — fail to disentangle genetic from environmental factors. If the case for a genetic cause fails in schizophrenia, then it is more likely to crumble when broader and less precise diagnoses, such as those of depression or anxiety, are dealt with.

Conclusions

In this chapter we have explored, in turn, each of the four main modes of explanation of mental distress and disorder, using depression and schizophrenia as model systems. We have devoted most time to the discussion of what are often regarded as the two major conflicting modes of explanation, the biological and the social, and you may feel that we have been overly critical of each. We certainly have not come out at the end with a tidy explanation: we cannot offer you *the* cause of any sort of psychopathology. That is at least partly because, despite the (sometimes strident) claims of those who believe in single cause explanations, there is certainly no such thing as *a* unique cause. By this we do not mean a sort of simplistic middle of the road position, that *sometimes* the cause is social, *sometimes* biological. Our position is that all phenomena are simultaneously biological *and* social, and cannot be partitioned into X per cent of one and Y per cent of the other. This should become even clearer in the next chapter when we look at treatments. Rather, the problem lies in the probability that 'depression' and 'schizophrenia' are not unique entities. Although each term may describe similiar types of behaviour, they are more likely to involve multiple processes and brain states. After all, why should you assume that postnatal depression and depression following the loss of a job are precipitated by a similar set of causes or involve similar biochemical changes in the brain merely because they have the same name and may be treated with the same set of drugs? There are much more likely to be multiple states of brain biology that correspond to the phenomenon called depression. It may well be (we do not know) that certain genotypes, in the particular social and physical environment of the late twentieth century Europe or America, are especially predisposed to respond to life-threatening events by evincing depression or schizophrenia. This says nothing about how such genotypes may respond in other environments. Nor does it give much guidance as to how to alleviate present distress.

Objectives for Chapter 8

When you have studied this chapter, you should be able to:

8.1 Distinguish between four broad types of explanation of depression and schizophrenia: as expressions of relationships between people; as caused by social and economic factors; as caused by events in a person's childhood; as caused by disordered bio-chemistry or genes.

8.2 Discuss what advantages there might be to being labelled 'mad' in a world which itself is 'mad'.

8.3 State the principal ways in which personal life-history explanations of adult depression differ from social and economic ones.

8.4 Explain why current biochemical theories of depression and schizophrenia centre on neurotrans-mitters and cite the principal evidence in favour of neurotransmitter and genetic theories.

Questions for Chapter 8

1 (*Objective 8.1*) Writing in the *New Scientist* on 7 June 1984 the psychologist Keith Oatley said:

> ... depression is not typically a mental disorder. Nothing is disordered or wrong with people's minds that they become depressed. It is in people's lives and social relationships that something has gone wrong. In the large majority of cases depression is occasioned by quite clear losses and disappointments, but it occurs only where their other interpersonal resources make it impossible, for a time at least, to experience themselves as worthwhile in alternative ways. The reason that more women than men, and more people of lower socio-economic status, become depressed in our society is quite simply that women and working class people on average have lives with more possibility of things going seriously wrong, and fewer social and economic possibilities for dealing with the kinds of things that do go wrong (Oatley, 1984)

Which type of explanation of depression, from among the categories given in this chapter, is Oatley adopting? Which is he rejecting?

2 (*Objective 8.2*) In what ways might Goffman, Laing and the defence counsel for a mass murderer differ in their arguments about the advantages of being described as mad?

3 (*Objective 8.3*) How far would a psychotherapist working in the psychoanalytic tradition agree or disagree with the Oatley thesis?

4 (*Objective 8.4*) How might a biological psychiatrist attempt to explain, in terms of underlying brain biology, the heightened or lowered emotionality, auditory hallucinations, loss of appetite or of sexual enthusiasm that may occur in schizophrenia?

9

The treatment of mental distress and disorder

So far we have discussed how people experience mental distress and disorder, and attempts to define and explain it, with little reference to treatment. Of course, the voices you heard on the audiotape associated with Chapter 6 were of people who have received therapy and the biochemical explanations analysed in the last chapter are partly based on arguments derived from the effects of therapeutic drugs. It is now time to treat the question of therapy a little more systematically.

We have discussed biological and social explanations of mental distress and disorder and, corresponding to these types of explanation, there are two broad types of therapy.

☐ Would you consider these two broad therapeutic approaches to be mutually exclusive?

■ No, they are not. Therapies may involve a range of treatments, some biological, some social.

☐ If you held a social theory of the cause of depression, would you necessarily advocate a social therapy?

■ Not exclusively. Socially induced suffering may still be alleviated by biological treatments.

True, certain explanations of mental distress exclude the possibility of individual therapy at all. You may believe that the distress is not real, but a matter of differential labelling of the powerless by the powerful. There is little you could do, short of a social revolution, to change the context in which the differential labelling occurs. From such a viewpoint the best you can offer is to drug the sufferer into acquiescence in an unjust world.

Similarly, a genetic explanation for depression or schizophrenia implies that little may be done to eliminate the problem. Genetics might offer a diagnostic tool. For instance, it has been claimed that it is possible to identify potential schizophrenia sufferers at the age of three. If true,

such a claim might have therapeutic implications of some significance, just as if there were an abnormality in a single gene (or two or three genes) in schizophrenia. Early detection might offer the possibility of either abortion or, in a future science-fiction world, gene therapy. The real world is not such a science-fiction world and, for the reasons discussed in the previous chapter, is never likely to be.*

If depression is, as Brown argues, primarily a social phenomenon, then it can be *resolved* only by changing the world in which the individual is embedded — changing their social circumstances, for instance, by getting a better paid and more secure job, or better housing and a more satisfactory sexual and emotional relationship. But it is open to treat the depression by a therapeutic approach that involves talking with the individual so that they better understand themselves and the context and limits of their power to change the world. It is also open to treat a person with drugs that either dull the pain of living or provide a buffer from the world behind which it is possible to reconstruct life. Even if you do not believe that toothache is caused by lack of aspirin, it may still be appropriate to take aspirin so that you can bear the pain.

Finally, even if you believe that depression is caused by a faulty balance of neurotransmitters in the brain, you could try to change the balance *either* by giving drugs or by altering the inputs to the brain. According to the materialist theory of mind–brain relationships given in Chapter 6, one way of 'altering the inputs' may be by talking with the sufferer. Talking therapies must change the biochemistry of the brain if they change a person's state of mind, just as drugs must change a state of mind if they change brain biochemistry.

*The ethics, technologies and prospects of gene therapy and abortion are discussed in Caring for Health: Dilemmas and Prospects. The Open University (1985) *Caring for Health: Dilemmas and Prospects*, Open University Press (U205, Book VIII).

Thus, there are extreme protagonists of the view that talking is a waste of time and that you should go straight for the biochemistry and, indeed, extreme protagonists of the reverse position that drugs and other physical interventions are part of the process of oppression. Most therapists in practice, however, work within some middle ground.

For most people suffering mental distress and disorder, the first problems are likely to be to recognise the need for help and to begin to find routes towards it. Loneliness and a sense of isolation may make it hard for people to take the first steps, they may not believe that they would be helped by therapy, or their doctors may appear unsympathetic to their problems. The family may not be able or know how to provide support — recall the accounts by Goffman and Pringle in Chapter 8. The sense of isolation makes it particularly hard:

> You're doing what you should be doing but you are so far away that nothing seems to touch you until someone physically touches you and then it gives you a shake. (*Janice,* quoted in Nairne and Smith, 1984, p.8)

Friends, people to talk to, can be a help:

> My friends were helpful by just being there. They were supportive and they were prepared to let me rabbit on and on and on. It must have been painful to them, but they put up with it because they were friends. Just being able to talk about it whatever it was at the time — that's what helped me get through my depression. (*Sally,* quoted in Nairne and Smith, 1984, p.120)

But there is a limit to most people's friends' patience and skills:

> I went to my doctor because I had to, and because at that time I didn't know who else to turn to. I felt that if I didn't get help from somewhere I would go mad. I was coping — but only just. I felt I was getting to breaking-point. My husband and my friends were trying to be supportive but they didn't understand what was happening to me any more than I did. (*Sandra* quoted in Nairne and Smith, 1984, p.133)

Psychotherapeutic approaches (*talking therapies*), based on a variety of theories from psychoanalysis onward, are available in Britain (mostly outside the Health Service). Medical opinion as to their effectiveness is sharply polarised between the biologically oriented and, on the other hand, the more socially oriented psychiatrists and psychotherapists. In general, talking therapies are more often offered for depression than for schizophrenia. Some such therapies are based on attempts to help the sufferer explore the presumed childhood origins of their present distress, whether they are the traumas of their own birth, or their early experiences and relationships with their mother, father and other close members of the family. Other approaches attempt to help the sufferer learn new ways of understanding the world and responding to it, by changing cognitive processes, or by attempting to change behaviour. Some therapies are based on working with groups of patients or the families of sufferers and offer a mix of methods. Perhaps the major problem is that they all take time — the therapist's time as well as the patient's. Although not all approaches are as demanding as psychoanalysis, with its hour of patient-analyst interaction, two, three or more times a week, the case load that any psychotherapist can take on, even those using a group therapeutic approach, is obviously limited. If Brown's figures about the amount of depression among urban working-class women are to be believed, it is simply not possible to imagine an individually based talking therapy service on a scale that could cope with the problem. In this context, the particular role played by support and self-help groups, from specific women's counselling groups to the national charities (e.g. the Schizophrenia Fellowship and Schizophrenia Association) should be mentioned. These groups can often supplement or go beyond the supportive framework currently available from the talking therapies offered by professional psychotherapists.

The problem of time for the talking therapies is coupled with the powerful impetus within the western medical tradition to seek reductionist and interventionist approaches to treatment. One approach, which is halfway between a talking therapy and chemical or physical interventions, but is based on a biological theory of mental distress and disorder, is *behaviour therapy*. It is based on the idea that mental distress and disorder are learned behaviours and that what is learned can be 'unlearned', or at least modified. Such 'unlearning' is achieved using a programme based on a particular type of psychological model called behaviourism and is especially associated with the Harvard psychologist B.F. Skinner. According to Skinner, most, if not all 'behaviours', which for him include most human actions (including speech) are learned, especially during childhood, but also in adult life. Learning is based on 'contingencies of reinforcement': that is, some behaviours are rewarded by, for instance, a child's parents or an adult's colleagues. Other behaviours are punished. Rewards may be material (a chocolate bar or money) or immaterial (a smile or a statement of approval). Punishment may be physical (a slap or withdrawal of cash or privilege) or immaterial (a scolding or a frown). If behaviours are produced by such contingencies of reinforcement then they can, in principle, be modified by designing alternative contingencies. In some sense, this rather obvious principle is the way that many, perhaps most, parents endeavour to bring up their children. Organised into a systematic approach, behaviour therapy is offered in the UK, especially to children classified as unruly or disruptive in ordinary schools. Several local authorities have 'special schools' for children that are run on behaviour therapy principles. Children live in a token economy in which they are rewarded for approved behaviour with privileges, from chocolate and spending money to being allowed out for the afternoon. For transgressions they are punished by withdrawal of such privileges. Behaviour therapy has been used with autistic children and in attempts to treat some adult types of mental distress and disorder, especially such conditions as the phobias.

The effectiveness of talking therapies is hard to evaluate in the clinical trials used by modern medicine, which uses double-blind procedures and placebos.

□ What are the difficulties in using such procedures for social interactions such as talking therapies?

■ One difficulty is that there is no placebo for a social treatment. *Any* interaction, however trivial, between a patient and a therapist or members of the therapist's staff has some therapeutic potential. Treatments are hard to standardise and measures of improvement are not easily achieved. Typically, patients are assessed on one of a number of standardised questionnaire-type rating scales, but there must always be an element of subjectivity. Another major problem is this. In a drug trial, double-blind procedures can be used in which neither the patient nor the medical staff can tell whether what is being administered is the drug under test, a different drug for comparison, or a placebo. The nature of a talking therapy, however, must involve both the therapist and the patient knowing which patient is receiving the therapy and which is receiving alternative treatment. (It is of course possible and, indeed, necessary to ensure that the person assessing the patient's condition does not know what therapy the patient has been receiving.)

Such problems mean that it has proved very difficult to evaluate quantitatively the success or failure of therapies based on social interactions. There have, however, been some examples of trials that have avoided these pitfalls. One example is provided by the work of Leff and his colleagues (Leff *et al.*, 1982). As you will recall from the last chapter, this group maintains that one of the precipitating causes in schizophrenia is the behaviour of the relatives with whom the schizophrenic patient lives. In particular, they maintain that schizophrenic patients are likely to live with relatives with whom they have a great deal of regular face-to-face contact (more than 35 hours a week) and who

have a high level of expressed hostility, in the form of critical comments made to the patient, and over-involvement with them. The approach adopted by Leff's group was to compare two groups of twelve schizophrenic patients, all of whom were receiving normal out-patient care, including long-term psychoactive drug treatment (see later). The close relatives of the experimental group were then given a package of treatments, including an educational programme of lectures, group discussions and family sessions with the psychiatrist and patient present. After nine months of such intervention, the relatives' scores for 'expressed emotion' were significantly lowered. So far as the patients were concerned, only one of the twelve patients in the experimental group showed a relapse into a 'floridly' schizophrenic condition, whereas half the patients in the control group relapsed and three had to be readmitted to hospital.

□ Does this study show that social intervention is sufficient to prevent schizophrenia?

■ No, it shows only that social intervention can mitigate the symptoms of schizophrenia and help to prevent relapses in patients with close relatives who show high expressed emotion.

□ Does the study show that social intervention alone is sufficient in such cases?

■ No, remember that the patients were receiving long-term drug treatment during the trial. What it does show is that under these conditions social intervention can be successful.

The combined use of talking therapies and chemical or physical intervention is characteristic of much of today's approach to psychiatric intervention, but there remain limits to what is available and what can be achieved by talking therapies. In fact, both patients and therapists may believe that the use of biologically based treatments — drug treatments or other physical interventions — is at least doing *something*. The pressure for biological 'solutions' is not merely a question of the professional preferences of doctors and the power of advertising by drug companies. In western cultures, patients and their close friends and family often press for such treatments too. There are many reasons for this. Theories and treatments that locate the origin of schizophrenia, for instance, in family relation-ships, can be seen as blaming the other family members. They may already feel so distressed and guilty about the suffering of the schizophrenic that they are not able to carry such an extra burden. This perhaps encourages the strong belief in biological explanations and treatments among a number of the support groups such as the Schizophrenia Association. It is therefore these treatments above all which we will review here. We can consider two categories, physical and chemical interventions.

Physical interventions

In the nineteenth century it was thought that madness could be cured by the administration of vigorous shock, for example by immersing sufferers in cold water. Modern physical interventions are the logical extension of such beliefs. From the 1920s on, a variety of techniques to induce prolonged unconsciousness were adopted, including insulin therapy, which puts subjects into a coma while the brain is temporarily starved of glucose. They are still in limited use today, but during the 1930s these treatments were largely superseded by *electroconvulsive therapy* (ECT). This originated with Ladislas Von Meduna in Budapest and Ugo Cerletti in Milan. They believed, erroneously, that schizophrenia and epilepsy were mutually exclusive diseases and, therefore, if they could generate convulsions that mimicked epilepsy, they might ameliorate the schizophrenia. Because of this belief, first camphor and later a drug called Metrazol were used to generate convulsions. Finally shock was used, administered through electrodes applied to the skull. The addition of anaesthetics or muscle relaxants diminished the wild convulsions, with the attendant dangers of bone fracture, that were a feature of the early treatments.

No particular beneficial effect of ECT has been found for schizophrenia, despite the early enthusiasms. By the 1950s ECT was tried in cases of depression and here it has been claimed to have a positive effect, particularly for some forms of depression that do not respond readily to drug therapy. ECT remains a quite extensively used procedure, though by the 1970s and 1980s a vigorous controversy had grown up over its use and there was a substantial campaign to have it stopped. There is rather little unequivocal evidence for the therapeutic effects of ECT and its physiological mode of action is obscure. Application of the current causes a sort of electrical storm of activity in the brain. Some cells will die and will not be replaced. As the shocked individual recovers, there tends to be some loss of memory. Recent memory is damaged because it is 'held' in the brain in the form of circulating electrical patterns of nerve cell activity. These are disrupted by the ECT, so the person who has had such shock treatment will almost certainly have no memory for the hour or so of events preceding the shock. It seems likely that there is also a loss of older, well-established memories for events years before the treatment. The reason for such random loss of memory, if it does occur, is not clear — it may be to do with cell death. Equally, if there *is* a therapeutic effect of ECT, the rationale for it in terms of brain physiology is quite unclear. There are, however, considerable difficulties in providing clear-cut evidence for such long-term memory loss. Initially 'lost' memories may be recovered slowly over a period of months after the ECT and establishing that such loss has occurred in patients who may be elderly or confused is obviously difficult.

Is there a therapeutic effect? Opinions are divided. Many psychiatrists are sure that there is, at least in particular types of depression, such as that which may occur in women after the birth of a child or around the menopause. Many patients speak strongly in support of the beneficial effect they are sure they have experienced as a result of ECT. The comedian Spike Milligan is one example. Other patients dread it and may see the offer of ECT in psychiatric hospitals as a threat rather than a promise. Opinion on the ethics of ECT is equally divided. Some would see it as a 'punishment' for refractory patients for whom the 'threat' of ECT may be enough to change their behaviour — a type of behaviour therapy, therefore. Some see ECT as a measure of last therapeutic resort, others as an unethical intervention applied to a patient who may not be able to give rationally informed consent.

> I had it in the days when they didn't give you an injection first. I had it five days a week for three weeks non-stop. I had a two-week break and I relapsed so I had it for another two weeks, five days a week. That's why I've got such a poor memory now. It deadened part of my brain I suppose. There are little gaps in my life I still can't remember. I used to say, 'Why couldn't you pick out the bits I don't want to remember? All of those things stayed with me!'
> (*Chris*, quoted in Nairne and Smith, 1984, p.148)

The image of ECT conjured by such accounts, or by films such as *One Flew Over the Cuckoo's Nest* do indeed make people uneasy and have added to public disquiet about ECT. Certainly, the use of ECT in many countries has been sharply reduced in recent years.

What is the evidence for the therapeutic effects of ECT?

Figure 9.1 The use of electricity to treat mental disorders has a long history. This electrical apparatus was used to give patients shocks to various parts of the body in 1885, at the asylum of La Salpêtière in France.

The problems of interpreting any apparent improvement in an individual as a consequence of ECT, as indeed of any therapy for mental distress and disorder, are substantial. For example, within a month of each other, at the end of 1980 and the beginning of 1981, two reports appeared, one in the *British Medical Journal* (West, 1981) and the other in *The Lancet* (Johnstone *et al.*, 1980). The first describes a double-blind, clinical trial in which patients suffering from depression were given ECT and showed significant improvement over matched control groups. The second describes a similar trial, but one in which patients were followed-up for up to six months after treatment. This second report found that initially there was a small, but significant improvement in the rate of remission for patients who had received ECT compared with the control group. Both groups improved so much during the six-month period, however, that by the end of the time no long-term beneficial effects could be claimed for ECT. This faster rate of improvement with ECT may, however, be helpful — perhaps even vitally so — to some depressed patients.

Thus one important factor in evaluating the effect of ECT or other treatments for mental distress or disorder is the time scale over which improvement is being assessed.

☐ There is another important factor to be taken into account in the design of trials to assess the effect of such treatments. What is it? You should be familiar with it from earlier discussion.

■ Placebo effects need to be considered.

There are indeed placebo effects in the use of ECT. For instance, there are reports that if a patient is simply placed in the ECT apparatus, given the muscle relaxant and anaesthetised without shock, improvement occurs.

Internationally, the status of ECT as a treatment — and its legality — varies markedly and this controversy will undoubtedly continue in Britain for several years yet.

Chemical interventions

Pharmacological intervention — the use of drugs in the control or alleviation of the suffering of mental distress and disorder — is by now far the most common treatment, in and out of hospital. The vast majority of the *psychoactive* drugs (drugs which interact with the central nervous system and affect moods and 'state of mind') have been developed in the immense growth of the pharmaceutical industry since the Second World War and psychopharmacology is still a major growth area. Many of the 'first generation' of psychoactive drugs were developed by exploring the active chemical substances present in traditional herbal remedies, followed by playing 'molecular roulette' — the process of synthesising chemicals with a similar molecular structure to the 'active principle' of the herbal remedies. First, their

effects on experimental animals were examined and later the effects on humans in clinical trials were tested. The fact that many such drugs turned out to interact with neurotransmitter systems in the brain has strengthened the belief that these systems *are* the sites of brain disorder corresponding to mental distress and disorder. It has also provided the basis for a more systematic approach to the search for newer psychoactive drugs. Pharmacologists can now orient their search towards substances known to have interactions with neurotransmitters.

The first major psychoactive drug to be introduced was the tranquilliser chlorpromazine (best known under the proprietary name Largactil), first employed during the 1950s.* Sometimes referred to as a 'chemical straight-jacket', chlorpromazine calms seriously disturbed patients and makes them more amenable to less brutal forms of social control. Its use in allaying the symptoms of patients in hospital is held to have been of major importance in transforming the conditions of mental hospitals.

It has been calculated that some 50 million people worldwide have received chlorpromazine since its introduction in 1952 and its use has been massive. It can be argued (indeed, it is commonly stated as a fact) that it was the introduction of chlorpromazine and the generations of psychoactive drugs that followed it, that made possible the opening up of the locked wards, the incorporation of mental hospitals into general hospitals, the reduction in the length of stay of mental patients and the reorientation towards their care in the community. International comparisons, however, suggest that there is no simple correlation between the introduction of psychoactive drugs and the opening of the hospitals in this way. It seems to have depended more on complex social and political factors, which differ from country to country. The move to deinstitutionalise mental patients, which has received political impetus both from the organisation of mental patients themselves (such as the Mental Patients' Union) and powerful social and political writers like Thomas Szasz and Ivan Illich has, however, certainly been advanced by the existence of the psychoactive drugs. It is worth pointing out that if deinstitutionalisation occurs without adequate promotion of facilities within 'the community' for the treatment of such patients, then 'community care' may transfer the responsibility for care from the institution to the family. In countries with a state-run health service, this may amount to a reprivatisation of public medicine at the expense of the family — if indeed there is a family to take responsibility. If there is no family or if no financial and counselling support is given, the consequence is likely to be

*In this chapter we give both the generic (chemical) name for the drugs we are discussing and, in brackets, the proprietary (brand) name under which it is commonly prescribed.

that those who had previously been in hospital care become vagrants and down-and-outs liable to arrest for petty crimes. They move from the concern of the hospital to that of the prison — from one institution to another.*

The scale of manufacture and prescription of psycho-active drugs is now prodigious. In the UK, one in five of all National Health Service prescriptions is for a drug acting on the central nervous system and, by 1979, some 53 *million* prescriptions were being written for psychoactive drugs — about one per head of the population — each year. Women are prescribed drugs more frequently than men by their general practitioner, although men tend to use non-medical mood adjusters, such as alcohol, rather more than women. The extent of reliance on such chemical adjusters to the social environment in contemporary society should give considerable cause to think of its implications. In 1983, a poll showed that 23 per cent of the adult population of the UK had taken a benzodiazepine drug, such as Valium, at some time, and that 35 per cent of these had taken the drug regularly for longer than four months. This represents 3.5 million people in the UK taking the drugs for much longer than ethically recommended. A survey of benzodiazepine users carried out by the television programme *That's Life* found that 62 per cent had taken the drug for more than five years and 40 per cent for longer than ten years. Four out of five of the users were women. Drugs have certainly become part of the popular culture and they certainly 'work' in the sense that they change mood and alleviate distress.

> Tablets enabled me to live normally at a time when I found the tiniest normal detail of life too much to cope with. In particular they helped me to sleep, which made all the difference to my ability to cope with the day. I knew they weren't a miracle cure for all my problems, but they did make it possible for me to survive an acute crisis and gradually to come to terms with those problems. I realised that in a sense my peace of mind was artificial, but I also knew that it was better than disintegrating altogether. I used anti-depressants exactly as a crutch is used by someone with a broken ankle — as a temporary aid, preferring to be able to get around somehow, rather than not to walk at all. (*Diana*, quoted in Nairne and Smith, 1984, p.139)

> I've come across a lot of condemnation not only of medication but of those who take it. This has only exacerbated the guilt and conflict I already feel about taking anti-depressants. But I have often owed my

continued functioning to those tablets and on more than one occasion agreeing to take them has kept me out of hospital. I have often been far too badly depressed to do anything and then I feel medication is the only way to get you active enough to start talking and wanting to do something. (*Ruth Elizabeth*, quoted in Nairne and Smith, 1984, p.139)

> After my father died I went to the Student Health Centre and I was put on anti-depressants. It was very badly handled in terms of how I felt — how they dealt with my grief — well they didn't deal with it at all. But I actually felt that those drugs helped me. They lifted my mood and made it easier to cope. I did also have a lot of emotional support through talking to a social worker. But if anyone else was going through a similar experience I wouldn't hesitate to say try an anti-depressant. (*Theresa*, quoted in Nairne and Smith, 1984, p.140)

For some people the drugs can merely mask feelings while complicating the problem further by opening the prospect of addiction (see Chapter 10).

> The first time I was given anti-depressants was *after* the first time I tried to commit suicide, I had been feeling very depressed for a long time, but nobody took any notice. (*Chris*, quoted in Nairne and Smith, 1984, p.106)
>
> Valium helps to ease the pain away, (you give me)
> Valium help me cope another day, (you give me)
> Valium when it's all too much to bear, but
> It won't pay the bills, it won't cure my ills, it'll teach me not to care. (Women's Liberation Song Sheet, quoted in Nairne and Smith, 1984, p.110)

Most of the patients in the *That's Life* survey said they did not want to be put on pills when they first consulted their doctor and 81 per cent complained of 'side effects' ranging from depression to panic while taking the drugs. Nonetheless, 57 per cent of the sample were still taking the benzodiazepines.

There are several ways of grouping drugs that affect brain and behaviour. For example, there is a category of *sedatives* — drugs such as the barbiturates — of which the best known effect is that of inducing rest or sleep. Closely related to these in effect are the *tranquillisers*, which are supposed to calm anxiety (anxiolytics) without sedation. These are now generally preferred in prescriptions outside hospitals as being safer than barbiturates and less 'heavy' in their effects.

The prescription of drugs by general practitioners varies not only with the gender, and probably the class, of the patient, but also, interestingly, with age. Look at Figure 9.2. This shows general practitioners' methods of treatment for

*Community care and its problems are discussed in Chapter 5 of *Caring for Health: Dilemmas and Prospects* (U205, Book VIII).

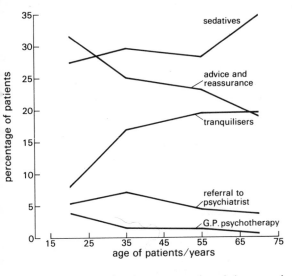

Figure 9.2 The methods of treatment adopted by general practitioners when faced with patients of different ages who were suffering from a psychiatric disorder. (Shepherd and Clare, 1981, Figure 13, p.155).

patients of different ages whom they identified as suffering from a psychiatric disorder.

☐ What is the most striking feature of this graph?
■ The graph shows the increase in the level of drug prescription with the age of the patient.

☐ What reasons might there be for this increase?
■ The severity of the psychiatric disorders diagnosed might be increasing with age, or the nature of the diagnosis might change. For instance, it is frequently said that older people find it harder to sleep than younger ones. This might account for the large increase in sedative prescriptions in the over-55 group. Doctors might be less prepared to listen to the problems of older people, hence the amount of 'advice and reassurance' might diminish with the age of the patient. There is also another possibility. As people tend to stay with the same general practitioner for quite a large number of years, the older the patient, the older the general practitioner they are likely to consult. Perhaps older doctors are more likely to prescribe drugs and less likely to offer advice and reassurance than younger ones?

To return to the classification of psychoactive drugs: among the tranquillisers, there is a group sometimes called 'minor tranquillisers' (e.g. Valium), which tend to be available on general prescription, and 'major tranquillisers' — sometimes called neuroleptics (e.g. chlorpromazine). Chlorpromazine's major medical use is in prescription in hospitals for treatment of psychoses, although it is also prescribed outside hospital as well. There is a category of

antidepressant drugs that are supposed to give a 'lift' to depressed patients when taken over a period of several weeks. Examples include amitriptyline, mianserin and a group of drugs known collectively for their biochemical effects on a particular neurotransmitter system as monoamine oxidase inhibitors (e.g. Marsilid and Nardil). Closely related to these in their claimed behavioural effects are psychomotor stimulants such as amphetamine (one formulation of which is sometimes popularly known as 'purple hearts').

In addition to these classes of complex chemical substances, there is widespread and increasing use of a simple inorganic substance, lithium, in the treatment of depression, especially of the 'bipolar' type. The biochemical mode of action of lithium is quite obscure, but since it is chemically rather similar to sodium (an ion involved in the maintenance of electric excitability of the nerve cells) it may work by interfering with the electrical properties of nerve cells in some way. Lithium is now used widely both in the treatment of depression and also as a prophylactic—that is, lithium is given to people to *prevent* the onset of the disorder. Finally, there is the group of *hallucinogens*, such as LSD or cannabis, which, although they have on occasion been used medically, are not generally regarded as appropriate at the present time. Substantial and often simplistic claims are made for how psychoactive drugs work and about the conditions under which they should be prescribed. It is therefore important to avoid being too rigid about the categorisation of drugs or taking an over-simple view of how the drugs affect individuals who take them. Just as the diagnosis of depression or anxiety, or other neuroses, is not straightforward, so the drugs themselves do not have single or unidimensional effects. A given dose of a particular drug can act on two different people in two different ways. At different times it can interact with a single individual quite differently, depending on the individual's prior history of use of the drug and the social context. It is commonly found that the more often a person has taken a particular drug, the greater the amount of the drug that is needed to achieve a given effect. This is called the *tolerance effect*. It is merely necessary to consider your own experience of, for instance, alcohol, assuming that you do drink. The changes of mood induced by alcohol depend partly on the quantity consumed, partly on the social context and partly on your own mood when you drink it. Presumably, all these have their biochemical correspondents, which must affect the cellular responses to the alcohol.

An interesting experiment shows this effect. A group of ten people are placed in a room. Nine are given a sedative and one is given a stimulant.

☐ How would you expect the person given the stimulant to react?

■ The person given the stimulant should become 'lifted' and active, but in fact, he or she tends to behave like the majority of people in the room, as if sedated.

The experiment can also be done in reverse. A person given a sedative will behave like those given the stimulants.

Thus, it is a mistake to think of psychoactive drugs as acting as some sort of *magic-bullet* with well-defined and immediate effects. Although psychopharmacologists sometimes speak of the 'side effects' of some drugs, this is a term largely derived from an earlier belief that drugs should have one main effect and that everything else is incidental. In reality, any agent is likely to show multiple effects. An example is provided by the drug L-dopa, which is used in the control of Parkinsonism (Chapter 8). When it was first available, it was regarded as an almost perfect 'magic bullet', which headed straight for the dopamine pathways involved in motor coordination. Later, all sorts of additional effects on individuals' behaviour and mood became apparent. People reported strange hallucinatory sensations and some began to show violent hostility to the use of the drug. The effect of L-dopa in generating schizophrenia-like behaviour became one of the starting points for the claim that irregularities in the amount of dopamine

Table 9.1 Major classes of psychoactive drugs

Class of drug	Examples	Action
Sedatives and tranquillisers		
Barbiturates	phenobarbitone (Luminal) amylobarbitone (Amytal) pentobarbitone (Nembutal)	Sleep or drowsiness-inducing. Depress electrical activity in brain. Can be addictive. Not now generally prescribed.
Minor tranquillisers and hypnotics (generally known as benzodiazepines)	meprobamate (Miltown) chlordiazepoxide (Librium) diazepam (Valium) flurazepam (Dalmane) nitrazepam (Mogadon)	Exert calming, anxiety-allaying ('anxiolytic') effect. Are also sedative to some extent and are widely used as hypnotics. May act via neurotransmitter receptors as they bind to nerve cells in the brain. Extensively prescribed in general medicine.
Major tranquillisers (antipsychotics; neuroleptics)	chlorpromazine (Largactil) haloperidol (Haldol) fluphenazine (Modecate)	Used in treatment of psychotic disorders, especially schizophrenia. Bind to dopamine receptors. Mainly prescribed in institutions (e.g. hospitals, prisons) for control of psychoses.
Stimulants	amphetamine (Dexedrine) methylphenidate (Ritalin) caffeine	Fast acting and transient. Increase arousal and motor activity, combat fatigue and drowsiness. Affect arousal system in the brain and mimic the effects of sympathetic nervous system.
Antidepressants		
Tricyclics and related agents	amitriptyline (Tryptizol) imipramine (Tofranil)	Improve mood and other symptoms of depressive illness, but only after 2–3 weeks. Not stimulant. Most are sedative. Interact with amine class of neurotransmitters. Extensively prescribed.
Monoamine oxidase inhibitors	iproniazid (Marsilid) phenelzine (Nardil) tranylcypromine (Parnate)	Inhibit the breakdown of some amine neurotransmitters. Similar in general action to the tricyclics, but little prescribed due to interaction with certain foods (the 'cheese effect').
Lithium		Claimed to 'even out' mood swings in 'bipolar' manic depressive psychoses and now also prescribed prophylactically. Mode of action uncertain, but believed to interfere with electrical activity of nerve cells because of similarity to sodium ion.
Hallucinogens (or psychedelics)	cannabis (marijuana, dope, ganja, hashish, grass)	Contains tetrahydrocannabinol. Derived from naturally occurring plants. Use results in mild euphoria or sensation of tranquillity. Can generate hallucinations. Mimics effect of sympathetic nervous system.
	psylocybins	Derived from varieties of mushrooms. Hallucinogens.
	lysergic acid diethylamide (LSD, 'acid')	Synthetic product derived originally from a fungus. Powerful hallucinogen.
	mescalin	Derived from cactus. Often taken as a fermented liquid extract known as mescal. Hallucinogen.

and in its metabolism in the brain were responsible for schizophrenia.

Table 9.1 lists the main classes of psychoactive drugs, but within each class there are a multitude of formulations. Some involve chemical modification of known active constituents. Drug companies will modify a drug in this way to improve effectiveness, diminish 'side-effects', or to produce a product to rival other companies. Some involve 'mixes' of different types of agent. Clearly, psychoactive drugs are effective in changing mood and allaying distress. Insofar as they make the person taking them less disturbing to others, they also make the patient easier to manage. This in turn, may serve to improve the relationship between the sufferers who take the drugs and those closely connected with them, so an upward spiral of improvement may occur. This is likely to be true even if the drugs are not as specific in their effects on behaviour or on biochemistry as their protagonists would have us believe. Part of the subtlety of these interactions is revealed by the placebo effect that always occurs when drugs are used in the treatment of neuroses. Double-blind clinical trials of antidepressants and related drugs generally show at least a 30 per cent improvement in patients (rated on various types of mood scales) after treatment with placebo. During the three months or more over which such trials are conducted, the best of the anti-depressants or tranquillisers are likely to show only an improvement over a placebo of a further 20–30 per cent.

The interesting question, not merely for psychoactive drugs, but for placebos in other types of drug treatment, in which the substances concerned are *not* supposed to be psychoactive, is how the placebo works. If the drugs work by way of highly specific biochemical effects on neurotransmitter systems, how can a placebo produce the same biochemical effects? If a placebo does not produce the same biochemical effect as the drug it replaces, it is arguable that a good proportion of the behavioural effect of that drug, too, may not be by way of its assumed specific site of action. Perhaps the effect has more to do with contact with the prescribing doctor showing that the patient's distress has been 'taken seriously'.

We should not forget that psychoactive drugs are also powerful agents with multiple and lasting biological effects. As their use has increased, not merely has there been a growth of new types of addiction, but also a whole new range of drug-induced disorders has slowly become recognised. Substances given to cure one problem generate another and the growth in such iatrogenic disorders is serious and disturbing. This is particularly the case for the major tranquillisers, such as chlorpromazine which, as we have said, has been used on a vast scale since its introduction in the 1950s. There has been a slow recognition in the past decade or so of a disorder category that has become known as tardive dyskinesia, particularly among hospital patients who have been long-term users of chlorpromazine. The symptoms include characteristic motor disabilities and uncontrollable gestures (for instance, movements of the mouth) and they do not necessarily disappear when the patient is taken off the drug. There are reports that from 10 to 40 per cent of those who regularly use major tranquillisers may suffer from tardive dyskinesia and about 50 per cent of those who get the disorder will have some irreversible brain damage. Nor are there at present any drugs to combat the effects, although tardive dyskinesia has now become a prolific 'spin-off' area of neurobiological research!

Objectives for Chapter 9

When you have studied this chapter, you should be able to:

9.1 Distinguish between talking therapies and biological interventions and explain their relationship to theories of disease aetiology.

9.2 Summarise the procedures involved in electroconvulsive therapy (ECT) and arguments for and against its use.

9.3 Comment on the strengths and limits of a pharmacological approach to the cure of mental distress and disorder.

Questions for Chapter 9

1 (*Objective 9.1*) Suppose your teenaged son began to be moody and withdrawn, to answer questions disconnectedly or apparently at random and sometimes to 'talk to himself', either in his room or walking down the street. You take advice from a psychotherapist who declares himself to be working in the Laingian tradition, from a psychiatrist interested in biological explanations of mental distress or disorder and from a lay association of relatives of schizophrenia sufferers. In what ways are the advice and treatment they offer likely to be similar and to differ?

2 (*Objective 9.2*) In the early 1980s, there were a number of Press reports of nurses working in psychiatric hospitals refusing, on grounds of conscience, to be involved in the administration of ECT to in-patients. Summarise the arguments that might be used by the nurses, and by those endeavouring to persuade them to apply the treatment.

3 (*Objective 9.3*) A new drug is to be tried out as a possible antidepressant. Twelve hospitalised patients diagnosed as sufferers from 'exogenous depression' and twelve randomly selected non-hospitalised volunteers are each given the drug treatment. Six of the depressed patients and six controls each receive the drug and the other six of each group receive a placebo that looks and tastes like the drug. Only the nurses who administer the drug or placebo know which is which. The nurses are asked to 'rate' patients and controls on a score sheet for a number of indices of depression over a period of four weeks. During this period *both* the control group receiving the drug *and* the patients receiving the drug are reported by the nurses to show significant improvement over those receiving the placebo.

How would you account for this observation and what criticisms do you have of the experimental design?

10

The boundaries of addiction

The advent of new psychoactive drugs and particularly their employment in the treatment of mental disorders reflect a fundamental belief by some that it is 'biology' that can go out of control and can be brought back into line. If this view is held, the best that can be hoped for is that drugs can hold down symptoms while the causative factors are identified and 'managed'. Although for some people things have always looked better when viewed through the bottom of a bottle, the variety of new agents available on prescription, or otherwise, has produced a number of undesirable and usually unforeseen effects — which add up to *dependence* upon the drugs. In the next few chapters we explore the nature of *addiction* (or dependence, as it tends to be termed in Britain today) and the way in which various explanations for the condition have shaped therapy.

Although the causative agents in, for example, cancers have yet to be fully catalogued, there is no doubt that cancers may be classified as diseases. Attaching the label of disease to some other conditions is, however, not at all straightforward and neither is it necessarily useful in terms of selecting a suitable and relevant means of amelioration. Reluctance to categorise a condition as a disease may reflect an ignorance of the causation of that condition or the lack of a suitable response to it. This will have become evident as you considered the classification of mental disorders (Chapters 6–9). Of course, there is also the question of symptoms. For example, someone who is obese may have either a passion for food that is rich in carbohydrates, or an aversion to physical exercise, or both. Alternatively, the obesity may be symptomatic of a disturbance in hormonal balance or of disordered regulation in the satiety centre in the brain. To take the obesity example further, we could replace the word 'passion' with 'addiction'. Are those who exhibit an uncontrollable urge to eat, or to gamble, or to experience the stimulating or tranquillising effects of certain drugs suffering from a disease? Are they displaying symptoms of a general discontentment with their lives, or are they simply indulging themselves?

At the mention of addiction in the UK, the first thought tends to be of a young person, probably male, with a criminal record, sitting in a lavatory near Piccadilly Circus in London trying to find a good vein in which to plunge a dirty syringe full of heroin. Alternatively, the picture evoked may be someone in multiple layers of clothes and newspaper, one of those unfortunates who inhabit the railway stations and parks of big cities, clutching cider bottles and attempting to get from you the 'price of a cup of tea'. These are caricatures and, by definition, they are misleading. The reality is that not all 'bag ladies' and 'bench bums' are addicted to alcohol and nor do those who regularly use heroin 'shoot up' in lavatories.

The problem with the concept of addiction is in defining its boundaries. Is there a difference between a man on a park bench holding a cider bottle and the executive on the second bottle of wine over lunch? What distinguishes the daughter who is 'snorting' cocaine from her mother who takes Valium? Why is the Christian wine ceremony acceptable in the UK whereas the Rastafarian ganja (marijuana) ceremony is a criminal offence?

The boundaries appear to be set by social attitudes and are conditioned by culture and legal status. Alcohol, nicotine and caffeine are so much part of everyday life in most societies that until recently it has been the abstainers who have attracted attention. At certain ages in the UK it becomes a legal right to purchase nicotine and alcohol, in the same way that people are thought to be responsible enough to drive and to vote. Alcohol and nicotine can thus become social symbols of maturity, of achieving some independence.

So far in this discussion the concept of addiction has been linked with chemical compounds that alter mood or perception. But the term may be applied to what is perceived as over-indulgence in sex, gambling and food. If addiction is a state of indulgence and of not being able to do without something, then everyone is addicted — be it to television, music, literature, sugar, salt, pets, or even to each other.

In these chapters we shall restrict the discussion to dependency on psychoactive drugs, a diverse group of both naturally occurring and synthetic compounds of which you know something already from Chapter 9 (see Table 9.1). Here we shall extend the term 'psychoactive' to include 'natural' substances (nicotine, caffeine, opium, etc.) that affect the nervous system. The practice of labelling these psychoactive substances as 'addictive' differs between cultures and, even within particular cultures, there may be dramatic changes over a period of time. For example, the use of opium in nineteenth-century England was widespread — as an analgesic, an anti-diarrhoea agent and, routinely, as a sedative (particularly for children). A century later, the possession of opium and its refined derivatives, such as morphine and heroin, carries the threat of a long prison sentence. On the borders of Afghanistan and Pakistan, dealing in opium is tolerated, but in the Soviet Union such dealing can carry the death sentence.

When the tranquillisers Librium and Valium were first marketed in the early 1960s they were hailed as wonder-drugs and were freely prescribed by doctors, especially to women. Librium and Valium replaced an earlier generation of sedatives, the barbiturates, which had caused concern because of the danger of accidental or intended overdose. (There were 2 000 such deaths in the UK in 1975.) Today, Librium, Valium and related compounds, generally called benzodiazepines, are seen as a major cause of drug dependency and prescribing habits will have to change. Will the possession of benzodiazepines become a criminal offence in the same way that the possession of opiate drugs has been?

From time to time throughout the past three hundred years, there have been sudden and often short-lived alarms about the use of particular psychoactive drugs in the UK. In the early eighteenth century, gin, the 'opium' of the working class, became the object of legislation. A century later, the sales of certain drugs were limited to pharmacists with the passing of the Pharmacy Act in 1868. Subsequent legislation at the turn of the century restricted the distribution of opium and cocaine. During the 1914–18 War it became clear to the British government that there was widespread use of cocaine by soldiers on leave. Under a new Defence of the Realm Regulation it became an offence for anyone, apart from those in the medical profession, to possess cocaine. In the early 1960s there was a sudden explosion in the number of people experimenting with psychoactive drugs — not only opiates, but amphetamines, sedatives and hallucinogens. This resulted in very restrictive legislation, the 1971 Misuse of Drugs Act.

In the past few years there has been increasing concern about the use of drugs. If some Press reports are to be believed then half the teenage populations of some large cities such as Liverpool and Glasgow are using heroin, those with money are buying cocaine and there is an epidemic of glue sniffing among school children. As yet there are no firm data.

To a great extent the boundaries drawn around the term addiction are determined by what society finds acceptable at a particular time. Commercial interests in the UK promote the view that alcohol, nicotine and caffeine are acceptable, though the costs to society in terms of treating people with liver and coronary disease and respiratory disorders are immense. Of course, to label something as a problem implies that something must be done. It indicates deviance and legitimises intervention.

Figure 10.1 'The problem . . . is in defining boundaries. Is there a difference between a man on a park bench holding a cider bottle and the executive on the second bottle of wine over lunch?'

In the following two chapters we shall first consider the explanations offered for the occurrence of a drug-dependent condition and then see how these varied explanations have shaped ideas about appropriate therapies. In searching for explanations it is not enough simply to look at the biological effects of psychoactive drugs. *Drug-related behaviour* is the interaction between the drug, the user and his or her environment. Therefore, in Chapter 11 the changing patterns of drug use, together with the experiences of those taking drugs, are described.

Objective for Chapter 10

When you have studied this chapter, you should be able to:

10.1 Illustrate how the boundaries of addiction can change over time.

Question for Chapter 10

1 (*Objective 10.1*) Give one example of a psychoactive substance for each of the following descriptions.

(a) It has been widely used in the UK for millennia and remains relatively freely available, despite evidence of its harmful effects and attempts to restrict its use through legislation.

(b) It has been widely used in the UK for four centuries with no attempt at legislation.

(c) It was widely used in the UK in the eighteenth and nineteenth centuries, but progressive legislation in this century has outlawed its possession by all except those registered by the Home Office.

(d) It is a synthetic drug that has never been officially marketed. It was used widely in the 1950s and 1960s and is now outlawed.

(e) This drug has been widely used in the UK since the sixteenth century, is often home-produced and, despite attempts to do away with legislation against this substance, it remains a criminal offence to possess it.

Figure 10.2 'The boundaries appear to be set by social attitudes and ... conditioned by culture ...'.

11
Explanations of drug dependency

In this chapter we describe the biological actions of psychoactive drugs and reiterate the various types of explanation that you have come across in earlier chapters.

At times you may need to refer back to *The Biology of Health and Disease* (U205, Book IV), especially for details of the central nervous system and for the aetiology of particular diseases.

Table 11.1 gives a great deal of information about the biological effects of particular psychoactive drugs — you should try to learn the general names of the more common types and their mode of action.

Drug dependency is a state, psychic and sometimes also physical, resulting from the interaction between a living organism and a drug, characterized by behavioural and other responses that always include a compulsion to take the drug on a continuous or periodic basis in order to experience its psychic effects, and sometimes to avoid the discomfort of its absence. (Kramer and Cameron, 1975)

This working definition of drug dependency attempts to describe the symptoms of the condition, but says little of causality. Why do people *begin* to take drugs? Are the reasons for beginning the same as those for *continuing* to use drugs?

☐ In Chapter 8 a number of broad types of explanatory principle were put forward, each of which attempted to account for depression and schizophrenia. Can you recall the three major types of explanation?
■ The three types are social, personal life-history and biological explanations.

In this chapter we shall look at drug dependency with these types of explanation in mind. First consider the other half of the interaction — the nature of psychoactive drugs and their physiological effects.

Psychoactive drugs and their effects
By definition, psychoactive drugs have effects on the nervous system. Table 9.1 in Chapter 9 listed four main classes of such drugs.

☐ Can you recall them?
■ The four classes are: (i) sedatives and tranquillisers, (ii) stimulants, (iii) antidepressants and (iv) hallucinogens (psychodelics).

The classes most commonly associated with dependency are the sedatives and minor tranquillisers, the stimulants and the hallocinogens.

☐ What substances other than those listed in Table 9.1

Table 11.1 Classes of psychoactive drugs known to produce dependency

Psychoactive drugs (examples in brackets)	Example of a commercial brand	General mode of action	Therapeutic use in the UK
1 **barbiturates** (pentobarbitone)	Nembutal	nervous system depressant	sedative/hypnotic (epilepsy/insomnia)
2 **ethyl alcohol**	most wines/spirits, etc.	nervous system depressant	none
3 **opiates** (morphine)	Duromorph	activates opiate receptors in nervous system	analgesic/sedative
4 **benzodiazepines**	Valium	activate particular receptors in nervous system	anti-anxiety/hypnotic
5 **amphetamines** (amphetamine)	Dexedrine	activates sympathetic nervous system and increases arousal and motor activity	stimulant (narcolepsy)
6 **caffeine**	most coffees and teas	generally raises level of cell metabolism; bronchodilator	stimulant
7 **nicotine**	most tobaccos	activates receptors producing parasympathetic effects	none
8 **cocaine**	—	nervous system stimulant	local anaesthetic; eye drops
9 **hallucinogens** (cannabis; mescalin from cactus; psylocybin from 'magic' mushrooms; lysergic acid diethylamide, LSD)	none	probably all mimic the actions of particular neurotransmitters	none
10 **solvents** (e.g. glues)	—	various	none

are implicated in dependency?

■   Others are cocaine and the opiates (heroin, morphine and opium), nicotine, alcohol and solvents (e.g. glue).

□   Now place the nine substances just mentioned into one of three categories according to what you think might be the number of regular users in the UK:
(a) 1 000 000 people or more
(b) 100 000 to 1 000 000
(c) less than 100 000.

■   (a) 1 000 000 people or more use alcohol, nicotine and caffeine.
(b) Tranquillisers (such as Librium) and hallucinogens are used by 100 000 to 1 000 000 people.
(c) Opiates, cocaine, barbiturates and solvents have less than 100 000 regular users.

This ordering may have surprised you! The opiates and cocaine — sometimes collectively termed *narcotic drugs* — solvents and the hallucinogens all attract considerable news interest, yet in comparison with alcohol relatively few people use them.

Psychoactive substances have been widely used in different societies for many thousands of years. The Greeks recognised the power of opium, both as a pain-killer and as a sedative. The practice of chewing coca leaves by Andean peoples to enable them to work long hours in the fields is unchanged. Nicotine and alcohol remain the major drugs of the industrialised countries.

Originally, the use of these plant-derived substances was twofold; as a means of sustaining health and, in religious ceremonies, as a means of transcending earthly experience. The wine ceremonies of the Christian faith and of Judaism, mescale drinking among the Indian tribes of Central America and ganja smoking among Rastafarians are all examples of the latter.

The pattern of use of such drugs in industrialised societies today can be traced back to these origins. What has changed is that people now have a far greater variety of psychoactive substances to choose from — a pharmacological diversity resulting from attempts both to alleviate physical symptoms of disease and to generate mood-affecting drugs for medical purposes.

Table 11.1 lists the major classes of psychoactive substances associated with dependency, their therapeutic value and biological sites of action, although for many substances the precise site and mode of action are, as yet, unknown.

As you can see, many of the substances derived from plants (e.g. heroin, caffeine, cocaine, etc.) and the synthesised drugs act by stimulating or blocking activity in the nervous system.*

*The biology of the nervous system is dealt with more fully in *The Biology of Health and Disease* (U205, Book IV).

☐ How do cells in the nervous system communicate, one with another?

■ They communicate by releasing chemical neurotransmitters that bridge the gap between one nerve cell and the next, causing an electrical impulse to be generated in the next cell in the pathway.

Heroin and morphine activate receptors that respond to opiate-like substances (called enkephalins) that normally circulate in the blood. The benzodiazepine tranquillisers activate receptors that promote the action of an inhibitory neurotransmitter in the brain.

Not all the effects of psychoactive drugs are to be found in the *central* nervous system (brain and spinal cord). Amphetamines produce effects similar to those found when the sympathetic nervous system is activated — elevation of heart rate and blood pressure. Nicotine mimics the action of acetylcholine, which is a major transmitter in the parasympathetic nervous system. The effects of some psychoactive drugs are very general. For example, caffeine raises the level of cell metabolism. Thus psychoactive drugs may produce changes not only in mood, but also in the general physiological state of the entire body. Alcohol diminishes the absorption of nutrients across the intestinal wall. Nicotine and caffeine promote a marked secretion of fluid into the intestine (hence their laxative properties). Opiates, on the other hand, produce constipation. Often it is these general accompanying effects that debilitate someone who is dependent on drugs rather than long-term changes in the central nervous system.

Now look at Table 11.2 which provides some data about the numbers of people who are dependent upon psychoactive drugs. Note that there are no data available for many drugs and that most people who are dependent use more than one drug.

The prescription of barbiturates and amphetamines is now reasonably infrequent and cocaine and the hallucinogens are rarely prescribed at all. The use of drugs in categories 6 and 7 is high. For example, in the UK about 35–40 per cent of people over the age of 16 smoke tobacco and *at least* that percentage take caffeine (in tea and coffee). Although we cannot quote accurately the number who are dependent on nicotine and caffeine, it is likely that they run into millions in the UK alone.

In Table 11.2 the distinction is made between two types of dependence. *Psychological dependence* is a condition in which a drug produces a feeling of satisfaction and a desire to administer the drug, periodically or continually, in order to produce pleasure or to avoid discomfort. *Physiological dependence* is an adaptive state that manifests itself by intense physical disturbances when the administration of the drug is suspended. These disturbances, referred to as a *withdrawal* (or abstinence) *syndrome*, are made up of specific psychological and physiological symptoms and signs that are characteristic for each drug type. A third distinction, that of *social dependence*, is sometimes evoked where the procuring and consumption of drugs form the subculture that the individual is a part of.

All the psychoactive drugs in Table 11.2 are associated with psychological dependency, but for cocaine and the hallucinogens there is no evidence of physical withdrawal symptoms if a regular user becomes, or is made, abstinent. On the other hand, all the substances listed in the table produce tolerance, which is a state of decreased responsiveness of the system to the pharmacological action of the drug as a result of exposure to that drug.

Now compare Table 11.2 with Table 11.3, which shows how psychoactive drugs are classified in the UK according to the Misuse of Drugs Act, 1971. This act lays down penalties for the unlawful possession of the different classes of drugs (e.g. the unlawful possession of heroin (class A) is considered to be more serious than the possession of cannabis resin (class B)).

☐ What is the most striking anomaly between Tables 11.2 and 11.3?

Table 11.2 Estimates of dependency on psychoactive drugs in the UK (where known)

Drug	Estimated number	Evidence of dependency	
		psychological	physiological
1 barbiturates	?	√	√
2 ethyl alcohol	750 000	√	√
3 opiates	4 371*	√	√
4 benzodiazepines	100 000	√	√
5 amphetamines	?	√	√
6 caffeine	?	√	√
7 nicotine	?	√	√
8 cocaine	?	√	—
9 hallucinogens	?	√	—

*Home Office figure for 1982. (Data from Office of Health Economics, 1981; Medical Research Council, 1983)

Table 11.3 The psychoactive substances listed in Table 11.2 as classified by the UK Misuse of Drugs Act, 1971

Class A	Class B	Class C
cannabinol	amphetamine	methaqualone
coca	cannabis	(sedative)
cocaine	cannabis resin	penoline
heroin	codeine	(stimulant)
morphine	methylamphetamine	
lysergimide (LSD)		
mescaline		
methadone		
opium		
pethidine		

■ The lack of correlation. Substances with a high incidence of dependency (shown in Table 11.2) are either not included (alcohol, nicotine, caffeine) or are easy to obtain on prescription (the minor tranquillisers).

How such a situation arose is something that we shall consider in Chapter 12. The reasons why alcohol and nicotine are freely available in Britain (as in most cultures) are predominantly commercial and fiscal and have a history that predates evidence about their harmful effects. Revenue from sales of alcohol and cigarettes is phenomenal — up to £7 000 million sterling was collected in government duty in the UK in 1981. Any legal measures to control either substance, therefore, run the risks for government of unenforcability, popular outcry and the need for alternative forms of taxation.

The attitudes of governments towards the production of drugs has always been ambivalent. The Opium Wars between Britain and China in the nineteenth century were not about controlling opium production within China, but about keeping China open for the sale of opium by the British. More recent attempts to control production include the US government's attempts to control heroin production in the famous Golden Triangle (Burma, Laos, and Kampuchea), to put pressure on Turkey's opium farmers to limit production and to limit coca-growing in Peru and Bolivia by the inducement of loans to these governments.

Figure 11.1

While the governments of industrialised countries attempt to limit the flow of opiates, cocaine and cannabis from east to west (and from south to north), the giant pharmaceutical companies of the west seek markets in countries with as yet few legal prohibitions — outlets for their massive production of psychoactive substances. This overspill of drugs into Africa, South America and the Far East is creating new problems of dependency.

All the dependency-related psychoactive drugs have been, and still are, of therapeutic value in some part of the world. In agrarian communities they represent the means of sustaining hard labour (e.g. alcohol, cannabis, coca) or of regaining a state of well-being (opiates, barbiturates and the minor tranquillisers). Their effects and the long-term consequences of their use depend upon the dose and on how they are administered.

In therapeutic terms, the *preferred* (simplest) way of administering *any* drug is by mouth, the substance being absorbed into the bloodstream through the wall of the small intestine. Most drug formulations have to take into account the speed of absorption and the detoxifying ability of the liver. (Blood from the wall of the small intestine passes first to the liver, where toxic substances are broken down before entering the veins that return blood to the heart and thence to the major organs.) Obviously, then, only a small proportion of any drug taken orally reaches the 'target'. More direct routes are provided by injecting the drug under the skin (subcutaneously), or into a muscle, or into a vein (intravenously). Drugs can also be inhaled or sniffed so that a substance of the correct chemical composition will enter the bloodstream through the thin membranes lining the lungs, nose or roof of the mouth. Any of these more direct routes will not only produce a faster effect, but will result in a higher dose reaching the target.

□ Can you think of any hazards associated with injecting drugs?
■ These are numerous. One is the danger of overdose. Ulceration at the site of injection, blood-poisoning (septicaemia) and hepatitis arising from non-sterile needles and syringes are also possible. Then the drug may be contaminated with toxic impurities (either accidentally or intentionally). For example, heroin may be cut (diluted) with other, cheaper substances. Finally, thrombosis (a blood clot) and embolism (the admission of air bubbles into the bloodstream) may result.

The continued use of drugs increases the chance of such infection and, in addition, may lead to liver damage (e.g. cirrhosis) and even hepatoma (liver cancer).

Invoking biological explanations

Taking *any* drug alters a person's existing physiological state. Homeostatic balance is upset and a new state is achieved. Drugs therefore have observable and measurable biological effects, but can drug dependency be explained entirely in biological terms?

With psychoactive drugs, the new state may be more tranquil (sedative) or there may be a feeling of heightened motivation (e.g. amphetamines). As the drug is broken down, in tissues such as the liver, and excreted, the pre-drug conditions return. To achieve the drugged state once again, more has to be taken. With regular use, various tissues of the body adapt to cope with the intake of drug, in other words, tolerance sets in. For example, a regular intake of alcohol raises particular enzyme levels in the liver and these more rapidly break down the alcohol. In the nervous system, if a cell is continually exposed to a neuro-transmitter-like substance, the cell becomes less responsive to it. This could explain why regular users of a drug become tolerant to a particular dose and require higher doses. (Tolerance to a dose of one of the opiates, however, seems to depend as much upon the individual as anything else.)

Associated with tolerance are the dangers of taking an overdose. Tolerance to opiates develops and is maintained by large and frequent doses. Any period of abstinence results in a loss of tolerance and there is great danger of an overdose if, when the drug is taken again, the amount used is too high. With the opiates there seems to be no limit to the dose at which one can become tolerant. With barbiturate drugs, the situation is quite different: there is an upper *lethal* limit — tolerance is possible only to a point! The incidence of overdosing with barbiturates is high and this led to the search for alternative tranquillisers, resulting in the development of the benzodiazepines.

In the same way that various physiological processes *adapt* to a persistent level of drug, so cells become highly sensitive when the drug is first withdrawn. Withdrawal symptoms may be very obvious. Examples are the tremors (DT's) between bouts of alcohol consumption, psychotic episodes ('cold turkey' — so called because of the appearance and feel of the skin) when opiates are withheld and loss of concentration during abstinence from nicotine. It is not universal that those regularly taking opiates, for example, exhibit withdrawal symptoms, nor that a *single* experience of heroin leads to dependence. William Burroughs, the American writer who became prominent during the 'beat' scene of the 1950s had this to say in his book *Junkie*: 'It took me almost six months to get my first habit, and then the withdrawal symptoms were mild. I think it no exaggeration to say it takes about a year and several hundred injections to make an addict'. (Burroughs 1969). Burroughs is no doubt overstating his case. He sees withdrawal as the first symptom of dependence.

☐   What may be another symptom?
■   The fact that someone repeatedly *injects* themselves.

Supporters of what is called *learning theory* suggest that some drugs, such as amphetamines, cocaine and opiates, can be powerful *primary reinforcers*. In other words, behaviour resulting in the administration of the drug increases. A reinforcing drug may not necessarily produce a pleasurable state, and even if it does, it is not necessarily the pleasurable state that leads to the drug-seeking behaviour.

The means of taking drugs may act as a *secondary reinforcer* and therefore may also be important in drug-taking behaviour. Note this revelation by a young opiate addict, injecting several times each day:

> I was mentally more dependent on the needle than on the drug ... I searched masochistically for the vein for half-an-hour, and when I eventually hit the vein and pushed the stuff in, the relief when I saw the blood coming into the syringe was fantastic. By then, getting the drug into my body had become a secondary consideration. Shooting the stuff in was just an obvious conclusion after hitting the vein. The relief came when I hit it. (quoted in Glatt, 1974)

From this it could be argued that the syringe and the needle have assumed secondary reinforcing properties through their association with the rewards of the drug itself.

Adherents to learning theory also argue that, for those drugs that produce marked withdrawal symptoms, drug taking is under the control of 'aversive stimuli'. In other words, drug use is continued in order to *avoid* the unpleasant experience of withdrawal symptoms. There is little evidence to support the theory, though many opiate-dependent individuals do claim that they take drugs for this reason.

Changing patterns of drug use

Although biological explanations may be valid means of describing tolerance and even withdrawal symptoms, they are inadequate on their own to describe why people start to use drugs or why they continue to use them. The roots of dependency can be traced back to the therapeutic use of drugs. For example, people known to be dependent upon opiates in the early part of this century in the UK (a few hundred, based on pharmacists' records and on prosecutions) were either patients who had been persistent-ly prescribed morphine, or doctors and nurses to whom such drugs were readily available. At this time, treatment of dependency on opiates was seen to be the preserve of the medical profession who controlled their availability through prescription. Of course, the widespread use of alcohol, tobacco and caffeine was already sanctioned.

What changed the drug experience in the UK in the 1960s were, simultaneously, a change in society and social values, and hardening attitudes towards the use of drugs. Disclosures by two famous addicts illustrate this change: In 1821, Thomas de Quincey wrote:

> Was it on a sudden overmastering impulse derived from bodily anguish? Loudly, I repeat, *Yes*; loudly and indignantly — as in answer to a wilful calumny. Simply as an anodyne it was, under the mere coercion of pain the severest, that I first resorted to opium. (de Quincey, 1821)

And 150 years later, William Burroughs wrote:

> The question, of course, could be asked: Why did you ever try narcotics? Why did you continue using it long enough to become an addict? You became a narcotics addict because you do not have strong enough motivations in any other direction. Junk wins by default! (Burroughs, 1969)

Whereas cannabis and psylocybin have a long history of use in the UK, cocaine, LSD and mescalin are relatively recent arrivals and few people used them until the 1960s. In a generation that demanded radical change, alcohol, the drug of the older generation, was too reminiscent of the existing social structure. Alcohol was also not a 'mind-expanding' agent like the hallucinogens. Advocates of mescalin, such as the novelist Aldous Huxley, and LSD, such as Timothy Leary, a Harvard psychologist, argued for their widespread use. In San Francisco, the emerging hippy culture of the mid-1960s was based on marijuana, as was the growth of Rastafarianism in the Caribbean. Old colonial links with India, Pakistan and the Middle East ensured a continuous import of cannabis to the UK, until it was realised that the British climate is quite suitable for growing *Cannabis sativa*. There was then a switch to home-grown 'grass'. The use of home-produced cannabis at least broke the contact with dealers and therefore minimised the exposure of cannabis users to other drugs.

It was at this time, in the 1960s, that the tranquillisers first appeared. Librium and Valium were hailed by many as the cure for all ills. Day-to-day anxiety and stress and associated problems with sleep became medicalised. Benzodiazepines were offered to women in particular and members of lower socio-economic groups were handed prescription after prescription.

More recently the pattern of drug use in the UK has again changed. The use of solvents by young people, common in Central and Northern America, has spread to the UK, particularly among boys. Solvents are both cheap and readily available, and inhaling the solvents in glues and plastic cements is an easy way of achieving a state of euphoria and hallucination. With regular use, solvents cause damage not only to the lining of the respiratory passages, but also to the liver and kidneys. Alcohol has now become more popular among young people and is still relatively cheap. Between 1949 and 1979 the relative price of alcohol fell by 50 per cent. The age at which people start drinking has fallen in recent decades and an early start to drinking appears to be associated with the subsequent development of heavier drinking patterns.

Experiencing drugs

In seeking explanations as to why individuals use drugs to the extent that they become dependent upon them, it would be folly to focus on the biology and to ignore the experience of those taking drugs.

English literature has many examples of writing while under the influence of drugs. Opium was commonplace in the lives of the early nineteenth century romantic poets such as Samuel Taylor Coleridge. William Wilberforce, who fought for the abolition of slavery, Clive of India, Edgar Allan Poe and Dante Gabriel Rossetti all used opium. Coleridge, troubled by toothache, had found relief in laudanum (tincture of opium) — not sleep but: 'a spot of enchantment, a green spot of fountains and trees in the very heart of a waste of sand'. A few weeks later in 1797 his poem *Kubla Khan* was conceived while sleeping off the effects of laudanum.

> In Xanadu did Kubla Khan
> A stately pleasure-dome decree:
> Where Alph, the sacred river, ran
> Through caverns measureless to man
> Down to a sunless sea.
> So twice five miles of fertile ground
> With walls and towers were girdled round:
> And there were gardens bright with sinuous rills;
> Where blossomed many an incense-burning tree;
> And here were forests ancient as the hills,
> Enfolding sunny spots of greenery.

For some, it seems, opium was a tonic, whereas for others it was an intoxicant and an aid to the imagination: 'a sensual pleasure — these trances, of profoundest reveries, which are the crown and consummation of what opium can do for human nature'. (Thomas de Quincey, 1821)

Around the time of the passing of the Dangerous Drugs Act in 1920, recreational drug use centred around London's artistic and theatrical circles. Of the 333 addicts known to the Home Office in 1956, 30 per cent were from the medical professions and the other notable group was 'a number of dance band musicians'.

Aldous Huxley, writing in the 1950s, had expounded upon the power of drugs:

> Most men and women lead lives at the worst so painful, at the best so monotonous, poor and limited that the urge to escape, the longing to transcend themselves if only for a few moments, is and has always been one of the principal appetites of the soul. (Huxley, 1959)

For ordinary people, it was the 1960s that provided contact with drugs. Gerry Stimson and Edna Oppenheimer, working at the Addiction Unit of the Institute of Psychiatry in London, undertook a study of heroin addicts between 1968 and 1978. Here are two quotations from some of the people in their study:

> I think I was bored really, it was just starting, a new craze.

> I think I was just curious. I took it slowly after the initial one, now and then. It opened up new things within you and you want to realise what you're taking and you want to find out more. (quoted in Stimson and Oppenheimer, 1982)

These are essentially *social* accounts of 'turning on'. In contrast, some people became addicted to heroin from a sense of loneliness or personal inadequacy.

> I just feel as if I've got to have these props. Yes, and I think it just became a ritual, like a religious ritual really. (quoted in Stimson and Oppenheimer, 1982)

The environment in the early 1960s — changing social values, the increase in real income, the search for new experiences, the availability of drugs for all eventualities — therefore contributed to the increase in the number of people becoming dependent upon drugs. At that time, a narcotic or barbiturate habit was not financially prohibitive — a few pounds a day at the most.

Stimson and Oppenheimer looked closely at the heroin addicts who formed the sample for their survey. A third were employed at the start of the survey in 1969. Twenty per cent reported income from employment as their only means of support and a third had an illicit source of income. Some two thirds of the sample were either 'stable' (working with legitimate incomes, conventional in appearance) or 'loners' (little contact with other addicts, supported by Social Security benefits). Less than 20 per cent were 'junkies', stealing and hustling to support themselves. Such a finding contradicts many of the stereotypes of heroin addicts (Chapter 10).

Whereas the route to drug dependency appears to be founded upon personal and social reasons, the continuing use of psychoactive drugs may have a physiological basis.

It is clear from Table 11.2 that many substances produce not only the desire to keep on taking them, but also physiological symptoms when they are withheld. With the growing level of tolerance that accompanies increased use of narcotics, there is a necessary build-up in the amount needed to produce a desired effect. At the same time, physiological changes take place in the body so that, when heroin, for example, is not taken, the individual starts to feel uncomfortable. For some it may be nothing more than a few aches, sweating and edginess, but for others:

> Your head feels like a typewriter that's all rusted up so that the words just do not come out properly. Physically, you're so lethargic, if that's the word, so sluggish and you can't sit down or lie down and rest because your body won't relax. At the same time you feel so weak when you get up to move. It's such an effort to go on living. (quoted in Stimson and Oppenheimer, 1982)

In Stimson and Oppenheimer's study, people spoke less about getting 'a buzz' and more about using heroin 'to keep me straight', 'to be able to walk and do normal things that people do without thought.'

Is drug-dependency a communicable disease?

So far, we have not used the term 'disease' in connexion with drug dependency. To label drug dependency as a disease, as it is in some cases, implies that treatment is required to rehabilitate the 'sufferer' to a point of well-being, of normality. With few exceptions, those who are drug dependent have become so by self-medication. The reasons for beginning that medication are diverse and numerous as we have seen. For some it was a need to experience a different reality or a way of dealing with the world as it was. For others, drugs provided a licence to behave in a particular way: they could opt out of responsibility and blame the drugs. Although we may invoke biological explanations for the physiological symptoms of drug dependency, such as withdrawal and tolerance, are there biological reasons for people becoming dependent? Where the use of drugs begins in a therapeutic setting then the answer is, yes, but not when drugs are taken for recreational reasons. Max Glatt, a psychiatrist and editor of the *British Journal of Addiction*, has argued that there is no such person as *the* addict. (Glatt, 1974)

> ☐ What factors can you think of that may be involved in the development of dependency?
> ■ Apart from the individual, the social surroundings and the drug itself seem to be important.

Glatt views these factors as a triad and draws an analogy with infectious disease. The individual is the host, the drug is the infectious agent and the social surroundings represent the environment. In Islamic countries, for example, there is no history of alcohol consumption and alcoholism does not flourish among the younger generation. In the UK, where tobacco is freely advertised and a source of revenue, there is a cultural acceptance and even an expectation of its use. Children, particularly those of parents who smoke, therefore experience pressure to smoke as well. According to this model the parents and cultural environment 'infect' the child with the disease — in this case a desire to smoke.

It is a commonly held view that those who become dependent upon drugs are emotionally maladjusted, weak individuals who require some sort of prop in life. In this chapter we have seen that routes to drug dependency are diverse — the need to conform to the values of a social group, to escape from an existing socio-economic order, or simply to experiment and experience something different. Seeking explanations for the initial use of drugs and their continued use, however, are not matters simply of academic interest. Treatments have been, and still are, based upon the type of explanation prevalent in a particular culture at a particular time and this has led to diverse and often ineffectual means of therapy, as we shall see in Chapter 12.

Figure 11.2 'Children ... of parents who smoke ... experience pressure to smoke as well.'

Objectives for Chapter 11

When you have studied this chapter, you should be able to:

11.1 Define and distinguish between the following terms: withdrawal, tolerance, psychological and physiological dependence, tranquilliser, hypnotic, hallucinogen, sedative, opiate, narcotic, stimulant.

11.2 Describe the general biological effects of heroin, nicotine, a benzodiazepine, amphetamine and a barbiturate drug.

11.3 Distinguish between different explanations of the routes to, and the state of, dependence.

Questions for Chapter 11

1 (*Objectives 11.1 and 11.2*) Which of the following pairs of psychoactive drugs have (a) similar effects and (b) contrasting effects on the body?

  (i) amphetamine and   (iii) heroin and morphine
      pentobarbitone   (iv) cocaine and Valium
  (ii) mescalin and LSD   (v) nicotine and caffeine.

2 (*Objectives 11.1, 11.2 and 11.3*) Which of the following produce (a) tolerance, (b) physiological dependency and (c) psychological dependency?

  (i) opiates
  (ii) hallucinogens
  (iii) stimulants such as amphetamines.

3 (*Objective 11.2*) Which of the following have major effects outside the central nervous system (brain and spinal cord)?

  (i) alcohol   (iv) caffeine
  (ii) heroin   (v) nicotine
  (iii) cocaine   (vi) amphetamine

4 (*Objective 11.4*) Which of the following quotations illustrate (a) social causation, (b) personal life-history, (c) a biological explanation, or (d) a mixture of any of these three?

  (i) 'Drug-dependent individuals have personality disorders in excess of that found in the general population'.

  (ii) 'Amphetamines and cocaine are primary reinforcers of drug-seeking behaviour'.

  (iii) 'There is a strong correlation between parents who take a lot of tranquillisers and drink, and their drug addict children'.

  (iv) 'Evenings were spent there, transactions were going on. Eventually one day I must have wanted to try. By that time everyone else was injecting'.

12

Drug dependency: contain or cure?

This chapter discusses various approaches to the treatment of drug dependency. Throughout, you should keep in mind the kinds of explanations that we put forward for the drug-dependent state in Chapter 11. You are required to study three short articles in the Course Reader (Part 4, Section 4.6) on 'Drug problems in the sociocultural context'. They deal with problems in Thailand (Vichai Poshyachinda), Egypt (G. M. Abu El Azayem) and the USA (J. Jaffe).

Social attitudes to drug dependence have varied with time and across cultures. The policies that have been formulated to deal with drug dependency aim either to cure or to contain. Based on the cost to society, some argue that the only valid policy is to cure. In the UK, the use of prescribed benzodiazepines cost the National Health Service £30 million in 1979. In 1981, the unwanted effects of alcohol consumption cost the UK £1 000 million in lost or decreased productivity (30 million working days were lost in 1982) and in medical care. The Health Service in the UK spends £150 million each year on smoking-related diseases.

Prohibition and criminalisation seek to contain drug taking and to diminish the number dependent on drugs. This has been the attitude of successive administrations in the USA and Eastern Europe. It leads to contradictions in deciding which drugs to ban. Whereas the use of narcotics carries heavy prison sentences, alcohol is readily available. Attempts to prohibit alcohol in the 1920s in the USA were a disaster and led to organised crime. In the same way, the outlawing of free narcotics prescriptions introduced a black market for the first time in the UK in the late 1960s.

Brewers, distillers and purveyors of alcohol provide 700 000 jobs in the UK, export over £1 000 million of alcohol and help the government to raise £3 500 million in revenue (Office of Health Economics, 1981). The duty on nicotine consumption raised £4 500 million in 1983. Together, the duty on nicotine and alcohol in 1984–85 amounted to 50 per cent of the cost (£14 700 million) of the National Health Service, which is the largest employer in the UK. On a cost–benefit analysis it would appear folly to introduce legal measures to prohibit or limit the availability of alcohol and nicotine, although these account for well over 90 per cent of all cases of drug dependence. Health care approaches to nicotine and alcohol dependency are left to the efforts of voluntary organisations such as Alcohol Concern and Alcoholics Anonymous, and pressure groups such as Action on Smoking and Health (ASH), which is run by the Royal College of Physicians and the Health Education Council. The pharmaceutical industry in the UK has exports worth £1 000 million a year and invests £50 million each time a new pharmaceutical compound is developed — a strong lobby in the event of new drug legislation (Office of Health Economics, 1983).

The other psychoactive drugs outlined in Table 11.1 attract attitudes that are very different. Persistent users of narcotics, such as heroin, cannabis and cocaine, do not produce wealth in terms of revenue: cannabis smoking does not help to raise taxes! Neither does the manufacture of these drugs provide mass employment, manufacturing opportunities and export markets for big businesses. Treatment of those who are dependent upon drugs costs money, both in terms of medical care and in providing the means to police the distribution of such drugs. In this chapter we shall look at various attempts to control dependency on alcohol and narcotics and current attitudes on the prescribing of benzodiazepines.

The prevention of harm related to alcohol

In the UK between 1959 and 1979, the amount of alcohol consumed per capita doubled. It has been calculated that a 1 per cent rise in real income increases the consumption of alcohol by 1–2 per cent and, therefore, a means of reducing its consumption is to increase its price considerably. One outcome of such a step may be that money is diverted away from food and clothing to meet the increased cost of alcohol.

How does advertising affect the consumption of alcohol? In the UK, the drinks industry spends more than £100 million each year on advertising. It was suggested that a 1 per cent reduction in advertising would lead to 0.2% reduction in alcohol consumption. This did not happen, however, when it was tried in the Province of British Columbia, Canada and although advertising is non-existent in most of eastern Europe, the alcohol problem still abounds there. (Of course, cocaine and cannabis are not advertised, but have high sales nevertheless.)

Another social strategy would be to reduce the availability of alcohol by limiting the number of licensed premises. Total prohibition does not work, as witnessed in the USA, and in those states that limit the number of outlets there is no obvious reduction in the amount of alcohol consumed. The converse, however, does appear to be true. When, in Finland in 1969, the restrictions on the outlets for the sale of beer were lifted there was a 50 per cent rise in alcohol intake.

All of these proposals involve legislation and policing. Together with health education, they may change patterns of drinking behaviour and influence a future generation, but there remain hundreds of thousands in the UK alone whose drinking patterns are firmly entrenched and harmful to health. One solution to this problem is in *self-help groups*. The chance meeting of a doctor and an alcoholic New York stockbroker in Akron, Ohio in 1935 led to the formation of Alcoholics Anonymous, which arrived in the

UK in 1947. Alcohol Concern as it is now known still holds the view of the Temperance Movement that *alcoholism* is a disease that affects only some people and the only cure is total abstinence. Unlike the Temperance Movement, Alcohol Concern sees the problem in the *individual* and not in the property of the *drug*. In Britain it now has around 1 200 groups totalling 10 000 members. Similar groups such as Al-Anon and Al-Alteen offer support to the partners and teenage children of alcoholics.

Within the British National Health Service, effort in the past 30 years has been aimed at the development of specialised centres for the treatment of alcoholism. There are now thirty of these in England and Wales and they treat 7 000 people a year. The debate in the Health Service is still whether or not *total* abstinence should be the goal. Some argue that controlled social drinking is a possible and appropriate alternative for a proportion of those currently dependent upon alcohol. Another question is whether long periods in hospital are necessary or, indeed, desirable. A British study (cited in Office of Home Economics, 1981) compared specialised hospital treatment and a single counselling session. It appeared that both were equally effective in helping people to break their dependence on alcohol.

The problem with benzodiazepines

The minor tranquillisers, a class of psychoactive drugs which includes the benzodiazepines, represent the most widely prescribed group of drugs in western Europe and the USA. In recent years, this high rate of prescribing has become a subject of concern for two reasons: first, many have expressed the view that their prescribing is indiscriminate and, secondly, it is estimated that there are now 100 000 people dependent upon benzodiazepines in the UK alone. General practitioners in particular have been singled out for criticism.

□ What factors can you identify that might influence a general practitioner in the prescription of tranquillisers?

■ You may have thought of some of the following:
1 Advertising and pressure from pharmaceutical company representatives.
2 The attitude of fellow general practitioners.
3 Whether the patient has already received the drug.
4 The sex and age of the patient.
5 The limited time available for consultation.
6 Seeing a patient's distress as having an exclusively biological basis.
7 Inability to offer any other form of help or support.

Jonathan Gabe and Susan Lipshitz–Phillips of the Social

Research Unit at Bedford College, London, carried out a study in 1981 which attempted to define the roles of general practitioners and their patients (all women) in the prescribing of benzodiazepines (Gabe and Lipshitz–Phillips, 1982). *All* the women expressed a strong antipathy to using drugs of any kind. This was surprising as an earlier study (Helman, 1981) had found that chronic benzodiazepine users come to accept their drug taking, seeing the pills as either food, fuel or a tonic. When questioned as to why they were taking tranquillisers, most of the distress or upset the women described was identifiable as anxiety.

The doctors in the Gabe and Lipshitz–Phillips study said that they prescribed benzodiazepines for 'anxiety and insomnia caused by interpersonal and domestic problems such as marital strife, child care difficulties and the 'empty nest''. Some doctors listed 'physical and/or psychosomatic conditions (rheumatism, menopause)' as the cause of anxiety and a few perceived 'stresses of poor housing or financial difficulties'. All the doctors felt that drugs were of some value in the acute stage of a crisis, but they also recognised the danger of patients becoming dependent on such drugs and treating them as 'magic pills'.

Considering the results from this type of study it is hard to see why benzodiazepines are prescribed as frequently as they are. Younger doctors, fresh from training, pointed out that the concern about over-prescribing had reached the medical schools. The doctors said that drug advertising had no impact on their prescribing habits and only a few admitted that they prescribed when pushed for time. This group of doctors did admit that they prescribed benzodiazepines more often to women than to men and more often to working-class patients, either because of an inability to communicate with them or because these patients wanted 'pills' rather than 'talk'.

In theory at least all the doctors said that they wanted to wean their long-term patients off benzodiazepines. Some, however, admitted that past experience had taught them that there was little point in trying, especially with elderly patients.

Opiate dependency: some health-care approaches

Chapter 11 included a caricature of a heroin addict and the media are often seen to present the addict as a 'down and out', a criminal living off others to maintain a habit that will eventually be fatal. To control the use of opiates some countries have outlawed these drugs and have thus made criminals of those who are dependent on them. For people who take heroin because of dissatisfaction with their view of themselves, such an approach can simply reinforce that view. Other countries have decriminalised drug dependents and encouraged them to seek treatment in clinics.

The World Health Organization (Edwards and Arif, 1980) suggests that there should be four elements to any policy designed to treat drug dependency:

1 Withdrawal and detoxification.
2 Drug maintenance and substitution.
3 Self-regulating therapeutic communities.
4 Psychological and social counselling, vocational counselling and follow up.

We shall now look at the attitudes of four countries: the UK, Thailand, Egypt and the USA to see if the World Health Organization's suggestions are included in their policies for treating drug dependency. As you work through these four accounts you will see that the first two items are commonly included in present policies, but the last two — expensive elements in any rehabilitation programme — are rare. Make notes on what each account reveals, particularly about the following:

1 The dominant explanation put forward for drug dependency.
2 Who has the responsibility for treatment.
3 The relative costs (financial and in terms of the number of health workers) of each treatment strategy.
4 The success rates and what 'success' means.
5 The type of experience that someone who is drug dependent might have under each regime of treatment.

The United Kingdom

Attitudes to the use of opiates in the UK have swung widely in the past two centuries. The use of opium in the 1800s was widespread, but the availability of opium and its derivatives (morphine and heroin) has been gradually restricted. This was mainly due to the medical lobby who apparently wanted a monopoly on the prescribing of opiates for reasons of their own incomes, rather than as a positive attitude to limiting its availability (Stimson and Oppenheimer, 1982). Until 1939, however, there were few prosecutions under the Dangerous Drug Acts of the 1920s. The use of opiates was viewed primarily as a medical problem rather than a criminal one. The few hundred addicts that there were could easily be identified through prescription records at pharmacists.

In the 1960s, this situation changed dramatically. The number of people using heroin for recreational purposes increased (see Figure 12.1).

Over the same period, the average age of those taking opiates fell. In 1960, 10 per cent were under 35, but by 1964 this age group represented 40 per cent of the total. In the following year (1961), the system whereby any general practitioner could prescribe opiates was questioned as this appeared to be supplying heroin to an illicit market and thereby creating new problems. It was decided to restrict those who *could* prescribe, while not necessarily curbing the *amount* prescribed to individuals.

Special centres were proposed where those who were

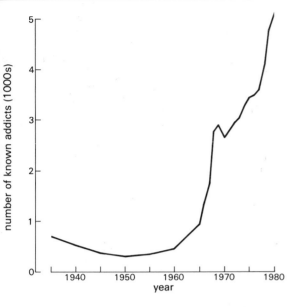

Figure 12.1 Numbers of narcotic drug addicts in the United Kingdom (mainly heroin addicts) known to the Home Office, 1935–1980. (Data from Stimson and Oppenheimer, 1982, Tables 2(2) and 11(1), pp.35–6 and 208–9).

dependent on drugs could undergo a course of treatment. There was thus a quite dramatic shift in policy from the medical treatment of individuals to the social control of dependency. From 1968 on, doctors required special Home Office Licences to prescribe opiates and cocaine, and the names of new patients had to be registered with the Chief Medical Officer.

In addition to heroin, methadone, a synthetic opiate, was also being prescribed. It acted as a reserve if the heroin was consumed too quickly between prescriptions. It also represented an attempt to wean people off heroin on to something that did not provide the heroin 'buzz' and also prevented withdrawal symptoms. The long-term aim was to dissuade dependents from injecting heroin and to encourage them to take methadone (orally) and thence to abstinence. An extensive black market, fuelled by imported Chinese heroin at inflated prices, grew up with the clinics. At this time, Gerry Stimson and Edna Oppenheimer set up their long-term study of heroin addicts (Stimson and Oppenheimer, 1982). They drew a representative sample of 128 patients who were being prescribed heroin from various London clinics. After the initial survey in 1969, the group was traced and again interviewed ten years later. Stimson and Oppenheimer found that fifty of their sample were still attending a clinic. Of those not attending, fifty were abstinent and nineteen had died. Of those still attending, half were receiving only methadone, whereas the others were receiving heroin with or without methadone.

All of those who had died were dependent upon drugs up to the time of their death.

☐ What conclusion might you draw from this study?
■ At first it seems that, within ten years, some 40 per cent of those originally attending a clinic became free of drugs. Of course, this could be either *because* of the clinic treatment or *despite* it — this group may have become abstinent anyway. Again, it seems encouraging that most of those still dependent upon opiates were still attending the clinic, but it could be argued that the clinics were prolonging their dependency by providing drugs. Sixteen per cent of the original group had died, a very high proportion of fatalities compared with those associated with the consumption of large quantities of nicotine or alcohol.

What are these clinics? Many remain unchanged from 1967. They are often isolated from the rest of the hospital and sometimes from other psychiatric clinics; they are cramped and rarely rehoused in new buildings. In 1981 there were 1 061 patients attending the fourteen London clinics. In charge of each is a consultant psychiatrist. The number of consultant sessions varies from clinic to clinic and there are probably not more than twelve consultants in the UK. Most clinics do not have training posts for doctors. The number of other staff varies widely from clinic to clinic and may therefore affect the type of treatment offered. One may have five or six nurses, while another has only one nurse and two or three social workers. It was originally intended that there be one social worker for every twenty-five patients. In reality, the ratio is 1 : 100. Few clinics have access to a psychologist and there is no formal training for any particular staff.

☐ What does the make-up of the staff at these clinics tell you about the attitude towards those who are dependent on drugs?
■ It suggests that the patients are regarded as mentally disturbed (psychiatrist and psychologist), ill (nurse) and have social problems (social worker).
☐ Can you think of others who might have been included in the therapy sessions? What do you conclude from their absence?
■ Some who might have been brought in are: clergy, the patient's own doctor, members of the family and close friends. Drug dependency is not seen as something stemming from religious or family problems, nor is the long-term medical history of the patient that the general practitioner could provide seen as pertinent. Of course, the practicalities of including a GP are complex.

Many clinics have rooms in which patients are allowed to inject and there is usually access to a detoxification programme (in-patient treatment to help dependents to become clear of drugs). Treatment policy in the clinics was, first, to deal with the heroin dependence (by providing the drug) and, second, to control it by gradually diminishing supplies. This was a difficult task — somehow to 'maintain' addicts and yet not prompt them to seek *extra* supplies of drugs from the black market. The clinics took the thrill out of 'scoring' drugs and forced order into what were often chaotic lives through a regime of regular attendance at the clinic. It is argued that this order brought stability to some addicts and contributed to their decision to come off drugs. Most of those who dropped the habit, however, pointed to changes in their lives that triggered an active decision to abstain. Some triggers were unpleasant shocks such as a prison sentence for drug-related offences or the death of a friend who was an addict. Others pointed to the beginning of a stable relationship or the offer of an interesting job.

> The Clinics are monotony, once I got off it and on to methadone ... I suddenly thought 'What the hell am I doing , I'm going to be an old lady, I'm going to be in the gutter as far as how people look at me. I am a person and I'm going to be in the gutter, and I'm going to spend my whole rotten life going to the chemist every morning'. And that was one of the things that decided to get me off. (Stimson and Oppenheimer, 1982)

> You don't realise just how much heroin blocks off your feelings and your emotions until you come off, it's like coming alive again. It's a completely new experience. (Stimson and Oppenheimer, 1982)

Have these clinics been successful? Anthony Thorley, who collaborated with Stimson and Oppenheimer, found in a detailed review of long-term studies of drug dependence that, in the UK, 25–33 per cent *more* addicts were likely to be abstinent after five years than addicts in other countries that had *not* set up the clinic system (Thorley, 1981). Some psychiatrists, however, believe the clinics are an expensive mistake. It is suggested that less than five per cent of those dependent upon opiates attend and that most patients believe that the clinics are unhelpful.

Apart from the health service there are a number of hostels run by church organisations and volunteer groups. They provide long-term halfway houses in an attempt to get those who are free of drugs back into the community. Outside these voluntary organisations, most health districts have no specialist services at all. At best there is a detoxification unit where the physical dependency is 'cured', but there is little support to help with the problem of psychological dependence.

Up to now, the process whereby those who are dependent on opiates can register, and so obtain drugs legally, means that the criminalisation of drug dependents does not take place. As Figure 12.1 has shown, however, the number of people dependent upon heroin has continued to grow and the black market thrives.

Now read the three articles in Part 4, Section 4.6 of the Course Reader on 'Drug problems in the sociocultural context'. They deal with Thailand (Vichai Poshyachinda) Egypt (G.M. Abu El Azayem) and the USA (J. Jaffe). As you read them, remember to make notes under the five headings we suggested earlier.

When you have read the articles and compared them with the situation in the UK, work through the following questions:

☐ What can be said about the way in which those using opium differ from those using heroin?

■ Opium, as used in Thailand and Egypt, is the narcotic of the older generation and is used therapeutically. Heroin is the narcotic more common among younger 'recreational' users.

☐ What are the major differences in the aims of the various treatments?

■ All four programmes probably aim for total abstinence, but it only comes near to being achieved in Thailand.

☐ Can you rank the various approaches in terms of success related to cost?

■ There is little doubt that the treatment given in Thailand is the most successful in terms of cost per patient. Next comes the treatment provided in Egypt and then that in the UK. It is difficult to assess in the US example, but, given its high cost, treatment in the USA is probably the least successful. Of course, it would be necessary to know the rate of recidivism before stating unequivocally which was the most successful.

☐ What types of explanation for drug dependency are the various treatments based upon?

■ In all four, there is a recognition that some of the problem is derived from personal life-history. Group therapy is used in Thailand and Egypt, but little attention is paid to it in the UK and the USA. Both in the UK and USA treatments are based on a biological explanation of dependence and so drugs are prescribed or substituted to deal with the problem. The description of treatment in Egypt is of particular interest because it shows a radical shift in thinking, from treating addicts as criminals towards encouraging them to attend clinics voluntarily.

☐ What sort of experience would someone attending the Buddhist temple in Thailand have compared with someone attending a methadone clinic in the USA?

■ The Thailand treatment is fairly stark. Basically, it is a way of providing group support during the period of withdrawal and then reinforcing people when they have become free of drugs. In a methadone clinic, heroin is simply substituted. The 'improvement' would be gradual and the treatment very much in isolation.

☐ Do you think that the treatment given in Thailand would work in the UK or USA?

■ The answer is almost certainly no. Treatment in Thailand, though voluntary, rests heavily on Buddhist belief and respect for the priests. Even when compulsory detoxification has been attempted in the West, the results have been poor.

National or international policies?

It is clear that there are wide differences in attitudes to opiate dependency and that both the style of treatment and the resources devoted to it vary. Does one system work better than any other? Is containment, as illustrated by both the USA and UK examples, as good as a determined effort to cure drug dependency, as in Thailand? Can a *single* policy be formulated to promote the alleviation of drug-related problems? The answer is, not surprisingly, no! Policies have to be designed for specific social situations and tailored to the scale of the dependency problem, the goal sought (containment or cure) and the resources available. In the Far East, where opium has a long and socially accepted history, the aim is to provide the means whereby people can seek help to become abstinent and have access to medical care so that their state of health will be monitored. In the West, the policies range from stabilising the dose taken to total prohibition. In a system like that in the USA, making the opiate user a criminal may add to the sense of social non-conformity; such a policy can create *more* crime.

The association of dependency on opiates with crime has also evolved in the UK over the past fifteen years. When the special clinics opened, the black market was no longer fed by excess psychoactive drugs from the Health Service, but by stolen or illicitly imported drugs. The clinics prompted many who were dependent on drugs to turn away from medical prescription (and the attendant health monitoring) to illicit dealers. The clinics placed more of a stigma on opiate dependency. No longer could people consult their own doctors, but were forced into anonymity; they were thus denied personal support and became 'just another junkie'.

In the UK, there is now a trend away from seeing drug dependency as an illness susceptible to medical treatment and towards regarding it as a vice, better dealt with by the police. Some view this as part of current government policy aimed at reducing state involvement in the provision of medical and social services, coupled with an emphasis on law and social order — more money for policing and harsher policies for young offenders.

Patrick Jenkin, as Minister for Social Services, indicated the government view in 1980:

'as with so many health problems, prevention is better than cure ... our first and most vital line of defence is obviously the police and the Customs' (*Drug Link*, 1980)

From a medical interpretation of 'prevention', through the social ideology of the multidisciplinary clinics of the 1960s and 1970s, we have now shifted to a 'ministerial' viewpoint. From being perceived first as a medical problem, than as a social or personal one, dependence on psychoactive drugs is now being seen as a problem to be dealt with by the forces of 'law and order'. Clearly, the police and customs have some role to play in controlling drugs, but the American experience suggests that the complete criminalisation of taking drugs would be a disaster.

Objectives for Chapter 12

When you have studied this chapter, you should be able to:

12.1 Provide at least two contrasting examples of the treatment of opiate dependency and show how they are consistent with the dominant explanation for dependency in that culture.

12.2 Describe one low resource and one high resource approach to containing drug dependency.

12.3 Compare and contrast social attitudes to the control of alcohol and heroin in the UK.

Questions for Chapter 12

1 (*Objective 12.1 and 12.2*) What are the major points of contrast between the treatment of opiate dependents in the Thailand temple and the US methadone clinics?

2 (*Objective 12.3*) What are the advantages and disadvantages for people who are dependent on opiates of receiving treatment within the special clinics in the UK? Are the advantages and disadvantages the same for people attending alcohol centres?

Being sick and being called sick

In studying this chapter, you will be referred to two articles in the Course Reader, 'Malingering' by Richard Asher (Part 2, Section 2.8) and 'Coping with migraine' by Sally MacIntyre and David Oldman (Part 6, Section 6.2). Reference is also made to the article by Erving Goffman that you read in association with Chapter 8. Some of the main topics of this chapter are touched on elsewhere: hysteria, the sick role, and medical authority in Book II; personal versus social responsibility in Book III; iatrogenesis and the placebo effect in Book IV.

At the end of the chapter you will be referred to another article in the Course Reader, 'Disability: whose handicap?', by Ann Shearer (Part 6, Section 6.3). You will then be asked to listen to the audiotape sequence *Disability and Sickness* (AC807, Band 2).

All diseases and disorders have one thing in common; to be sick is not merely to suffer a special condition of the mind or body, it is also to inhabit a special social world. That world, its nature, its morality, its economics, its politics and its intermeshing with the wider human world is the subject of this chapter.

The kind of social world in which the sick live, its relationships and dilemmas has of course been touched on throughout this book. Now we shall attempt to draw these various threads together. To do so is a difficult task. The sick may have some things in common, but lumping them all together can also do a gross injustice to the singularity of their condition. Every disease differs in its impact, every individual has a unique biography and personality and every sick person is bound up in a distinct set of social and economic relationships — this particular family, that particular doctor, this job, that hospital and so on.

Since sickness is a fundamental aspect of human experience, many social scientists have gone beyond merely describing the experience and on to construct a *model* of its basic features: that is, a theoretical framework that gives structure to what has been observed. The classic modern analysis of the social relationships of sick and well people was produced in 1951 by the American sociologist Talcott Parsons. According to his model, sick people take up what he called the *sick role*. When in this role, they have two rights and two obligations.

On the one hand they can claim exemption from many normal responsibilities (those with flu may stay in bed) and they can also claim the right to be cared for by the well. In return for these potential rights, they also have two duties. First, they are obliged to do all they can to get well (if this is possible) and, secondly, as part of this, they are obliged to seek and follow the advice of others — friends, relatives and, particularly, healers — in other words, to obey 'doctors orders'.

So Parsons' model of the experience of sickness refers not only to rights and obligations of the sick individual, but also to the many other roles, and rights and obligations, of relatives, friends, doctors, nurses, colleagues and so forth. It involves not just the role of the sick person, but a set of relationships. Parsons' model is *not* a description of how doctors, patients, relatives or friends actually behave. It outlines instead a kind of morality — a set of *rules* for how people feel they *ought* to behave in these circumstances. In practice, people do not always behave in the way they feel they ought and, in any case, they may be subject to other, conflicting rules for behaviour that stem from relationships other than those Parsons discusses in his model.

Parsons derived his analysis of these rules mainly from a study of paediatric clinics in Boston, Massachusetts in the 1930s, although he believed that his rules were of universal significance. Why might this be so? Why should this particular cluster of rights and obligations so commonly guide, in some fashion at least, the relationships of the sick and the well?

Consider first the duties of the well towards the sick, particularly their obligation to care for them and their duty to exempt the sick from some of their normal obligations. One obvious reason for these rules is that such measures may help the sick recover.

   □ Why should the well be interested in restoring the health of the sick?

   ■ They may love the sick or feel some human sympathy for them, but another reason is that of reciprocity. Those who are well now may be sick later. Yet a third reason is that sickness is a terrible waste of human resources. Not only may it stop the sick from contributing to human society, or lessen their contribution, but extra resources must be devoted to their care.

So the duties of the well towards the sick could be seen to stem from a potent mixture of interest and affection. What about the duties of the sick towards the well? In particular, why should the sick subject themselves to some form of medical authority? There are several answers to this question. The most obvious one is that doctors or other healers may have useful advice and treatment to offer that the sick should follow to minimise their ills. There are other grounds, however, for some measure of medical authority besides the possibility of medical expertise and patient incapacity. What if the sick role merely gave patients rights without any corresponding duties? Sickness would then offer exemption from normal obligations without any requirement to undergo medical examination, or to be subject to medical authority, or to make serious efforts, where possible, to get better. In such circumstances, sickness might prove a universally attractive proposition. Anyone faced with an unpleasant commitment merely has to claim, 'Sorry, I am sick'. This possibility, Parsons argues, is a crucial reason why the sick role involves the certification of illness, not just its mere assertion.

Even where doctors and healers have no effective therapy to offer, their authority alone, and the patient's confidence in it, can often have a strikingly beneficial effect, as is evident from the placebo effect discussed earlier. The fact that the sick have faith in their healers may itself be therapeutic, regardless of whether the actual treatments used are effective. The mere act of placing yourself in the hands of doctors and having confidence in their advice may bring about an important measure of relief. The importance of a good bedside manner is more than a matter of mere politeness.

Variation in the use of the sick role

There are, therefore, powerful reasons why the morality of the sick role should be so commonly found in human societies. Of course, there is a great difference between the very general rules attaching to the sick role and people's behaviour on any particular occasion. The actual form that the sick role takes varies enormously. In practice, it has endless permutations, an extraordinary variety of adjustments, shadings and forms, some minor, others major.

   □ Give examples from the conditions discussed in this book of the ways in which patients' experiences of the sick role are modified by the kind of illness from which they are suffering.

   ■ There are many different ways in which the type of illness can modify the patients' role. First, the length of time for which people are sick varies enormously. Chronically sick or disabled people may be in a kind of patient role all their lives. At the opposite extreme, a headache may last only a few minutes or hours. Similarly, just as the length of role may vary with the condition, so too does the extent to which sufferers are released from normal duties. The man in the last stages of terminal cancer, the woman with peritonitis, the floridly psychotic mental patient, all these are exempted from any ordinary social obligations. Also, the neurotic, or the mildly alcoholic, or people with a mild headache are often excused duties to some extent.

Just as this exemption from duties varies for patients, so too do the duties owed by others. Those with a pain in their head are owed less sympathy than those with a tumour in their breast and there is controversy over how far some of the drug addicted are owed any sympathy at all. Finally, although there is a general obligation for the well to aid the sick and for the sick to seek professional aid, how far this is true is heavily dependent on the type of illness — not everyone with a headache is expected to seek aid from others or visit a doctor.

Since there are many conditions for which medicine has

no effective treatment, there is always the possibility of patient revolt against the ethic of medical authority. However much medicine advances, this possibility will remain, for as soon as one problem is solved another takes its place. In industrialised countries, infectious diseases may no longer be the killers that they once were, but they have given way to illnesses such as cancers and heart disease. If solutions are one day found to these conditions, then other illnesses will replace them in their turn.

How the sick role operates is also shaped by the culture, wealth and organisation of the society in which the sickness occurs. Indeed, in extreme circumstances the sick role may cease to exist altogether.

☐ Can you think of any societies where the sick role has been abolished?

■ The Nazi solution to the problems of the 'mentally retarded' was simply to gas them. Likewise, many of those who fell sick in Nazi concentration camps were exterminated. Here there was no sick role, merely a death sentence. Those who could not labour were considered of no use to the camp regime. Other examples occur in human groups living in extreme conditions on the very margins of survival. In these circumstances, the sick may simply be left to die and, sometimes, the sacrifice may be voluntary. Captain Oates, on the British expedition to the South Pole led by Scott in 1912, walked out into the snow rather than be a burden to his colleagues.

Although the sick role may sometimes disappear, there is an important sense in which it is potentially present in every encounter between human beings. Health and sickness are relevant to every aspect of human lives and aspects of the sick role can, in consequence, be imported to every conversation, every relationship. Consider, for example, all the routine comments that fill up everyone's daily life: 'You look tired', 'Eat up your greens, they're good for you', 'You've put on a bit of weight since I last saw you', 'You sound flat', 'I'm sorry, I've got a headache', 'God, I feel knackered', 'How are you?'. Such remarks may be comments on your own state of health or the health of others. They may simply be a greeting, or they may express concern for your own or someone else's health and well-being. They could also be tactical weapons, a means of avoiding obligations, making excuses, changing the topic, or undermining the credibility of the speaker. To suggest someone is tired may be to hint that what they have just said should not be taken seriously. Similarly, to tell someone they should eat up their greens may be to assume parental rights, to claim authority for oneself and incompetence for the other. The roles of both healer and sick person are always available and may be used by them for all kinds of purposes, not just for health.

Thus the concept of the sick role is a way of explaining the inherent tension between the interests of the sick and the interests of society. These conflicts occur on two stages. The first we might call the *micropolitical* stage of the individual sick person and their immediate context of family, friends and doctors. Then there is the *macropolitical* stage of the individual in the context of wider social forces: employers, ideologies concerning ethnicity and gender, and the state itself. Let us begin with the micropolitics.

The sick role and sickness

Consider the claim that the way the sick role is sometimes applied may not only be inappropriate, but may actually increase or even create sickness. As a result of a person adopting a sick role, can some conditions be made worse, or more complicated, and can sickness develop where there was none before? All medical treatments can have side-effects and, if the sick role can exert a powerful placebo effect, should we not also expect it to be a major source of iatrogenesis? It is on this last type of iatrogenesis that we shall concentrate here.

Why might it be that, even where someone who is actually sick adopts the sick role, things can still be made worse? There are two reasons. The first concerns the many practical difficulties facing the well who care for the sick and the second concerns the manner in which all sickness is stigmatised. Both have been studied in detail by a largely North American sociological tradition, commonly, if awkwardly, known as *interactionism*.

For the interactionists, among whom Goffman is the most prominent, the individual is fundamentally shaped by the day-to-day interactions that he or she has with others. The way we see ourselves, our personal *identity*, is thus moulded by the way that others see us, and treat us, during our daily interaction with them. Their acts towards us, what they do as much as what they say, tell us a lot about their opinion of us. Of course, we do not place exactly the same value on everyone's opinion. Some opinions we readily dismiss, others are more crucial to our self-esteem, but whoever we choose to listen to, in the end, our self-evaluation is crucially dependent on other people's estimation of our worth — or so the theory argues.

☐ On this theory, how would the relationships attaching to the sick role mould the personal identity of the sick?

■ The precise way the well treat the sick would have crucial consequences for the sick's sense of self-esteem and for their future behaviour.

Sociologists of the interactionist tradition have therefore explored the daily response of the well to the sick: the problems that sickness in others poses for the well, the solutions they try out, the way that other relationships cut across their ties to the sick. In turn, they have also studied the reactions of the sick to the way they are treated by the well, seeing how each affects the other as the interaction proceeds.

The problems of caring for the sick

A family member may be ill and need care, but the family also needs care. A colleague may have serious problems in coping with the strains and stresses of work, but the work itself must go on. Even institutions set up specifically to care for the sick, hospitals and the like, have their internal dynamic, their own essential needs. Staff must be trained, resources found and schedules organised. The patients' needs must be set against demands from many other quarters. In other words, sick-role relationships are not the only ones in life, they must compete for people's attention with a whole host of other relationships and activities. As a result, the relationships between the sick and the well may, on occasions, increase or amplify rather than cure or diminish illness.

Take first an example from the family. A well-known study conducted in the early 1960s by George Brown and some psychiatric colleagues found that, on discharge from hospital, schizophrenics returning to their families had a worse prognosis than those who went to hostels instead (Brown *et al.*, 1962). One reason for this suggested by Brown's study, already referred to in Chapter 9, is that, where relatives are critical, hostile or show distinct signs of heavy emotional involvement, patients are particularly prone to relapse.

There may well be other factors involved in sick-role relationships, factors that hinge on the way that families are organised — the structures of relationship and identity that they involve. Consider, for example, the problems that may face a husband who has been an alcoholic for many years, but has now dried out, is sober once more and wishes to resume normal family life:

> With the continuation of sobriety many problems begin to crop up. Mother has for years managed the family and now father wishes to be reinstated once again in his former roles ... Even if the wife is willing to hand over some control the children often are not able to accept this change easily. Their mother has been both parents for so long that it takes time to get used to the idea of consulting their father on problems and asking for his decisions .... Used to avoiding anything which might upset him, the wife often hesitates to discuss problems openly. At times, if she is successful in helping him to regain his roles as father, she feels resentful of his intrusion into territory she has come to regard as her own. (Jackson 1968, pp.63–4)

Wives and children in such circumstances, so Jackson argues, are often torn between their new relationships and their old, and between the new identity that goes with the new relationships and that which they had before. This tension can sometimes seriously damage the transition of the husband from the sick role.

Now consider the reverse problem: what happens when someone starts to become sick? The impact this may have on others is discussed in Goffman's article in the Course Reader and the extract from Pringle in Chapter 8.

☐ What did these writers suggest might happen to family relationships when a member began to suffer from manic–depressive disorders or schizophrenia?

■ Normal family relationships were thrown into turmoil.

Now consider a very different situation, this time not in a family or in an ordinary work setting, but in an institution that has been created specifically to house sick-role relationships, a hospital. Here too, so it would seem, organisational relationships do not always square with the ethics of the sick role. The following is an extract from the diary of Rosemary Firth, an anthropologist, who spent twelve days under observation in a hospital for tropical diseases after her return from research abroad:

> Day Ten: Tuesday — This morning, being the Professor's day (the day he visits the ward), we were kept in bed the whole morning, and for lunch. I put on a dressing-gown and strolled onto the balcony. A nurse reproved me: 'You should not go onto the balcony in your dressing-gown. You might catch cold'. 'I think it's warm enough', I replied. 'Well that's up to you', was her sharp retort. Am I an adult seeking specialist advice in this hospital, or a child who knows nothing of what is good for it?
>
> I felt so frustrated by visiting time that when R came in alone, without my father — due to some misunderstanding — I was unreasonably upset and disappointed. To make matters worse we could not find any private place to sit and talk, and R was clearly uncomfortable, being unable to converse naturally in the small wards filled with guests and patients. The formal salutation by kiss as we prepared to separate on his departure was acutely embarrassing. Yet an unexpected visit from a student shortly before visiting hours were over, was more comfortable, even more pleasurable, because less emotionally loaded. (Firth, 1977, pp.153–4)

☐ What sorts of everyday things could the author no longer carry out inside the hospital?

■ She could not choose when to get out of bed and her rights to wear whatever clothes she might choose were restricted. There was no private place to talk, or to embrace intimately. The ward, in fact, was better suited to relationships with relative strangers.

□ How much of this seems to be for the convenience of staff?

■ Staying in bed and the restriction on type of clothing both seem to fit the bill. The lack of privacy is perhaps more related to hospital architecture and, indirectly, to the amount of money the public is willing to spend on hospitals.

Rosemary Firth concluded that while the hospital may have done something for her physical health, it had the reverse effect on her psychological state. Such effects may be tolerable for twelve days. They are, perhaps, a minor price to be paid for medical treatment. What happens to patients who are confined to the same institution for many years, even perhaps for the rest of their lives? Hospitals themselves may therefore be the source of a further type of iatrogenic disorder, 'institutional neurosis' as it is sometimes called. As a result, long-term institutions, mental hospitals, old people's homes and institutions for the handicapped have all come under severe suspicion in some quarters. Such doubts are nothing new. In the early eighteenth century, Daniel Defoe wrote of those who had to enter madhouses, 'If they are not mad when they go into these cursed houses, they are soon made so by the barbarous usage they there suffer'. The most influential modern statement of this point of view was made by Goffman. He pointed out that mental hospitals, old people's homes, institutions for the handicapped, TB sanatoriums and isolation hospitals all shared certain crucial characteristics with other seemingly very different institutions — prisons, boarding schools, orphanages and monasteries. He noted that in modern society 'the individual tends to sleep, play and work in different places, with different co-participants, under different authorities, and without an overall rational plan'. On the other hand, in what he termed *total institutions* things were different:

The central feature of total institutions can be described as a breakdown of the barriers ordinarily separating these three spheres of life. First, all aspects of life are conducted in the same place and under the same single authority. Second, each phase of the members' daily activity is carried on in the immediate company of a large batch of others, all of whom are treated alike and required to do the same thing together. Third, all phases of the day's activities are tightly scheduled. Finally, the various enforced activities are brought together into a single rational plan purportedly designed to fulfil the official aims of the institution. (Goffman, 1968, pp.5–6)

□ Why do institutions operate in this way?

■ To solve the practical problems of caring for lots of people with few staff. For instance, moving people about in large blocks is a bureaucratic solution by which very large numbers of inmates can be managed by very small numbers of staff, whose main activity is thereby surveillance.

Institutions' rules are commonly justified by an appeal to their official goals: reform, education, religion or, in the case of medical institutions, care and therapy. The fundamental similarities in their operations suggested, at least to Goffman, that these overt aims are often no more than a rationale which conceals a shared bureaucratic method.

In such circumstances, he argued, 'Staff tend to feel superior and righteous. Inmates tend ... to feel inferior, weak, unworthy and guilty'. Staff tend to see patients, prisoners and pupils alike as 'bitter, secretive and untrustworthy', while the inmates gradually undergo 'a series of abasements, degradations, humiliations and profanations of self', as they are transformed into 'objects that can be fed into the administrative machinery of the establishment, to be worked on smoothly by routine operation'.

Goffman's analysis is of course simply a model. It simplifies, abstracts and exaggerates. No institution is completely 'total', completely cut off from the outside world, and institutions also differ from one another in many important ways. Some are relatively small, others are of enormous size — some American mental hospitals in the 1950s had as many as 15 000 patients. Moreover, most staff try to do their best for their patients in what are very difficult circumstances. Nonetheless, Goffman's basic argument still seems plausible. The immense organisational problems in running total institutions may sometimes have severe psychological consequences for the inmates on whose behalf they are run.

Stigma

Now turn to yet a further matter which may crucially affect the sick. We began this chapter with a summary of the ethics of the sick role. In that morality, the well had various duties towards the sick. They owed them sympathy, care and help. How far is this actually the immediate human response to sickness in others? So far we have considered the way other social relationships can affect sick role relationships and seen how many external factors can exert a potentially harmful influence on the sick. We now consider something which seems far more personal and far more elusive — the immediate feelings that sickness conjures up in others. Like the placebo effect, this aspect of sickness is something that is little understood, though its own effects seem powerful enough.

Imagine that you are told that someone you know has been admitted to a mental hospital. You do not know them very well, but you are surprised. You are asked if you would mind visiting them and it is convenient for you to go. Your relationship with the person has always been reasonable in the past and there is no suggestion that this should be a regular visit. You have never been to a mental hospital before.

☐ What emotions, besides surprise, sympathy and a desire to help, might you experience in thinking about this?
■ A great variety of other feelings are possible. You may experience some or all of the following: a fear of hospitals; a fear of the disorder itself (mental disorder conjures up many frightening thoughts); a sense of awkwardness and uncertainty (just how should you behave when talking to someone in these circumstances?); a sense of shock and even, perhaps, a sense of disgust (mental disorder is definitely not a nice thing); a feeling of curiosity (you may be interested in seeing just how they are behaving and what a mental hospital looks like); a sense of shame at feeling all these things; and, finally, a sense of guilt (the thought that you, perhaps, might have had a part in causing the illness).

This complex mixture of thought and emotion does not apply simply to the problems of mental disorder. It can be just as true of physical illnesses and conditions, and is systematically reflected in the behaviour of the well. The memorial service for British troops killed in the Falklands War of 1982 was attended by many men who were injured in the conflict, but not by those who had sustained severe burns — their injuries were considered too shocking for the public to see.

As this suggests, some conditions are considered far more shocking than others — colds inspire a good deal less repulsion than cancers. In some cases, relatively minor things can cause extreme reactions, facial injuries being a classic example. Moreover, the number of conditions that are often thought shocking is large. Besides mental disorder, burns and cancers, there are mental handicap, cerebral palsy, incontinence, Down's syndrome, multiple sclerosis and many others.

The sufferers from many conditions are therefore faced with a complex barrage of reactions, some of which are recounted in the following extract. It is taken from the memoirs of a man whom Goffman, very small himself, described as an 'aggressive dwarf':

There were the thick-skinned ones, who stared like hill people come down to see a travelling show. There

were the paper-peekers, the furtive kind who would withdraw blushing if you caught them at it. There were the pitying ones, whose tongue clickings could almost be heard after they had passed you. But even worse, there were the chatterers, whose every remark might as well have been, 'How do you do, poor boy?' They said it with their manners and their tone of voice. I had a standard defence — a cold stare. Thus anaesthetised against my fellow man, I could contend with the basic problem — getting in and out of the subway alive. (quoted in Goffman, 1968, p.163)

☐ What does this suggest about sympathy?
■ That this too can be handicapping because it marks the recipient out as different, as abnormal, as someone to be pitied.

What the well are reacting to in cases of mental disorder, cancers or severe burns, and what the man who happens to be a dwarf is reacting against, is known by social scientists as *stigma*. Contained within this concept is the notion that all forms of illness, however caused, have the power to spoil the sufferer's social and personal identity. Certain kinds of illness and impairment separate their victims from the rest of humanity, define them, however minimally and temporarily, as abnormal, mark them out as different.

Just how different the sick actually are is another matter. The stigma of illness, however, can mark its sufferers out as fundamentally and essentially different, different in the very core of their being. The 'basic problem' of the dwarf quoted above is not that at all though — given his small height, it's getting in and out of the subway alive. On top of that problem, however, he also has to cope with a barrage of problematic reactions; reactions that are all premised on the assumption that he is fundamentally different. Consider the following remark about a blind person:

His once most ordinary deeds — walking nonchalantly up the street, locating the peas on his plate, lighting a cigarette — are no longer ordinary. He becomes an unusual person. If he performs them with finesse and assurance they excite the same kind of wonderment inspired by a magician who pulls rabbits out of hats. (cited in Goffman, 1968, p.26)

In other words, in addition to the disability imposed by illness or other medical conditions, there is often a social disability created by the assumption that the illness extends far wider than it actually does, crippling the sufferer in any and every aspect of their lives.

Thus the addicted become 'addicts', those with mental disorder are simply 'mad', those who cannot see are just the 'blind'. Instead of being just one part of an individual, usually a small part, their medical condition is seen as the most basic fact about that person, something which underlies every aspect of their life and informs their every action. The stigma grows until it encompasses their entire being — even to the point where we, earlier in this chapter, simply refer to 'the sick' in contrast with 'the well'. This powerful *halo effect* can distort the actions of professional carers quite as much as the behaviour of passers-by. For example, when the American sociologist Robert Scott compared the theories about blindness held during the 1960s by institutions for the blind in three different countries (the UK, the USA and Sweden) he found a striking difference between Sweden and the others. In the USA for example:

> Many experts believe that the loss of vision is a basic blow to self and personality so that deep shock inevitably follows the onset of this condition. Grief and depression also occur; the former because of the loss of basic skills for coping with everyday life, and the latter because of the resulting disorganization of the total personality. A basic goal of rehabilitation is adjustment to blindness. In most expert theories, a blind person is viewed as adjusted only when he has faced and fully accepted that he is blind. (Scott, 1970, p.260)

It was precisely this doctrine that the Swedish institutions had challenged. Blindness there was treated as merely a part of a person's life that could be readily dealt with through appropriate aids. There was also, it should be noted, one further unusual thing about the Swedish institutions for the blind — they were controlled by the blind themselves. They had organised so effectively that they had gained control of all the main organisations that catered for the blind and effected by-laws that prevented any seeing person from holding executive office in such institutions. On their analysis, the sighted, however well-intentioned, could not be trusted to run the affairs of the blind. How far this possibility is open to other groups is uncertain. Not only is it hard for certain groups to run their own affairs — people with severe mental handicap are an obvious example — but there may also be a problem with the way the stigmatised react to stigmatisation.

Thus the problem with stigma is not simply that others stigmatise sufferers from particular conditions, but that the sufferers may see themselves in this way also, may accept the valuation that the wider culture places on them. Some may rebel, like blind people in Sweden or the example of the dwarf with his cold stare, but many others cannot. An article in the Course Reader (Part 6, Section 6.2) by two British sociologists, Sally Macintyre and David Oldman, illustrates the different situations in which sufferers are placed and some of the various ways in which they may react to their condition. Both of the authors suffer from a similar type of migraine, but their social experiences have been very different. You should now read this article.* When you have read it, answer the following question:

☐ In what way may medical theories of both cause and treatment shape the subsequent psychological health of the sufferer?

■ Theories which stress the physical origins of the condition and prescribe physical treatments, such as drugs, allow sufferers to define themselves as 'a basically normal person' who is 'merely a host for occasional physical disturbances'. On this account, the condition is 'a morally neutral matter'. By contrast, theories of migraine that emphasise the role of personality and conflict, and stress the need for major personal change, are far from morally neutral. On changing doctors, Sally Macintyre states, 'I was redefined from a blameless, passive host to an active producer of migraines'. This in itself may possibly be sufficient in some cases to result in serious damage to health. From being simply a migraine sufferer, she went on to become depressed and agoraphobic. Her problems in coping with migraine were, for a time, transformed into a general fear about her capacity to cope with life. For David Oldman, however, his mother had also suffered from migraine and prescribed her own 'physical' forms of treatment — the classic British sick-role treatment of bed, a hot-water bottle and Lucozade. Gender may also be important. Psychological theories may, perhaps, be more readily applied to women.

Mental theories of illness therefore possess an especially stigmatising and polluting power. So too do any of those which stress the importance of individual life-style, of how much we exercise, of what we eat, drink and smoke. All illnesses for which such theories are held may induce blame from some and guilt in those who suffer them. Treatments too may result in such feelings. The depressed woman on a course of drug treatment may feel guilty at her inability to fight off her depression and shame at her dependence on drugs. Yet if sexism and inadequate child-care facilities are major influences on her condition, then to think solely in terms of drug treatment is to 'blame the victim', not the social structures which have powerfully shaped her plight.

---

* Some of the technical vocabulary may be unfamiliar: 'anomic' means to be in a state where a person's actions are not guided by any social norms or rules as to how to behave; 'physicalist' is yet another word for 'biological' as opposed to 'mental'; 'agoraphobia' is a condition whose sufferers fear open spaces, travel, crowds and any situation which they cannot readily leave; 'prophylaxis' means preventive treatment.

The macropolitics of sickness

In moving from the family to the total institution and stigma, we have moved a long way from micropolitics to macropolitics, but there is further to go yet. Look at Figure 13.1, which shows the proportion of conscripts to the American Army who were disqualified from service on medical grounds. It dates from 1968, the height of the American intervention in Vietnam.

□ What might explain the fact that significantly more whites than blacks were exempted from military service on medical grounds?

■ There are three main possibilities. First, blacks might have been significantly fitter than whites. Second, blacks might have been keener to fight than whites and therefore less prone to invent an illness and more likely to conceal one. Third, US Army doctors might have been keener to pass blacks as fit than whites.

The first explanation, that of greater fitness among black conscripts, seems unlikely. In the United States as a whole, the black mortality rate is roughly a third higher than that of whites and mortality is closely linked to morbidity.* Moreover, blacks in the US are poorer than whites and poverty is strongly associated with much higher rates of morbidity and mortality. What about the second explanation, that blacks were more anxious than whites to be drafted into the army: that is, whites were more often malingering? Note that the war was unpopular with many people, but for poor unemployed young blacks it offered the possibility of an escape. Their richer white brethren with jobs may have been far less willing to serve, far more prone to malinger. As for the third explanation, US army doctors, themselves mostly white, might have at least two possible motives for passing blacks as fit more often than whites. On the one hand, they too might have felt that the war offered blacks an opportunity which it did not offer to whites. In these circumstances, they might have examined blacks less thoroughly than whites. On the other hand, they might also have been prejudiced against blacks and more willing to find them fit to fight because fighting was all that blacks were fit for. They may have felt that white lives were more precious. It is striking that the greatest discrepancy between the rates of disqualification occurred in the South of the US, long known as the area of greatest racial prejudice.

We shall return later to the influence of poverty, employment and ethnicity on definitions of illness, but let us consider for a moment the whites who were found unfit. Was this part of a phenomenon of avoiding social duties by

* For a definition of these terms you should refer to *The Health of Nations* (U205, Book III).

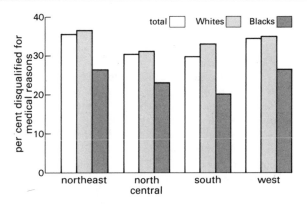

Figure 13.1 Variations in the proportion of conscripts from white or black skinned ethnic groups who were disqualified from service in the American army for medical reasons in different geographic areas of the USA in 1968. (Waitzkin and Waterman, 1973).

feigning or exaggerating illness — malingering? If so, then malingering is not just an individual act, nor simply a sign of weakness, cowardice and bad character. The propensity to malinger is shaped by powerful social and economic forces. Only some can afford it. Equally, successful malingering depends on its acceptance by others. If there were whites who found it easier to avoid service in Vietnam, most likely they did so at least partly because of white doctors' prejudices. Everyone may be a malingerer at times, but some people are allowed to malinger more than others.

Just how common is malingering? One view to which we can turn is that of the British psychiatrist, Richard Asher. Parts of his essay 'Malingering' have been reprinted in the Course Reader (Part 2, Section 2.8). You should now read this and then answer the following questions:

□ What is the difference between malingering, hypochondria and hysteria?

■ It is difficult to distinguish clearly between these conditions, although clear malingering seems to be rare. Whereas the malingerer deliberately imitates illness, merely pretending to be ill, hypochondriacs worry obsessively that they really are ill, so much so, in fact, that they would seemingly almost prefer to be ill. Hysteria is different again. The hysteric actually experiences major physical symptoms such as intense pain and even, in extreme cases, paralysis, all without any observably faulty biology. To the sufferer, however, the illness is no less real, no less unpleasant than if the symptoms were produced by a 'real' biological disease.

□ What can you tell from Asher's account of medical attitudes towards sufferers from extreme forms of these conditions? (Everyone of course, has minor forms of these problems).

■ The tone throughout Asher's article is fairly

jaundiced. Such patients are, for the doctor, familiar and tedious, albeit lucrative to those in private practice. They are also, as in the case of Munchausen's syndrome, a source of detective work.

□ What is Asher's explanation for such conditions?

■ Apart from the general point about human beings being fools (part of a quotation on the matter from the poet Robert Burns), his main explanation is loneliness and a desire to be noticed. Implicitly, he seems to be arguing that some people have so few other rewards in life that the sick role, for all its incapacitating nature, is actually preferable.

Asher is primarily concerned with conditions in which the sick role becomes a way of life. In such circumstances, the charge of malingering seems inappropriate, but what of isolated episodes? Surely all of us go in for malingering on occasions? The following extract is taken from a monthly government report on employment published in 1981. The research which it summarises was undertaken by the Office of Health Economics, a research organisation funded by the British drug industry.

During 1979 the record loss through sickness absences cost the Exchequer nearly £1.5 billion in sickness and invalidity benefits, a 44 per cent increase since the start of the decade. But the OHE [Office of Health Economics] estimates that the real cost to the community was around £5.5 billion in lost production. It compares this figure with Government expenditure in that year of £7.8 billion on the National Health Service and £5.4 billion on housing. The 371 million working days lost in 1979 represent approximately six per cent of potential working days available.

Figures show that sickness was by far the most significant cause of lost working time in 1978/9. It accounted for 40 times as many days as those lost through strikes and 25 times as many lost days as industrial injuries. But Britain's performance appears no worse than that of its partners in the European Community.

New claims for sickness and invalidity benefits have subsequently sustained a general decline. Between March 1978 and 1981 unemployment in Britain increased by 70 per cent. ... The average weekly intake of new claims for sickness or invalidity benefit for the first ten months of 1980/81 was 14 per cent below the corresponding figure for 1979/80 which in turn was 12 per cent less than that for 1978/9.

The OHE's report shows that males currently have an average of 10 days of certified absence each year. The figure contrasts sharply with the 12 days recorded in the mid-fifties. It is also apparent that there has

been a significant increase in the volume of short-term incapacity: in 1978/9, 34 per cent of male's absence lasted for a week compared with 23 per cent in the mid-fifties. ... More trivial ailments such as sprains, strains, nervousness, debility or headaches have become an important cause of non-attendance at work. In 1978/9 nearly 23 million days, or over six per cent, were lost and attributed to those ailments. This was almost five times the number recorded in 1954/5 when they accounted for just 1.7 per cent of overall absence.

At the same time, there has been an increase in the number of very long-term spells of incapacity. These make a significant contribution to the annual total of lost days. It is estimated that approximately 40 per cent of all days of certified absence among the male workforce in 1978/9 were attributable to claimants whose incapacity lasted through the 12 month period. This proportion was 35 per cent just seven years earlier. (*Employment Gazette*, 1981)

□ What are the two main trends that have occurred in sickness absence in the UK since the 1950s?

■ The first trend is the major increase in absence from work due to sickness since the 1950s and the second is the significant decline in such absences since 1979 with the onset of high unemployment.

□ Bearing in mind that there is evidence that unemployment increases morbidity and mortality*, what does this trend suggest about the relationship between claiming sickness benefit and the state of the British economy?

■ That during periods of economic growth people are more willing, or more able, to allow themselves to be sick. This applies to both minor and major complaints. In periods of economic recession and high unemployment, however, the reverse occurs. On the one hand, people may be afraid of losing their jobs or less able to tolerate the loss of income. On the other, employers may feel that they no longer need to employ the half-fit or those with recurrent illness or absences.

The Office of Health Economics' figures on the loss of total production as a result of sickness absence need to be taken with a pinch of salt — these are purely notional calculations. Nonetheless, sickness does seem to be a major cost to society as well as to the individual. Is the decline in sickness absenteeism from 1979–81 a sign that previously people were malingering more, or is the explanation really the other way round — is the low rate of sickness absence from work in the 1950s an indication of just how hard

* This is discussed in *The Health of Nations* (U205, Book III).

pressed the work-force generally was then? Consider the following quotation. It is from a 66 year-old man with lung cancer. He had worked most of his life as a miner, but had taken a job in a munitions factory for the last few years before retirement:

> I could feel my chest getting tight, so, of course, I thought it was a cold on the chest, having been so fit, and of course it got worse and worse ... I had not had it like this before. Oh, I said, it will pass and I let it go, but it got acute and that was about last December, but even then I wouldn't go to the doctor's. Eventually I didn't bother and I didn't go to see any doctor right up until I retired 17th June ... It was a hard struggle, but I had to work up to my notice on the 17th June for my gratuity and, of course, up to that year, if I finished I would have full gratuity for the years I have been in [the] colliery ... if I went to see the doctor he would definitely put me on the sick and that would be knocked off my gratuity. I didn't go because of that you see. I thought I would stick it out ... As I got to retirement age, I thought the gratuity would be very useful ... I hadn't saved anything for my old age, you see — it was the biggest mistake of my life doing that. (Murcott, 1971)

☐ What does this suggest about failure to consult early with cancer?
■ That it may sometimes result from powerful economic pressures.

Of course, some might still argue that it was all this man's fault anyway — he shouldn't have smoked, he should have saved money for his old age. Personal factors do have their role, but it is hard to see how this man is personally responsible for the state of the coal-mining industry, or the nature of his pension, or for the state of the national economy.

As with the young men in the USA who were or were not passed as fit to fight, depending on their skin colour, so it is with the lung cancer victim above. Definitions of sickness or fitness are imposed upon the individual as a consequence of larger social, economic and political forces.

The politicisation of psychiatry

All aspects of sickness may, as we have seen, be the terrain of political as well as medical questions. Nowhere, however, is this more apparent than in psychiatry. The power of medicine and the medical model is such that there is always likely to be a temptation, indeed, a likelihood, to use that power for the maintenance of the social institutions which sponsor it. Within this context, the definition of a person's problem as emerging from a crisis of their own

mind and brain becomes only too tempting to defenders of the status quo. By contrast, opponents of the present social order may be tempted to define away individual problems as purely socially constructed.

The point is, psychiatry is often simultaneously a means of liberation, of helping people understand the nature of their problems and thereby arming them in the struggle to transform their lives, and a means of control. This use of psychiatry thus runs the danger of becoming a subtle and apparently humane way of *blaming the victim*. If depression is caused by disordered neurotransmitters, the plight of working-class mothers in Camberwell cannot be blamed on job insecurity, high rise buildings, inadequate child-care facilities or the institutionalised sexism of society. That such 'blaming the victim' does occur is suggested by the possibility that doctors, when consulted about a variety of symptoms, may offer a psychiatric rather than a physical diagnosis more frequently to women than they do to men. Dishing out the Valium is one response to the difficulty of such consultations. Hence the drug is used as a way of masking the 'real problem', making life bearable for the person in an otherwise unbearable situation. The offer of a psychoactive drug may seem the only solution for the patient who is trapped in a particular situation and for the doctor who can offer no other way out of it. If this analysis seems stark in the context of our own society, it may be easier to see in another. Consider the case of the Soviet Union, for instance.

In the early 1970s, rumours of a wave of political dissidence among the Soviet intelligentsia, particularly scientists, began to reach the ears of Western journalists. The dissidents were raising a variety of issues: their desire for greater freedom to travel and make contact with scientists abroad; their concern over the direction of Soviet internal and foreign policy; and what were later to become known as 'human-rights' issues. The response of the Soviet state to these challenges was only in the last instance one of direct political or administrative repression. More frequently, individual protestors were harassed, brought in for psychiatric investigation, diagnosed as being mentally disturbed (typically, schizophrenic) and then incarcerated in psychiatric hospitals. A typical case was that of the biochemist Zhores Medvedev, who has written books discussing the weaknesses of Soviet science and the censorship system. In 1974 Medvedev was subjected to involuntary psychiatric examination, diagnosed as suffering from 'schizophrenia without symptoms' and put in hospital. In hospital, Medvedev was 'threatened' with the use of psychoactive drugs and only pressure from inside and outside the Soviet Union, and the energetic intervention of his brother Roy, resulted in his release after a few weeks and subsequent exile in the UK. (This is discussed in Medvedev and Medvedev, 1974.)

The protests concerning this plainly 'political' use of psychiatry among concerned journalists and academics in the West were strong and there was much pressure on the World Psychiatric Association to censure Soviet psychiatry (it eventually passed an appropriate resolution in 1977) and to boycott Soviet–organised meetings. The Association showed obvious reluctance to take up a position, although it seemed clear in this and similar cases that the role of psychiatry was to describe a *political* question in medical terms and, by doing so, to turn the essentially political nature of the individual's protest into a non-political question of his or her state of health. (Block and Reddaway, 1977)

☐ How do you think an orthodox Soviet psychiatrist might explain the hospitalisation of Medvedev?
■ They might (and did) argue that as the Soviet Union is a benevolent and free society, to criticise it and to communicate this criticism to external enemies of the state must indicate mental instability or incipient mental disorder in a person so obviously 'out of joint' with society.

From the point of view of the Soviet authorities it was not so much that the protestors were being punished for their protest, although the protestors themselves and many people outside the Soviet Union clearly believed they were. Rather, the Soviet State might be seen as being concerned to *invalidate* a social and political protest by declaring the protestors to be *invalids*, sick, in need of care and protection to cure them of their delusions. The forensic and other psychiatrists who were asked to diagnose the 'disease' of the Soviet protestors were using criteria which were probably not so far different from those used by their counterparts in the West. By such criteria one way of looking at Medvedev is that he was in need of hospital treatment, just as were Rosenhan's pseudo-patients described in Chapter 9. How does Medvedev's book writing differ from the pseudo–patients' 'compulsive note-taking'?

Do cases like that of Medvedev occur in Britain as well? Consider the following report about a young black man, Cirus Noor, who had been charged with attempted arson against a London police station. His action, so he said, was a protest against what he considered to be the murder by police officers of another black man, Colin Roach:

The authorities are now trying to suggest that Noor is mentally disturbed. Home Office spokesman Ian Porter has made 'off the record' remarks to inquiring journalists to the effect that Noor was both violent and mentally disturbed. Noor says he was being held in the hospital wing, daily visited by psychiatrists and told that if he didn't take his 'treatment' he would be

'sectioned' — classified as mentally disturbed and put in a psychiatric institution.

It is not unusual for the Home Office to equate protest by young black prisoners with insanity. Richard 'Cartoon' Campbell died in Ashford Remand Centre in 1980 after being classified as mentally disturbed — although he was examined by an independent psychiatrist who found him 'lucid' and without any sign of mental illness.

Noor, who was awaiting trial at the time of the incident, was acquitted at the Old Bailey last week on four charges of attempted arson at Bethnal Green police station. He was convicted on two lesser charges of possession of an offensive weapon and was sentenced to two years in prison.

In court he was coherent and rational. He claimed that he had the offensive weapon — milk bottles filled with paraffin — as a protest to draw attention to the death of Colin Roach. (O'Halloran, 1983)

☐ Does this account remind you of a description you have read earlier in this book?
■ Remember the case of Calvin Johnson in Chapter 6.

There seems little doubt about the accuracy of the allegations against Soviet prison psychiatry, for the psychiatrists themselves have admitted their actions, although they argued in their defence that political dissidence is a sign of insanity. What of the charges against British prison psychiatry? Prison psychiatrists would reject the charge that they are behaving in a similar way to their Soviet counterparts, yet it is striking that the prescription of sedatives, tranquillisers and other psychoactive drugs is actually far *lower* in British prisons for the psychiatrically disturbed, such as Grendon, than it is in some general prisons such as Brixton and Holloway. In 1979, the average prescription rate for psychoactive drugs at Grendon was 11 doses per inmate per year, in Brixton it was 229, in Parkhurst 338 and in the women's prison Holloway an astronomic 941 doses per inmate per year (Owen, 1981).

☐ How might an opponent of the use of drugs in prison explain this phenomenon?
■ Drugs are being used as a sort of 'chemical straight jacket' to sedate and contain recalcitrant prisoners.
☐ How might a supporter of the use of the drugs defend their use?
■ Conditions in prison are so distressing for the inmates that the drugs are a way of helping them sustain their morale.

It is interesting that ex-prisoners themselves, discussing their experience of drugs in prison, have tended to argue both these positions. In any event, the implications are very disturbing. If prison is a microcosm of the world, the world is either full of people so distressed that their minds need to be continually adjusted by psychoactive agents, or the world is so distressing that the use of mind-adjusting agents, even to the point of addiction, becomes necessary for self-preservation. Either argument throws a particular responsibility on psychiatrists who have to dispense judgements about a person's psychic state and prescriptions for drugs. It is this question of responsibility that formed the focus of the arguments of the 'anti-psychiatry' and radical psychiatry movements of the 1960s and 1970s. If the Russian psychiatrists are seen as agents of social control, how many Western psychiatrists avoid confronting a similar dilemma?

None of this, of course, is intended to 'justify' in any way the actions of the Soviet authorities. What it suggests instead is that we can see in the action of the Soviet state a disturbing mirror reflection of a medicalising tendency, a type of biological determinism, that is also present in Western society. Seeing it thus so distorted helps us understand some of the problems of the borderline between therapy and social control. It is to arguments about the scale of this medicalisation that we now turn.

Medicalisation

We noted earlier that the sick role was capable of being imported into every aspect of social life — every action, every conversation could be judged in these terms, even greetings, such as 'how are you', might carry subtle medical implications. Moreover, as in the case of British prisons and Soviet dissidents, there have been persistent allegations that the use of medicine was being extended in illegitimate ways; politically motivated acts were transformed into psychiatric conditions.

Some writers, however, have gone far beyond these particular claims. They argue that the very success of modern scientific medicine, its development of powerful techniques coupled with the huge growth in its size, means that all areas of life are becoming *medicalised*. What was once merely potential is now actual. Every aspect of human behaviour, so they argue, is now the subject of medical investigation and medical control. Medicine on this account, is a disease — a disease that threatens, like bubonic plague, a whole society.

To illustrate this ultimate form of iatrogenesis, we can consider a disease state that arose in the US over the period of the 1960s and 1970s. It affects children, normally aged between 9 and 14, and is diagnosed by psychiatrists as 'hyperkinesis' or 'minimal brain dysfunction' (MBD), sometimes now classified as 'attention disorder.' The diagnosis is typically made of children who have been referred by their teacher at school for psychiatric examination because they are poor learners or disruptive in class. The diagnostic signs for minimal brain dysfunction may include any of the following: overactivity, unusual energy, inability to sit still in the classroom and at mealtimes, talking out of turn in the class, disrupting the class, being easily distracted, not getting work done at school, day-dreaming in the classroom, ignoring teachers and parents when they try to give directions, unable to take part in card games, being impulsive, unable to save money, saying tactless things and blurting out secrets, being cheeky to teachers, showing off. The diagnosis is more often applied to boys than girls and is much more frequent in the US than in the UK. There are no 'biological' signs of brain abnormalities, despite the name 'minimal brain dysfunction'. Up to 600 000 American school children are claimed to be suffering from the disorder (Schrag and Divoky, 1975) and children so diagnosed are treated by giving them an amphetamine-related drug, Ritalin. Ritalin is a powerful drug. Its use may result in loss of appetite, sleeplessness, irritability and abdominal pain and it can interfere with normal growth in youngsters. It also sedates them and makes them less of a nuisance in class, whatever effect it may have on their learning ability. Indeed, some of the proponents of the use of Ritalin have even claimed that in minimal brain dysfunction there is a disease of hypo-amphetaminosis: that is, too little amphetamine in the brain. This is a classical example of what was described in Chapter 7 as 'pharmacological logic', detecting the existence of a disease on the basis of the medical treatments of drugs that affect it (this is discussed in detail by Rose, Lewontin and Kamin, 1984). According to the American psychiatrist, Paul Wender, children under the drug often begin to behave in a manner consistent with their parents formerly unheeded 'oughts' and 'shoulds'. 'One bright 8 year-old referred to d-amphetamine as his "magic pills which make me a good boy and make everybody like me"'! The child turns from a 'whirling dervish' into being 'quiet, compliant' and with an 'improved class behaviour, group participation and attitudes to authority under medication' (Wender, 1971).

Is it appropriate to assume that, because a child does not get on with his teachers and his behaviour is perhaps unacceptable even to his parents, he is therefore sick? Some might argue that there is hardly a child who could not be fitted into such a list of symptoms. In a study cited by the New York child psychiatrist, Eli Messinger (1978), teachers were asked to rate the behaviour of their kindergarten pupils. Forty-nine per cent of boys showed 'restlessness', 48 per cent 'distractibility', 46 per cent 'disruptiveness', 43 per cent 'inattentiveness'. Are all these potential or actual sufferers from minimal brain dysfunction?

☐ Minimal brain dysfunction is not diagnosed to

anything like the same extent in Britain as in America. How else might British teachers or educational psychologists explain the type of behaviour that leads to this diagnosis?

■ They might define children as plain naughty, to be disciplined rather than drugged. They might define them simply as suffering from 'behaviour disorder' or as suffering from the consequences of being 'educationally subnormal'. You may be aware of the use of these terms in British schools.

This British response may reflect a cultural difference between approaches to school discipline and learning. It may reflect different concepts of normality — perhaps inattentiveness to teachers is regarded as part of the 'normal' range of a child's behaviour in Britain. The British may choose to punish their 'naughty' children, or segregate them in special schools, rather than doctor them. 'Bad' rather than 'mad' may reflect ideas of original sin rather than brain dysfunction, yet it may still be a way of 'blaming the victim'. Examples such as this have led some to fear that biochemistry might be used to control all aspects of human behaviour. Such fears are not confined to the potential use of the natural sciences; social science too may be used to the same effect. *Birth to Old Age: Health in Transition* (Book V) described the increasing use of social science by medicine to survey entire populations. David Armstrong, a doctor and a sociologist, concluded a recent survey of the history of this process with the remarks:

> Sociology made its principal contribution in the post-war world when its mastery of survey techniques made it of value to a medical gaze intent on exploring the surveillance possibilities of this newly discovered technology. Sociologists, in close alliance with medicine opened up areas of the health experiences of 'ordinary' people through survey of health attitudes, of illness behaviour, of drug taking and of symptom prevalence. More recently, as the medical gaze has focused on individual idiosyncracies, personal meanings and subjectivity, sociology too has turned its attention to fresh possibilities. (Armstrong, 1983, p.114)

☐ What does this suggest about the stress on personal experience that has been a central theme of this book?

■ It raises the possibility that this approach, far from providing a liberation from an exclusively biological emphasis, may in fact offer further means for medicalisation as doctors and their allies discover yet more about human beings.

The supporters of the medicalisation thesis differ over who principally benefits. For some, such as Ivan Illich, a Latin American theologian, it is merely one instance of the rise to power in social life of the 'experts'. To others, such as the Baltimore-based doctor, Vincente Navarro, doctors and other such experts are merely the agents of a far more powerful force, the modern state, and the ruling class which controls the state. Not everyone would accept Illich's or Navarro's claim and not everyone would regard medicalisation, if it is occurring, as a threat to human liberty. Others argue that demedicalisation as well as medicalisation is taking place and would point to the Italian community approach to the mentally disordered as an example of this.

Pressures both to medicalise and to demedicalise human life come from all quarters, not just from experts, states or ruling elites. Individuals and organisations, families and economies, all mould the sick role in their own fashion. Moreover, as we have seen throughout this book, although there is much that we do know about diseases, there is much that we do not know and much that seems likely to remain a subject for debate. It is hard to believe, for instance, that the precise status of addictions or mental disorder will one day be settled for ever. Our explanations and treatments may continue to improve, but health and disease will always offer plenty of scope for uncertainty and plenty of room for exploitation by those with an interest in the matter — and in this particular matter, everyone has an interest.

The medicalisation and demedicalisation of disability are discussed further in 'Disability: whose handicap?' in the Course Reader (Part 6, Section 6.3) and in an audiotape sequence, *Disability and Sickness*. Read the article first and then listen to the tape — it provides a powerful conclusion to this chapter and to the book.

Objectives for Chapter 13

When you have studied this chapter, you should be able to:

13.1 Describe the sick role and its determinants.

13.2 Describe the various forces that can shape the actual use of the sick role — individual, familial, group (e.g. ethnicity and gender), organisational, political and economic — and discuss why they have this power and the manner in which they operate.

13.3 Discuss reasons why some of the ways the sick role is applied may actually increase illness, including stigma and the practical and emotional problems that the sick can present for the well.

13.4 Discuss the notions of medicalisation, biological determinism and 'blaming the victim' and consider the extent to which these phenomena occur in modern industrialised societies.

Questions for Chapter 13

First read the following quotation which is taken from an analysis of the special characteristics of US Army psychiatry by the American sociologist, Arlene Daniels:

In World War I, when men broke down with' hysterical or psychiatric symptoms considered 'illness', they were evacuated to hospitals in the interior as medically, that is psychiatrically ill. Others then became 'ill' in the same manner. A contagion of psychiatric symptoms would often decimate the ranks of a unit. These cases were never able to return to active duty . . . .

By World War II, however, American Army psychiatrists had a new doctrine.

. . . It was argued that evacuating a man with a mental illness label might make a permanent neurotic cripple of him by 'fixing' the temporary symptoms. 'Fixing' occurred when the expression of symptoms was rewarded by removal from the stress situation . . . In addition, a man may be injured by guilt and remorse feelings at leaving his comrades in those difficulties from which he has escaped through an ambiguous 'mental breakdown'.

These . . . ideas were conceptualised as the theory . . . known as 'combat psychiatry'. . . . [through combat psychiatry] psychiatrists were able to reduce drastically the numbers of soldiers incapacitated by 'combat exhaustion' [or 'shell shock' — the World War I term]. When soldiers exhibited symptoms of combat exhaustion, psychiatrists interviewed the officers and buddies of the victim in order to discover the circumstances surrounding the breakdown. They minimised the seriousness of the symptoms to the man whenever possible in order to prevent him as well as others from defining the problem as one of mental illness. When men were screaming, weeping, vomiting, hallucinating, or engaging in other forms of extreme or bizarre behaviour, they were 'supported' rather than 'treated'. They were told that they had experienced a normal 'stress reaction'. They were offered sedatives on the spot and told that within twenty-four to forty-eight hours of sleep, rest, quiet, hot food, and other such comforts, they would be all right. They were assured that they could return to performing their duties without fear of 'going crazy'.

The success of this treatment procedure was that it enabled many 'casualities' to return to the field. Unfortunately . . . it is not known what percentage of those declared in a state of remission (symptom-free) were able to function effectively upon return to combat. Comparisons of survival rates for soldiers who have and who have not been treated for combat exhaustion and returned to duty have never for example been made. (Daniels, 1972, pp.149–50)

1 (*Objective 13.1*) In what ways does Arlene Daniels' account illustrate Parson's analysis of the determinants of the sick role?

2 (*Objective 13.2*) List ways in which this account illustrates the ambiguity of mental disorder.

3 (*Objective 13.2*) Just who was the client of the US Army psychiatrists — the troops themselves or someone else (the Army, the US government, or the American people)?

4 (*Objective 13.3*) How does the doctrine of 'combat psychiatry' resemble the other American doctrine of 'interactionism'?

5 (*Objective 13.4*) Is the change in treatment of soldiers with psychotic symptoms between the two world wars an example of medicalisation or demedicalisation?

References and further reading

References

AITKEN-SWAN, J. and EASSON, E.C. (1959) Reactions of cancer patients on being told their diagnosis, *British Medical Journal*, 5124, pp. 779–83.

ALDERSON, MICHAEL (ed.) (1982) *The Prevention of Cancer*, Edward Arnold.

ARMSTRONG, D. (1983) *Political Anatomy of the Body: Medical Knowledge in Britain in the Twentieth Century*, Cambridge University Press.

BALINT, MICHAEL (1968) (2nd edn) *The Doctor, His Patient and the Illness*, Pitman.

BARSKY, ARTHUR, J. and KLERMAN, GERALD, L. (1983) Overview: hyponchondriasis, bodily complaints and somatic style, *American Journal of Psychiatry*, 140:3, pp. 273–83.

BLOCK, S. and REDDAWAY, P. (1977) *Russia's Political Hospitals: Abuse of Psychiatry in the Soviet Union*, Gollancz.

BRISTOL CANCER HELP CENTRE (1983) *Cancer Help Centre*, BCHC. Booklet sent to people requesting preliminary information.

BROHN, PENNY (1983) quoted in, The will to live, *Radio Times*, 12–18 March 1983, p. 10.

BROWN, G.M., MONCK, E.M., CARSTAIRS, G.M. and WING, J.K. (1962) Influence of family life on the course of schizophrenic illness, *British Journal of Preventive and Social Medicine*, 16, pp. 55–68.

BUNGAY, G.T., VESSEY, M.P. and MCPHERSON, K. (1980) Study of symptoms in middle life, *British Medical Journal*, July 19, 281, pp. 181–3.

BURKITT, DENNIS, P. (1977) The aetiology of appendicitis, *British Journal of Surgery*, vol. 58, no. 9, pp. 695–9.

BURROUGHS, WILLIAM (1969) *Junkie*, New English Library.

CAIRNS, JOHN and BOYLE, PETER (1983) Cancer chemotherapy, *Science*, 220, pp. 252–4.

CANCER RESEARCH CAMPAIGN (1982) *Trends in Cancer Survival in Great Britain: Cases Registered between 1960 and 1974*, Cancer Research Campaign.

CARROLL, K.K. (1975) Experimental evidence of dietary factors and hormone-dependent cancers, *Cancer Research*, 35, pp. 3374–83.

CARTLEDGE, SUE (1983) An approach to death, *Spare Rib*, November, no. 136, pp. 6–8 and 34.

CHAMBERLAIN, JOCELYN (1983) Screening for cancer, *Community Medicine*, 5, pp. 283–6.

COCHRANE, R. (1977) Mental illness in immigrants to England and Wales: an analysis of hospital admissions, *Social Psychiatry*, 12, pp. 25–35.

CREED, FRANCIS (1981) Life events and appendicectomy, *Lancet*, vol. 27, June, pp. 1381–5.

CURLING, GAY (1981) Asymptomatic breast screening, *Nursing*, November 1981, pp. 1348–51.

CURRIE, G.A. (1983) personal communication.

DANIELS, A. (1972) Military psychiatry: the emergence of a sub-speciality, in FREIDSON, E. and CORBER, J., *Medical Men and Their Work*, Chicago, Aldine, pp. 145–62.

DE QUINCEY, THOMAS (1821) *Confessions of an English Opium Eater* (1978 edition), Penguin Books.

DISEASES AND REMEDIES: A CONCISE SURVEY OF THE MOST MODERN METHODS OF MEDICINE (1898) Published at the office of The Chemist and Druggist, London.

DOHRENWEND, B.P. *et al.* (1980) *Mental Illness in the United States: Epidemiological Estimates*, New York, Praeger.

DOLL, RICHARD. (1980) The epidemiology of cancer, *Cancer*, 45, pp. 2475–85.

DOLL, RICHARD and PETO, RICHARD (1976) Mortality in relation to smoking: 20 years' observation on male British doctors, *British Medical Journal*, 2, pp. 1525–36.

DOLL, RICHARD and PETO, RICHARD. (1981) *The Causes of Cancer*, Oxford University Press.

DOYAL, LESLEY *et al.* (1983) *Cancer in Britain: The Politics of Prevention*, Pluto Press.

Drug Link (1980) vol. 14, no. 1.

EDWARDS, G. and ARIF, A. (1980) *Drug Problems in the*

Sociocultural Context, World Health Organization.

ELLMAN, RUTH and CHAMBERLAIN, JOCELYN (1983) Improving the effectiveness of cervical cancer screening. Paper presented to the *Society for Social Medicine Conference,* Sheffield, September 1983.

Employment Gazette (1981) Employment brief: OHE report on absence, September 1981, p. 379.

EPSTEIN, SAMUEL (1978) *The Politics of Cancer,* Sierra Club Books (hardback). An expanded paperback version was published by Anchor/Doubleday Press in 1979.

FARIS, R.E.L. and DUNHAM, H.W. (1939) *Mental Disorders in Urban Areas,* Chicago, Hafner.

FIRTH, R. (1977) Routines in a tropical diseases hospital, in DAVIS, A. and HOROBIN, G. (eds) *Medical Encounters,* Croom-Helm, pp. 143–58.

FITZPATRICK, R.M. and HOPKINS, A.P. (1981) Patients' satisfaction with communication in neurological outpatient clinics, *Journal of Psychosomatic Research,* vol. 25, no. 5, pp. 329–34.

FOUCAULT, MICHEL (1971) *Madness and. Civilization,* Tavistock Publications.

FREI III, EMIL (1982) The national cancer chemotherapy program, *Science,* 217, pp. 600–6. An edited version is reprinted in BLACK, NICK *et al.* (eds) (1984) *Health and Disease: A Reader,* The Open University Press.

GABE, JONATHAN and LIPSHITZ-PHILLIPS, SUSAN (1982) *Sociology of Health and Illness,* vol. 4, pp. 203–4.

GARDNER, H. (1977) *The Shattered Mind: Reason After Brain Damage,* Routledge Kegan Paul.

GENERAL MUNICIPAL BOILERMAKERS AND ALLIED TRADES UNIONS (1984) Cancer and work: guidelines for workers taking collective action over health hazards, in BLACK, NICK *et al.* (eds) *Health and Disease: A Reader* (1984) The Open University Press.

GLATT, MAX (1974) *A Guide to Addiction and its Treatment,* Lancaster, Medical and Technical Publishing, pp. 15–46.

GOFFMAN, E. (1968) *Stigma,* Penguin Books.

GOFFMAN, E. (1968) *Asylums,* Penguin Books.

GOLDBERG, D. and HUXLEY, P. (1980) *Mental Illness in the Community,* Tavistock Press.

GOLDIE, LAWRENCE (1982) The ethics of telling the patient, *Journal of Medical Ethics,* 7, pp. 128–33.

GROVE, J.L., BUTLER, P. and MILLAC, P.A.H. (1980) The effect of a visit to a neurological clinic upon patients with tension headache, *Practitioner,* 224, pp. 195–6.

HALDANE, J.B.S. (1964) Cancer's a funny thing, *The New Statesman,* 21 February 1964.

HELMAN, C. (1981) Tonic, fuel and food: social and symbolic aspects of the long-term use of psychotropic drugs, *Social Science and Medicine,* 15B, pp. 521–33.

HUXLEY, ALDOUS (1959) *The Doors of Perception,* Penguin Books.

JACKSON, J. (1968) The adjustment of the family to the crisis of alcoholism, in RUBINGTON, E. and WEINBERG, M. (eds) *Deviance: The Interactionist Perspective,* New York, Macmillan, pp. 50–66.

JOHNSTONE, E.C. *et al.* (1980) The Northwick Park electroconvulsive therapy trial, *Lancet,* 8208–8209, pp. 1317–20.

KALACHE, ALEX (1981) Risk factors for breast cancer: a tabular summary of the epidemiological data, *British Journal of Surgery,* 68, pp. 797–800.

KETY, S.S. (1978) Hereditary and environment, in SHERSHOW, T.C. (ed.) *Schizophrenia: Science and Practice,* Harvard University Press.

KNOPF, ANDREA (1974) *Cancer: Changes in Opinion after Seven Years of Public Education in Lancaster,* Manchester Regional Committee on Cancer.

KORAN, LORRIN, M. (1975) The reliability of clinical methods, data and judgments (Part 1 and 2), *New England Journal of Medicine,* 293, 13 and 14, pp. 642–6 and 695–701.

KRAMER, J.F. and CAMERON, D.C. (1975) *Manual on Drug Dependence,* World Health Organization.

LAING, R.D. (1967) *The Politics of Experience and the Bird of Paradise,* Penguin Books.

LEFF, J. *et al.* (1982) A controlled trial of social intervention in the families of schizophrenic patients, *British Journal of Psychiatry,* 141, pp. 121–34.

LEWIS, I. (1979) The grumbling appendix (letter), *British Medical Journal,* 1, September, p. 552.

LICHTNER, SIGRID and PFLANZ, MANFRED (1971) Appendectomy in the Federal Republic of Germany, *Medical Care,* IX, 4, pp. 311–30.

LIDZ, T. and BLATT, S. (1983) Critique of the Danish-American studies of the biological and adoptive relatives of adoptees who become schizophrenic, *American Journal of Psychiatry,* 140, pp. 426–31.

LITTLEWOOD, R. and LIPSEDGE, M. (1982) *Aliens and Alienists,* Penguin Books.

MACBETH, R.G. (1965) Malignant disease of the paranasal sinuses, *Journal of Laryngology and Otology,* 79, pp. 592–612.

MACFARLANE, ROBERT (1934) Headache, in LANE, Sir W. ARBUTHNOT (ed.) *The Hygiene of Life and Safer Motherhood,* British Books.

MAGUIRE, PETER *et al.* (1980) Effect of counselling on the psychiatric morbidity associated with mastectomy, *British Medical Journal,* 281, pp. 1454–6.

MEARES, AINSLIE (1982) Stress, meditation and the regression of cancer, *Practitioner*, 226, pp. 1607–9.

MEDICAL RESEARCH COUNCIL (1983) *Annual Report 1982–83,* MRC.

MEDVEDEV, Z. and MEDVEDEV, R. (1971) *A Question of Madness,* Macmillan.

MESSINGER, E. (1978) Minimal brain dysfunction, *Health Pac Bulletin,* 67, pp. 10–21.

MEYEROWITZ, B. *et al.* (1978) Psychological aspects of adjuvant chemotherapy for breast cancer, *Proceedings of the American Association for Cancer Research,* 19, p. 359.

MURCOTT, A. (1971) unpublished.

NAIRNE, K. and SMITH, G. (1984) *Dealing with Depression,* London, The Women's Press.

OATLEY, K. (1984) Depression: crisis without alternatives, *New Scientist,* 7 June 1984, pp. 29–31.

OFFICE OF HEALTH ECONOMICS (1981) *Alcohol* (paper no. 70), OHE.

OFFICE OF HEALTH ECONOMICS (1983) *The Future for Pharmaceuticals,* OHE.

OFFICE OF POPULATION CENSUSES AND SURVEYS (1980) *Cancer Statistics: Survival 1971–73 Registrations, England and Wales,* London, HMSO.

O'HALLORAN, T. (1983) Screws turned on prisoners, *New Statesman,* 9 December 1983, p. 5.

OPEN UNIVERSITY (1981) SD286 *Biology, Brain and Behaviour,* Module D2, *Minds, Brains and Conciousness,* Module D3, *Madness, Sanity, Therapy and Control,* The Open University Press.

OSMOND, C., GARDNER, M.J., ACHESON, E.D. and ADELSTEIN, A.M. (1983) *Trends in Cancer Mortality Analysis by Period of Birth and Death 1951–80,* London, HMSO.

OWEN, T. (1981) *The Abolitionist,* 7, pp. 3–6.

PARSONS, J.A., WEBSTER, J.H. and DOWD, J.E. (1961) Evaluation of the placebo effect in the treatment of radiation sickness, *Acta Radiologica,* 56, pp. 129–40.

PETO, RICHARD (1983) *The Guardian,* 10 November 1983.

PRINGLE, JOHN (1972) *Mind and Mental Health Magazine,* Spring issue.

RANG, E.H., FAIRBAIRN, A.S. and ACHESON, E.D. (1970) An enquiry into the incidence and prognosis of undiagnosed abdominal pain, *British Journal of Social and Preventive Medicine,* vol. 24, no. 1, pp. 47–51.

ROBINSON, JEAN (1982) Occupational risks of husbands and wives and possible preventative strategies, in *Preclinical Neoplasia of the Cervix, Proceedings of the Ninth Study Group of the Royal College of Obstetricians,* London, Royal College of Obstetricians, pp. 11–27.

ROSE, STEVEN (1982) From causations to translations: a dielectical solution to a reductionist enigma, in ROSE, STEVEN (ed.) *Towards a Liberatory Biology,* Allison and Busby, pp. 10–25.

ROSE, S., LEWONTIN, R.C. and KAMIN, L.J. (1984) *Not in Our Genes,* Penguin Books.

ROSENHAN, DAVID (1973) On being sane in insane places, *Science,* 179, pp. 250–8.

ROSENTHAL, D. and KETY, S. (eds) (1968) *The Transmission of Schizophrenia,* Pergamon Press.

ROSSER, JANE and MAGUIRE, PETER (1982) Dilemmas in general practice: the care of cancer patients, *Social Science and Medicine,* 16, pp. 315–22.

ROYAL COLLEGE OF PHYSICIANS (1977) *Smoking or Health,* Pitman Medical.

ROYAL COLLEGE OF PHYSICIANS (1983) *Health or Smoking?* Pitman Medical.

SABISTON, D.C. (ed.) (1981) *The Davis-Christopher Textbook of Surgery,* (12th edition), Philadelphia, Saunden.

SEDGWICK, P. (1982) *Psychopolitics,* Pluto.

SCHRAG, P. and DIVOKY, D. (1975) *The Myth of the Hyper-Active Child and Other Means of Child Control,* New York, Pantheon.

SCOTT, R. (1970) The construction of conceptions of stigma by professional experts, in DOUGLAS, J. (ed.) *Deviance and Respectability,* New York, Basic Books, pp. 255–90.

SEAL, ANDREW (1981) Appendicitis: a historical review, *Canadian Journal of Surgery,* 24, pp. 427–33.

SHEPHERD, MICHAEL and CLARE, ANTHONY (1981) (2nd edition), *Psychiatric Illness in General Practice,* Oxford University Press.

SIMONTON, O. CARL, MATTHEWS-SIMONTON, STEPHANIE and CREIGHTON, JAMES (1978) *Getting Well Again,* Los Angeles, J.P. Tarcher Inc.

SONTAG, SUSAN (1983) *Illness as Metaphor,* Penguin.

STIMSON, GERRY and OPPENHEIMER, EDNA (1982) *Heroin Addiction,* Tavistock Publications.

SZASZ, THOMAS (1977) *The Manufacture of Madness,* Harper and Row.

THORLEY, ANTHONY (1981) Long-term studies of drug dependence, in EDWARDS, G. and BUSCH, C. (eds) *Drug Problems in Britain: A Review of the Year,* Academic Press, pp. 117–69.

WAITZKIN, H. and WATERMAN, B. (1973) *The Exploitation of the Sick Role in Capitalist Society,* New Jersey, Prentice-Hall.

WENDER, P.H. (1971) *Minimal Brain Dysfunction in Children,* New York, Wiley.

WEST, E.D. (1981) Electric convulsion therapy in depression,

British Medical Journal, 282, pp. 355–7.

WORLD HEALTH ORGANIZATION (1973) *Schizophrenia: An International Pilot Study*, WHO.

ZAKELJ, MAJA PRIMIC, FRASER, PATRICIA and INSKIP, HAZEL (1984) Cervical cancer and husband's occupation, *Lancet*, March 3 1984, p. 510.

Further reading

Chapter 2

FITSPATRICK, RAY *et al.* (1984) *The Experience of Illness*, Tavistock Publications.
This book reviews the growing body of evidence about the crucial importance of pyschosocial factors in understanding the experience of illness — how people interpret and respond to symptoms and how social and psychological factors influence treatment of particular diseases.

Chapters 3–5

CURRIE, GRAHAM and CURRIE, ANGELA (1982) *Cancer: The Biology of Malignant Disease*, Edward Arnold.
A concise, well-organised account for readers with some knowledge of biology. It stops short of discussing oncogenes.

DOLL, RICHARD and PETO, RICHARD (1981) *The Causes of Cancer*, Oxford University Press.
The classic over-all view of what is known and not known about cancer causation, from two of the world's most distinguished cancer epidemiologists.

GYLLENSKÖLD, KARIN (1982) *Breast Cancer: The Psychological Effects of the Disease and Its Treatment*, Tavistock Publications.
The findings of a research study into the effects of breast cancer on women in Sweden. It contains extensive transcripts of interviews.

SONTAG, SUSAN (1978) *Illness as Metaphor*, Penguin Books.
A powerfully argued essay about the use of cancers and TB as metaphors for 'sickness' in society and the stigmatising effect of this on sufferers.

Chapters 6–9

CLARE, A. (1980) *Psychiatry in Dissent*, Tavistock Publications.
A humane orthodox psychiatrist's account of the main issues in mental disorder and distress.

ROSE, S., LEWONTIN, R. and KAMIN, L. (1984) *Not in Our Genes*, Penguin Books.
Discussion of biological determinism and the biology and politics of mental disorder and distress.

SCULL, A. (1980) *Museums of Madness*, Penguin Books.
Discusses the origins of asylums in nineteenth century Britain.

SEDGWICK, P. (1982) *Psychopolitics*, Pluto.
A critical account of the fashionable 'anti-psychiatry' theories of the 1960s and 1970s.

WING, J.K. (1978) *Reasoning about Madness*, Oxford University Press.
Clear discussion of issues around the diagnosis and aetiology of mental disorder.

Chapters 10–12

CASTANEDA, C. (1970) *Teachings of Don Juan: Yaqui Way of Knowledge*; (1975) *Journey to Ixtlan: Lessons of Don Juan*; and others, Penguin Books.
A series of books that supposedly chronicle the development of a relationship between a Californian anthropology student and a New Mexico Indian 'teacher', Don Juan, who advocates the use of hypnotics in his teachings.

HUXLEY, A. (1959) *The Doors of Perception*, Penguin Books.
A personal account of experimenting with mescalin in the 1950s.

STIMSON, G.V. and OPPENHEIMER, E. (1982) *Heroin Addiction: Treatment and Control in Britain*, Tavistock Publications.
An extremely readable account of the long-term study of individuals in the London clinics who are dependent on heroin.

Answers to self-assessment questions

Chapter 2

1 (a) Most people seem to get headaches. There is, however, considerable variation in their frequency. Some people get them only rarely, others suffer several times a week. They are also more common in women than in men and in the young rather than the elderly.

(b) Current medical practice distinguishes between primary and secondary headaches. Those classified as 'secondary' are due to another condition such as flu, sinusitis or very, very occasionally, a tumour. In 'primary' headaches, there is no other disease present. Primary headaches in contemporary analysis fall into just two main groups, tension or muscle-contraction headaches and migraines. In migraines there is good evidence of some biological disorder, though stress may precipitate some attacks. Modern medical opinion tends to favour a psychological explanation for tension headaches, although the matter needs considerably more research.

2 A standard modern explanation of appendicitis relates its incidence to the amount of fibre in the diet. People who eat a less refined diet seem to suffer far less from the disease. Five hundred years ago very few people ate a highly refined diet.

3 Gender, class, age, anxiety, pain threshold, degree of attention to bodily states, culture, anxiety and social stress, the extent to which the pain is overwhelming: all these can affect the description of symptoms. Moreover, the fact that such variations occur is well-known to patients as well as doctors and therefore have to be taken into account by doctors when making their diagnoses.

4 These variations might be due to differences in morbidity: that is, differences in the incidence of appendicitis. These in turn might be due to variations in diet — the Swedes, perhaps, eat more fibre and the Austrians less. The death-rate from appendicitis, however, includes those people who died as a result of appendicectomy (all operations carrying a certain risk). These figures, therefore, might also reflect national variations in the propensity of surgeons to operate when presented with a case of abdominal pain. This latter explanation seems more plausible. There is no present reason to believe that there are major differences in the fibre content of the diet of people in these countries. Moreover, stress-produced abdominal pain is both common and can closely resemble that caused by appendicitis. Some surgeons may therefore be misled by this. Finally, surgeons in the German-speaking countries at that time were known to have removed many more 'lilywhite' appendices than their colleagues in England and Wales.

Chapter 3

1 Although the incidence of cancers does rise very rapidly with increasing age, so too does the incidence of other life-threatening diseases such as heart disease, bronchitis, pneumonia and strokes. Beyond the age of 50 or 60, therefore, a smaller percentage of this age group die of cancer, despite the increased risk of developing it, simply because other causes of death are claiming an increasing number of lives.

2 Cancers of the breast or the female reproductive tract account for more than half the fatal cancers among women shown in Table 3.1 (excluding skin cancers). With the exception of cancer of the ovary, these types of cancer show 'better than average' survival five years after diagnosis. By contrast, cancers of the lung account for just under half of male cancers and these have a relatively poor prognosis. Paradoxically, this could be used to argue that women are *more* susceptible to cancers since mortality due to lung cancer in men would drop sharply if everyone gave up smoking, whereas mortality from most 'female' cancers would probably remain the same. Cancers are the *commonest* cause of female mortality between the ages of 30 and 59, whereas men are more likely to die from heart disease, but women are far less likely to die before old age from *any* cause, including cancers. Each year 10 000 more men than women die from cancers. Sweeping generalisations about cancers and gender are, not surprisingly, difficult to evaluate!

3 The writer sees cancer as something that invades her secretly from outside, not as a part of her own body that is

misfunctioning. She believes that it attacks her with a purposeful and malevolent intent and is 'clever and sneaky'.

4   Lung cancers occur about twelve times more frequently in smokers than in non-smokers, thus the *biological* cause of this disease is the damaging effect of the oils and tars in tobacco smoke on cells in the lungs, trachea and bronchial tubes. The decision to take up smoking and continue to smoke daily over a number of years could be argued to be a *personal* one. Numerous people never make this choice and increasing numbers who did so once are 'kicking' the habit. There are, however, numerous *social* influences that put pressure on people to smoke, from the cash poured into advertising, peer-group pressures that consider smoking fashionable, 'adult' or 'sexy', boredom at work, or the relative inexpensiveness of cigarettes compared with other 'treats' such as alcohol, dining out or holidays abroad.

Chapter 4

1   All three extracts present cancers as biologically different from the body in which they grow: the disease 'seizes upon' parts of the body like a crab; is likened to the 'onslaught of bacterial and viral infections'; and acquires 'territory' of its own. The effect of describing the disease as 'it' and moreover ascribing 'it' with purposeful emotions (obstinate, steady, remorseless, inexorable, power-crazy, never satisfied) is to represent cancers as essentially 'foreign' and unlike normal body tissues. Viewing cancers as non-'self' facilitates their personification as 'all-conquering' 'dictators' that (by implication) overwhelm the 'immunological and other defensive forces' that are ranged against them.

This conflicts with the most recent biological explanation of cancers as resulting from the re-activation of genes that normally regulate key features of embryonic development (cell division, mobility, lack of differentiation, adhesiveness and contact inhibition). In this explanation, cancer cells regain essentially normal characteristics, but at the wrong time in development. This view undermines, but cannot totally demolish, the logic behind the hypothesis of immune surveillance against spontaneously occurring cancer cells.

2   Contraceptive pills began to be used in the UK by women of reproductive age, 15–44 years, in the years 1961–65. Women aged 45 years or more in 1961–65 would never have been prescribed the 'pill' and neither would women aged 55 years or older in 1976–78. Thus, women in the three oldest age groups in Table 4.4 have never used hormonal contraception and the increases in breast cancer in women in these groups (ranging from 16.5 per cent to 11.2 per cent) cannot be attributed to the 'pill'. In the youngest age group, 15–44, more women were 'current pill

users' in 1976–78 than was the case in 1961–65, but their mortality from breast cancer *declined* slightly over this period. The most impact might be expected in women aged 45–54 since none were pill-users in 1961–65, whereas many women of this age would have been ex-pill-users by 1976–78. The increase in breast cancer of 14.0 per cent in this age group, however, is very close to that experienced by older women during this period, for whom contraceptive pills can have had no effect. Richard Peto commented that *The Guardian* headline should have read, 'Breast cancer trends in pill generation remain similar to those among their mothers and grandmothers'.

3   You would need to ask the following questions:

Is the programme effective at offering adequately spaced screening relative to the 'risk' of cervical cancer among women of different ages, social class, personal history, etc?

Is the programme effective at allaying anxiety among women who have been screened or does it arouse fear in some of them?

Is the test reliable: that is, to what extent are women who have (or will develop) cervical cancer being detected by the test and are the women who do not have cancer, or would not have developed it, being treated as a result of 'false positive' tests or pre-malignant changes that would have reverted to normal spontaneously?

Is the cost of screening the most effective use of funding or would some other use of this resource have saved more lives?

Chapter 5

1   The doctor states clearly that he thinks the news should come from someone who knows the patient intimately and not from himself, a stranger. He knows from experience, however, that close relatives 'very frequently' don't want the patient to know the diagnosis, so telling *them* amounts to entering into a collusion in which the patient is protected from knowledge about the disease. You might wonder about the extent to which this doctor is protecting himself from the distressing interview he might have had with the patient.

2   The advantages we touched on were: a more frank and unembarrassed attitude about cancer; staff who may be more skilful in treatment and counselling of patients, at least for some cancers; the availability of expensive diagnostic or therapeutic equipment; the contribution to research and testing of new treatment strategies.

The disadvantages were: distance resulting in additional expense for patients and visitors; isolation of patient far from family and friends.

3   The orthodox practitioner might offer these criticisms of alternative methods:

There is no evidence that they prolong life and controlled trials have not been performed to evaluate their effectiveness.

Patients may be lured away from orthodox treatments that have a proved probability of success.

If patients 'take responsibility' for their disease, they can feel guilty and self-critical if they don't make progress.

You may also have recalled from Chapter 4 that alternative therapies usually ascribe the biological basis of their methods to enhancing immune surveillance, a concept that is now in serious doubt.

The alternative practitioner might offer these criticisms of orthodox methods:

They discourage the patient from taking any responsibility for their treatment, fostering depression and helplessness that reduce not only the quality, but possibly the quantity of life.

Treatment is solely of the biological manifestation of the disease and ignores the emotional or spiritual dimension of the 'whole person'.

The treatments are themselves damaging to healthy tissues and may destroy natural defence mechanisms which could contribute to regression of the cancer.

Some orthodox treatments have not been evaluated in clinical trials.

Chapter 6

1 (a) Yes. The theory assumes that brain states correspond in some way to existential states, so Mr Davies' brain state in one existential state (depression) should differ from that in another (mania).

(b) Not necessarily. The theory does not say that for *all* people the same brain state corresponds to the same existential state. Also if you simply control for age, class and ethnic background, there are many factors left unaccounted for, such as childhood experience, diet and so forth. You might expect, however, that there would be *some* features of Mr Davies' brain state which differed from that of other 'normal' men when he was depressed or manic.

(c) No. The relationship in the theory is not about causation. It is a statement of identity, or *correspondence*. Mr Davies' changed brain state is, in another way of talking about, the *same as* his changed existential state. It is just that in one case we talk in the language of mental processes, thoughts, consciousness and emotion, and in the other in the language of biology, nerve cells, neurotransmitters, etc.

Chapter 7

1 Of the various distinctions discussed in the text, the crucial one is that in neurological or 'biological' disorders the sufferer's existential sense of self and personality are not affected, but the person may have difficulties in carrying out tasks or actions; in a psychological or 'functional'

disorder the person's sense of self and personality are profoundly altered.

2 (a) Neurosis.

(b) Psychosis.

(c) You should be hesitant! After all, it is just possible, objectively, that the individual in the second case has some prior knowledge that Martians have landed! The first individual might be suffering from vitamin deficiencies, or malnutrition, or suffering from a drug overdose — or she might be anxious that if she goes outside the house she will be attacked by her husband. Without a more detailed investigation, do not jump to conclusions; even *with* more detailed investigation, you should be careful.

3 (a) There are, of course, genetic differences between men and women associated with the Y versus the extra X chromosome. However, while the admission rate for personality disorders in Northern Irish men is about twice that for Northern Irish women in England and Wales, that for English and Welsh men is roughly the same as that for English and Welsh women, and that for American men is just over half that for American women. No simple genetic differences between men and women could account for the variation, which would seem to be more simply ascribed to culture.

(b) You cannot conclude that the Irish as a group have a genetic predisposition to anything on the basis of this data. You will recall from Book I that the social ascription 'Irish' does not map onto a biologically defined genetic group or race. Even if it did, you would need to know what the personality disorder admission rates for the Irish in Ireland were, why there were such substantial differences between the rate for people born in Northern Ireland and the Irish Republic and what happened to the children of Irish parentage born in England and Wales. You would have to consider all these factors before you could begin to unpick some of the variables involved in interpreting these simple statistics. You would also need to know about doctors' *expectations* of how they should diagnose people from a particular cultural background.

4 The main problem is that there is considerable variation in the biochemistry of 'normal' people. If one finds a particular level of a biochemical substance in the post-mortem brain of a depressed person, one cannot be sure that it is not a consequence of aspects of that individual's genotype or development that has nothing to do with the depression at all. It might be a consequence of drugs taken to combat the depression. Or the individual might, for instance, smoke, or live in a polluted environment, and have consequential brain changes. To match post-mortem samples of 'control' brains that properly 'pair' with the samples from the depressed individual requires a degree of

matching that is generally very difficult to achieve. Finally, any observed difference might be a consequence and not a cause of the depression.

Chapter 8

1 Oatley is clearly *rejecting* the view that depression is caused by events in a person's mind and, hence, in the biology of their brain. He accepts that the phenomenon of depression exists and is not merely a way of describing a particular relationship. Depression, he argues, occurs because of losses and disappointments likely to be experienced disproportionally by people of lower social and economic classes. Hence depression is also not *directly* the consequence of formative experiences in early childhood, according to Oatley.

2 For Goffman, being called mad redefines a personal relationship with family and friends. It *relieves* the individual of particular obligations and, instead, enables that individual to *claim* particular privileges. For Laing, it is a retreat into sanity or, at least, away from an intolerable set of human relationships from which there is no other possible escape. For a defence lawyer, it enables the murderer to plead 'diminished responsibility', which absolves the defendant from being expected to understand the consequences of murder and, therefore, of the need to be punished for that crime. For all three, therefore, there are advantages to being called mad, but advantages of quite different kinds from one another.

3 A psychoanalytically inclined psychotherapist would, perhaps, ask the question: why does this *particular* person become depressed? After all, not everyone in poor socioeconomic circumstances who has suffered disappointment or loss becomes depressed — not everyone would see some particular event as a loss or disappointment. What was it then about the particular early life history of the person that might have *predisposed* him or her to depression? In particular, the psychoanalytic tradition would concentrate not on socioeconomic factors, but on the individual's relationships in his or her early years with mother, father and other close relatives, such as brothers and sisters.

4 All these aspects of a person's behaviour, thought and action are seen as products of the activity of particular regions of the brain. For instance, sounds are processed in the auditory cortex. If the nerve cells of the auditory cortex show abnormal electrical activity, this might produce the sensation of sounds: that is, auditory hallucinations. Appetite or sexual activity are affected by a number of regions of the brain, especially the nerve cells in an area called the hypothalamus (Book IV). If these nerve cells are electrically abnormal, then appetite and sexual drive are changed. Similarly, 'emotionality' (or 'affect') is related to the activity of cells in many parts of the brain, also including the hypothalamus. The electrical activity of nerve cells is affected by their responsiveness to signals arriving on the surface of the cells from synapses made by other nerve cells. Electrical activity therefore can be affected by changes in the amount or effectiveness of the neurotransmitter which carries the signal across the synaptic junction. These changes in the amount or effectiveness of a neurotransmitter could be produced by changed activation of the enzyme responsible for making or breaking down the neurotransmitter, or changes in the properties of the nerve cell membrane with which the transmitter interacts. These changes could themselves be the result of drugs, and of genetic factors, or of diet, or many other environmental inputs.

Chapter 9

1 Both the psychotherapist and the psychiatrist are likely, of course, to begin by taking a detailed case history, both of the teenager and of his close relatives. Their intentions in doing so are likely to be different, however. In the psychotherapist's case it is likely to be in order to explore those factors in the young person's relationships with his family which may underlie his strange behaviour. The therapist may advocate that the teenager should leave his family environment, which he may believe contributes to the boy's distress, and enter a 'therapeutic community' where he can be encouraged to discuss his condition and feelings, and to be given an opportunity to develop his own sanity sheltered from an 'insane' world.

The biological psychiatrist might pursue the question of whether other members of the family showed any 'psychopathology'. The next step might be a biological investigation of the patient and the use of drugs, particularly phenothiazines if the diagnosis was schizophrenia. An effort would be made to keep the teenager in the family — admission to hospital would be a measure of last resort.

The lay relatives' group would endeavour to provide support and advice for the family. They would quite likely agree with the psychiatrist on drug treatment, but they might also encourage trying alternative dietary approaches — for instance, high fibre, or gluten-free, or junk-additive-free foods, in the hope that this might alleviate some of the symptoms.

2 The nurses' arguments centred on the following issues:
(a) ECT is likely to cause irreversible, even if mild, damage to the brain and treatments which cause irreversible effects are to be avoided.
(b) Patients should not be subjected to treatments without being able to give informed consent. Obtaining such consent from severely distressed patients — or their

relatives — is difficult because you can never be sure how 'freely' the consent is given and how fully the consequences of the treatment have been explained.

(c) The conditions of the use of ECT in psychiatric hospitals are such that for many patients it may appear as if it is being administered as a punishment for non-compliance or non-improvement, rather than as a therapy.

(d) Evidence for the long-term beneficial effect of administering ECT is not strong.

Apart from the question of whether nurses had the right to comment on the clinical judgment of medical staff, the response of the clinicians and the hospital administrators were along the lines that:

(a) The modified way in which ECT is now administered is much less likely to cause long-term damage and, in any case, proving that such damage has occurred is very difficult.

(b) All that could be done to explain the nature of the treatment to the patient was being done and a doctor had a responsibility to attempt to improve the patient's condition. Arguments about ECT were no different in kind from those about drugs.

(c) The short-term beneficial effects of ECT were clear, even if the long-term effects were uncertain. Providing short-term relief enabled other treatments, including psychotherapeutic ones, to be offered.

3   On the face of it, both depressed patients *and* controls on the drug do better than those on the placebo. That would seem surprising, because you are not told that the controls are depressed to begin with. But note that the *nurses* who score the subjects know who is on the drug and who is on a placebo. The test is *not* double blind but 'single blind' — only the subjects don't know. Hence the nurses — you are not told whether they know who are controls and who are patients — may *expect* those on the drug to do better and hence rate them as improving, as indeed they do. Thus the interpretation that the drug is an effective antidepressant is invalidated by flaws in the experimental design. Note, by the way, that the controls are not an adequate group. Randomly drawn volunteers may imply that the distribution of age, sex, physical health, etc., is very different from the patient group. The appropriate controls would be *matched*.

Chapter 10
1   (a) Alcohol.
(b) Caffeine. Nicotine has attracted some legislation.
(c) Opium (morphine and heroin are later derivatives). Cocaine would also fit this description.
(d) Lysergic acid diethylamide (LSD or 'acid').
(e) Marijuana and derivatives such as cannabis resin and cannabinol (extract).

Chapter 11
1   (a) Drugs that have a similar effect on the body are:
  (ii) mescalin and LSD — both hallucinogenic.
  (iii) heroin and morphine — both sedative.
  (v) nicotine and caffeine — both stimulants.
(b) The other two pairs of drugs have a contrasting effect on the body. Amphetamine is a stimulant, while pentobarbitone is a major tranquilliser. Cocaine is a stimulant, whereas Valium is a minor tranquilliser.

2   (a) All of the types of drug listed produce tolerance.
(b) Opiates and stimulants produce physiological dependency.
(c) All produce psychological dependence.

3   Caffeine, nicotine and amphetamine have major effects outside the central nervous system. Alcohol has effects on the liver and intestine, but primarily it affects the brain. Heroin and cocaine effects are mainly in the central nervous system.

4   (i) (d)
   (ii) (c)
  (iii) (b)
  (iv) (a)

Chapter 12
1   There are four major points of contrast between the two treatments:
(a) The cost of treatment — low in Thailand, high in the US.
(b) The time scale — short term in Thailand.
(c) The goal — complete abstinence in the Thailand treatment, gradual reduction in the US.
(d) Support during the treatment — group support in Thailand, drug substitution in the US.

2   The advantages of the special opiate clinics are:
(a) Legal availability of drugs.
(b) Access to a detoxification programme.
(c) Medical surveillance of health as related to drug-dependency.
The disadvantages are:
(a) As there are so few clinics then much time is spent getting to them.
(b) They tend to depersonalise those who are attending them.
(c) Rarely is there access to social workers.
Many of these disadvantages are in common with alcohol centres (e.g. few of them, possibility of hospitalisation).

Chapter 13
1   Parsons places great stress on both the human capacity for malingering and on the wider social interest in making

sure that this does not happen. Both themes are evident here. There is the argument that shell shock in World War I produced contagious hysteria and also the stress in World War II on getting the men to 'perform their duty'.

2   Mental disorder is seen as something relatively fluid that can be modified by social circumstances: that is, by the way that people react to it. Note also the use of radically different terms to describe the same phenomenon — 'supporting' rather than 'treating', 'stress reaction' or 'combat exhaustion' rather than 'shell shock'.

3   Both the individual soldiers, on the one hand, and the US Army, the government and the American people, on the other, were the clients of the US Army psychiatrists. The doctrine of combat psychiatry could be said to be in the troops' interests as there were many fewer episodes of combat exhaustion and therefore, presumably, of permanent neurotic disorder. On the other hand, the doctrine is also clearly shaped by the interests of others who wish as many troops to be in the field as possible. The aim is to minimise the sick role. Moreover, since we do not know the relative death-rates of those troops who were returned to battle after this 'support', we cannot say whether or not they were helped or sacrificed.

4   The key resemblance is in their common emphasis on the importance of others' *reaction* to the episode. Note also the similar concern about the problematic nature of responsibility — the worry, here, that the men who had left the battlefield would feel a crippling guilt.

5   Supporters of the medicalisation thesis might point to the use of both modern drugs (sedatives) and modern social theories (combat psychiatry in the service of the armed forces). Medicine might be seen as penetrating the battle-field in an increasingly sophisticated fashion. Critics of the medicalisation thesis might argue that sedatives and new psychiatric techniques were used to keep people out of the sick role and did, in fact, do so. Both points of view seem plausible.

Entries and page numbers in **bold type** refer to key words which are printed in *italics* in the text.

Index

Acknowledgements

Grateful acknowledgement is made to the following sources for material used in this book:

Text
W.H. Auden, 'Miss Gee', in *Collected Shorter Poems 1927–1957*, Faber and Faber, and Random House Inc., 1966; J.B.S. Haldane, 'Cancer's a funny thing' in *The New Statesman*, 21 February 1964; R. Littlewood and M. Lipsedge, *Aliens and Alienists*, © R. Littlewood and M. Lipsedge, 1982, Penguin Books; H. Gardner, *The Shattered Mind*, © 1984 Howard Gardner, Alfred A. Knopf, Inc. and Routledge and Kegan Paul; J. Pringle, Living with schizophrenia, in *Mind and Mental Health Magazine*, Spring 1972; T. O'Halloran, Screws turned on prisoners, in *New Statesman*, 9 December 1983.

Figures
Figure 2.1 G.T. Bungay *et al*. Study of symptoms in middle life, in *British Medical Journal*, July 1980; *Figure 2.2* E.H. Rang *et al*., An enquiry into the incidence and prognosis of undiagnosed abdominal pain, in *British Journal of Social and Preventive Medicine*, vol. 24, no. 1, 1970; *Figures 2.3 and 2.4* J.L. Grove *et al*., The effect of a visit to a neurological clinic upon patients with tension headaches, in *The Practioner*, vol. 224, 1980; *Figure 2.5* copyright reserved. Reproduced by gracious permission of Her Majesty the Queen; *Figure 2.6* from Vesalius, de Humani Corporis Fabrica, Basel, 1543, p361. Courtesy Wellcome Institute; *Figure 2.7* F. Creed, Life events and appendicetomy, in *The Lancet*, June 1981; *Figure 2.8* S. Lichtner and M. Pflanz, Appendectomy in the Federal Republic of Germany, in *Medical Care*, IX, 1971; *Figure 3.3* R. Peto, in *The Guardian*. 10 November 1983; *Figure 3.4 Trends in Cancer Survival in Britain: Cases Registered between 1960 and 1974*, Cancer Research Campaign, 1982; *Figure 4.3* K.K. Carroll, Experimental evidence of dietary factors and hormone-dependent cancers, in *Cancer Research*, vol. 35, 1975; *Figure 4.4* Courtesy Dr. G. Canti, St. Bartholomews Hospital; *Figure 4.5 Mary Makes Up Her Mind*, leaflet from Manchester Regional Committee for Cancer Education; *Figure 4.6* G. Curling, Asymptomatic breast screening, in *Nursing*, vol. 31, 1981; *Figure 5.1* Courtesy TEM Instruments Ltd; *Figure 5.3* from *Getting Well Again* from O. Carl Simonton, Stephanie Matthews-Simonton and James Creighton, copyright © 1978 by O. Carl Simonton and Stephanie Matthews-Simonton, reprinted by permission of Bantam Books, Inc., all rights reserved; *Figure 7.1* from D. Curran and M. Partridge, *Psychological Medicine*, Livingstone, 1969; *Figure 9.1* Mary Evans Picture Library; *Figure 9.2* M. Shepherd and A. Clare, *Psychiatric Illness in General Practice*, Oxford University Press, 1981; *Figure 10.2* Charles Marriott; *Figure 11.1* Drawing by Peter Brooks, *New Society*, 19 October 1972; *Figure 11.2* John Topham Picture Library; *Figure 13.1* H. Waitzkin Latent functions of the sick role in various institutional settings, in *Social Science and Medicine*, 5 no. 67, 1971, Pergamon Press.

Tables
Table 4.1 adapted from R. Doll, The epidemology of cancer, in *Cancer*, vol. 45, 1980; *Table 5.1* J. Aitken-Swan and E.C. Easson, Reactions of cancer patients on being told their diagnosis, in *British Medical Journal*, vol. 5124, 1959.

Illustrations
Frontispiece The Munch Museum, Oslo; Mary Evans Picture Library.